GREENS GUIDE

to collecting
TV, MUSIC & COMIC BOOK ANNUALS

PRICE GUIDE
1950-2001

First Edition

Paul Green & Laura Taylor

INTRODUCTION

Well here it is... the first edition of Green's Guide. I know you realise how much work, research and sweat it takes to gather all the material for such a massive undertaking so I won't bore you with my tales of working from dawn 'til dusk and beyond. I just hope you enjoy the fruits of our labour. I'd like to thank Doug Sulipa for his encouragement and invaluable background info on the American/Canadian market and Mark Towers for his informative feature on that great British soccer icon Roy of the Rovers. Also D.C. Thomson for their kind help in contributing cover material and Fleetway for providing a list of current copyright holders. Gary Graham for sharing his insights on his extensive annual collection and of course my co-writer Laura Taylor for her continued support and enthusiasm. And most of all I'd like to thank my father and late mother for buying my first 'Cheyenne' Annual and introducing me to the colourful world of annuals.

Paul Green

.... And finally! I can't believe we made it! Having come up with the idea some two years ago, I can't tell you how good it is to finally see Green's Guide going to print. It has taken an awful amount of hard work and many many hours buried underneath annuals. Believe me.... my children even forgot what I looked like. The only time they ever saw me was when I'd sneak out of my room to raid the biscuit tin! Green's Guide has been a major achievement for me personally and professionally. Since I was a little girl I had always dreamed of writing a book, I have spent my whole life surrounded by them and the UK annuals contain so much information that at the beginning I really was overwhelmed with the whole idea. That said, now that our 'First Edition' is complete, I can't wait to get started on the next one! So watch this space...... I hope you all have many hours of enjoyment out of our guide, and I'm sure many of you will be delving into your loft spaces to search out those rare old annuals to see how much they are worth. All that remains to be said is, before you decide to put those rarities up for auction or sell them to your local collectors, take a moment to browse through them, feel the nostalgia and remember the happiness you had as a child when you opened up those beautiful new shiny books and devoured them page by page! Happy reading!

Laura Taylor

This book is dedicated to Gary who without his love and support, this book wouldn't have been possible (not to mention the countless cups of tea during the early hours of the morning!) and my children Gemma and Jessica who love me no matter what.

GREEN'S GUIDE TO COLLECTING TV, MUSIC AND COMIC BOOK ANNUALS

THANKS TO OUR CONTRIBUTORS

* Mark Towers * Doug Sulipa * Gary Graham * D.C. Thomson *

DISCLAIMER

GREEN'S GUIDE TO COLLECTING TV, MUSIC AND COMIC BOOK ANNUALS
ISBN 0 9538768 0 2

Published by GT Publications, 79 Hamilton Road, Great Yarmouth, Norfolk NR30 4LX

FIRST EDITION 2000
10 9 8 7 6 5 4 3 2 1

CORRECTIONS AND ADDITIONAL MATERIAL CAN BE SENT TO:
79 Hamilton Road, Great Yarmouth, Norfolk, NR30 4LX

Printing: Redwood Books Limited, Kennet Way, Trowbridge, Wiltshire BA14 8RN

CONTENTS

WHAT IS AN ANNUAL?

BY PAUL GREEN

The 1950's saw the birth of the TV Generation. Up to that point the major pop culture influences had been radio and the cinema. With the success of TV Western shows such as Cheyenne and Wagon Train and with traditional radio and cinema serials such as Lone Ranger and Hopalong Cassidy making the transition to TV the market was ripe for the plucking.

Publishing companies such as World Distributors used a mixture of studio based artists and writers and freelance staff to produce annuals based on the popular TV shows of the time. World Distributors was founded in 1946 by the Pemberton family, who started the company after buying up comic pages from Sunday newspapers. World War Two had savaged the comics industry and paper shortages and salvage drives made comics a rare commodity. The Pembertons capitalised on a gap in the market and commenced publishing children's annuals aimed at the Christmas market.

1950's World titles usually consisted of U.S. comic strip reprints and UK produced illustrated text stories and features. The fine cover illustrations, produced mainly by Walter Howarth, Ron Smethurst and Edgar Hodges, were often the highlight of the annual. Rival publishers, Purnell, Adprint and Daily Mirror usually featured annuals consisting entirely of new UK material and credited the artists and writers.

Other traditional publishers such as the Scotland based D.C. Thomson continued to publish annuals based on their highly successful comics which included the Beano and the Dandy and the classic characters Dennis the Menace and Desperate Dan.

Girl's titles in the fifties were usually based on themes such as ballet, hockey, boarding schools, ponies and romance. With the explosion of the pop music scene in the sixties and the 'teenybopper' craze in the seventies, girl's comics and annuals increasingly featured a large pop star content in the form of photo features and pin-ups. Fans of various pop stars and bands such as David Cassidy, The Osmonds, Marc Bolan and Slade can find them hidden away in numerous girl's titles. Our comprehensive Cross Reference Guide lists all the various pop and movie stars and the annuals they can be found in.

The following is a selected list of annual titles based on genre.

TV based annuals include: Bewitched, Beverly Hillbillies, Cheyenne, Baywatch, Knight Rider, Dukes of Hazzard, Dr Kildare, The Saint, Laramie, Maverick and Doctor Who

Music based annuals include: Fab 208, Popswop, Abba, Boyzone, Disco 45, David Cassidy, Top of the Pops, David Essex and Kylie Minogue

Sport based annuals include: Shoot, Scorcher, Roy of the Rovers, Striker, Question of Sport, Match of the Day and Match.

Annuals based on UK comics include: Beezer, Topper, Beano, Dandy, Sparky, Victor, Hotspur, Eagle, Tiger, Valiant, Lion, TV Century 21, TV Tornado, TV Comic and 2000AD.

DC and Marvel titles are often reprinted in UK annual form. These aren't to be confused with the American comic annuals! The UK comic book annuals often contain UK produced text stories and include: Superman, Batman, Wonder Woman, Superboy, Spider-Man, Hulk, Fantastic Four, Avengers, X-Men

Movie based annuals include: Back to the Future, Star Wars, Raiders of the Lost Ark, Annie, Conan, Lost in Space, Godzilla and The Flintstones

A genre often overlooked by overseas collectors are the titles based on **UK girl's comics and magazines.** These often contain some of the best UK and European artwork and annuals include: School Friend, Girl, June, Debbie, Judy, Bunty, Jackie, Diana, Misty, Penelope, and Princess Tina.

Pre-school titles often evoke the greatest nostalgia among collectors, annuals include: Camberwick Green, Playhour, Harold Hare, Andy Pandy, Sooty, Ivor the Engine, Thomas the Tank Engine, Bagpuss, Twinkle, Teletubbies, Teddy Bear, Clangers, The Flumps, and Bimbo

Long running titles still being published include, Dandy, Beano, Bunty, Mandy, Dennis the Menace, Bash Street Kids, Beezer, Twinkle, Blue Peter, Rupert, Shoot, Barbie and Sindy. You can check the full list of 2001 annuals later on in this Guide.

AMERICAN MARKET

DOUG SULIPA

Doug Sulipa has been a Senior Advisor for the Overstreet Comic Guide for the last 25 years, so who better to provide us with an overview of the current market.

Which titles are the best sellers at the moment?
In the last few years it has strongly gravitated toward the mid 70's to mid 80's period. The most popular has been the well known and highly collected cartoon charaters like He-Man, She-Ra, Transformers and most Hanna Barbera. But also extremely popular are the Captain America Annual with Jim Steranko art and pre-1975 Marvel and DC Superhero annuals. Bringing record prices is the Emergency Annual! Also anything based on a popular USA character, that has non USA reprint material is more desirable. The more original UK material the better! In music annuals the trend is similar. 1970's Partridge Family are more requested than Monkees! In TV annuals, the most requested are Charlie's Angels, Dukes of Hazzard, A-Team, rather than (the still popular) Green Hornet, Space Family Robinson, Bewitched and Beverly Hillbillies.

Which titles aren't selling?
Slowing in interest are the Western hero annuals, although they still bring prices far above the traditional UK market prices. Anything with no USA characters is slower, including Dr Who! But Gerry Anderson items still have a decent following.

Would you compare the market to investing in stocks and shares? One minute hi-tech stocks are hot and the next everybody's dumping them. Do you see this trend in Annual/Comics investors?
I simply see UK annuals as a "dormant giant" that has yet to waken! When we compare the 60's hardcover annuals to similar vintage USA comics, the annuals seem absurdly low! The market is in stasis! Real supply and demand has yet to hit the market! From our point of view, we see these books are no longer plentiful. Smart USA dealers are snapping up these bargains and the supply is diminishing. We get the impression that these books have long had low regard by the market they were made for! Why else would many a vendor price most of his 25-45 year old annuals in the same range as common new books, or even less? It might suprise, that almost all USA and Canadian collectors

do not know the annuals even exist! We are very attached to our own creations and will pay world record prices for nice collectibles on same. But awareness has not yet hit! With the fast expanding Internet and world market, we expect this to change rapidly! When awareness does hit, we will first see true supply and demand in action. We expect most of the high grade and best product to be sold to American collectors, before UK collectors know what hit them. They are accustomed to low priced annuals and will initially not want to compete versus USA and the world market for these great collectibles. Prices are still far too low for dumping. Once prices rise to more sensible levels, good collections will surface, in turn activating the market, causing rising prices. At that point we will see what is scarce and what is not.

Do you have a personal favourite comic strip, character or annual?
My personal favourites are all comics related:

(1) Uncle Scrooge
(2) Spider-Man
(3) Jonah Hex
(4) Superman

I love the 1950's and 60's DC Superhero annuals, mainly for the crude original UK cover art. I also favour annuals with great UK original art by Bolton, Bolland and all the better UK artists!

Which annual have you sold for the highest price?
I sold a perfect NM copy, based on strict USA condition guidelines, for $75! If I could find high grade 50's DC Superhero annuals, I could easily top this! On eBay Emergency! annuals have been fetching above this level too!

How long have you been collecting and selling?
I have been a fan from age 6 back in 1962, a collector since the Batman TV series in 1966, a dealer from 1971-date by mail order and I had a store from 1974-1996. I am currently very busy selling by want lists, mail order and internet from my 8000 square foot warehouse!

What made you get into the business?
I started as a reader, and became obsessed with comics! I

became a avid collector. To feed my passion, I started dealing. Back in 1974 it was considered a bit crazy to make a go of it just on "used" collectibles. The market has changed countless times, in countless ways. Once I began dealing I gained more interests and branched into records, magazines, books, toys, posters, movies and almost anything related to pop culture!

Do you ever get requests for obscure titles?

In USA collectibles my entire market has gone toward obscure! Obscure usually means scarce! As more and more people worldwide enter the internet market, billions of items are coming onto the market. Traditionally collected items, that had localized scarcity, are suddenly very common on the world market. These traditional collectibles fast loose their appeal when one can get them any time one wants it. Prices are falling on "overvalued" for the new world market items. Items we long term dealers threw out for the last 30 years are now the only things truly scarce and are skyrocketing in price. It is all simple supply and demand, with a new set of rules! In traditional collectibles, the market has grown for high grade copies. Only "as new", very strictly graded condition copies, are now scarce on many items! Depending on the collectible, a NM/M item that had once brought 4 times the G price, can easily command 10 times the G price, and as much as 20 times, 50 times, even 100 times the G price This is supported by professionally graded items, which are "slabbed" or sealed in cases which can't be opened,

without voiding the grade. This is an unstoppable force in most serious money collectibles.

Is it true to say that the majority of American/ Canadian collectors aren't aware of the existence of most UK annual titles?

I estimate 99% of Collectors and 98% of all dealers in USA/Canada do not know they exist! Most when they first see them, will instantly love them!

What is your personal opinion of the quality of the UK annual in terms of artwork and stories?

Just as the USA items vary in quality, so do the annuals. But in general I think the printing is far above the quality of most vintage USA items! The artwork and stories can be very crude to extremely nice! But the key for me is they are "different"! Having seen so many material, over so many years, I maintain they are uniquely great items! We missed a lot not having an annual Xmas gift "Prize" like this to pick from!

The hottest titles in the UK come from the Scottish

publisher D.C. Thomson. First editions of 'The Beano Book' and 'The Dandy Book' sell for thousands of pounds. I understand these titles aren't highly regarded in America and Canada. What are the reasons for this?

Since we did not grow up with them, they are totally foreign to us and have near zero appeal. They will have great appeal to any market where they were typically availiable. But they just did not get worldwide market appeal. USA characters have always tended to reach around the world, which is the big difference. I see them being stuck in the localized markets they came from, unless they one day become a pure investment vehicle for a foreign market speculator! It is rather unfortunate, because most of us have no clue of what we are missing!

What are your views on the future potential of the annual market?

I feel they remain one of the most overlooked of all collectibles! They have worldwide appeal! They are scarce in high grade condition! Demand is big when people become aware! Supplies are getting smaller daily! Pure supply and demand principles point in one direction only! An EXPLOSIVE potential market for collectablility and investment!

Douglas W. Sulipa of Comic World was interviewed via email by Paul Green

COMIC WORLD; BOX #21986; STEINBACH, MANITOBA;
CANADA R5G 1B5. PH:(204)-346-3674

DOUG SULIPA'S COMIC WORLD

IN MAIL ORDER
BUSINESS
SINCE 1971!

** [E-MAIL address; cworld@mb.sympatico.ca
** [FAX to; 1-204-346-1632]
** eBay Auctions= " dwscw "!
** [Phone # for Saturday ONLY; 1-204-633-9641]

WE TAKE VISA & MASTERCARD

Senior Adviser to Overstreet Annual Price Guide

AN INTERVIEW WITH...

PAUL GREEN

aul Green was born in Lincoln England in 1955 and attended Oldham Art College. He worked as a staff artist for World from 1974-1977 before going freelance for Stafford Pemberton, Grandreams, Marvel and World Regular titles he worked on include 'Masters of the Universe' (1985-89) and Scooby Doo (1983-86). He also worked on annuals for Superman, Batman, Wonder Woman, Buck Rogers in the 25th Century, Tom & Jerry, Terrahawks, Star Fleet, Happy Days, John Travolta, Battle Beasts, Popeye, Alias Smith and Jones, She Ra and Dukes of Hazzard.

How did you get your first job as a staff artist and who was it for?
My first job was for World Distributors who were based in Lever Street, Manchester. I decided to look for work before I completed my three years at Oldham Art College. At first I had this naiive view that I'd get work easily but walking around Manchester with my portfolio and knocking on the doors of various advertising agencies proved me wrong. I was becoming quite depressed with my lack of success. However the boss of one of the studios I visited recommended I try World Distributors. As soon as I entered the offices I knew I wanted a job there. The walls were covered with various annual covers. But I soon learned it took much more discipline to produce these covers than I'd experienced in all my time at art college.

What was the first annual you ever worked on?
That was a very boring title called Schoolboys'. My first attempts were rejected and I really felt I wouldn't survive my three months trial period. The difference to art college was a shock and I realised that most of what I'd been taught just didn't transfer into the workplace experience. His first published work was for World Distributors in Manchester on the Star Trek annual 1975.

What was the last annual you ever worked on?
Polly Pocket 1995. This was a title based on a toy range for young girls.

What was the most memorable annual you worked on and why?
Probably the two Superman Annual covers from 1979 and 1980. I became interested in comic art because of the wonderful DC Comics from the sixties. My favourite artist was Curt Swan. He drew the Superman titles and I was

thrilled to be part of the Superman tradition.

What character did you most enjoy drawing and why?
I enjoyed drawing the He Man and the Masters of the Universe characters, mainly because I was asked to illustrate the comic strips. Unlike the American system of dividing tasks between various artists, in the UK, artists usually both pencil and ink their own work. I also had to colour my work using gouache paint for covers and inks for the strips and text story illustrations.

Which character did you find the hardest to draw and why?
I always found the nursery titles hardest to draw. World published quite a few pre-school titles including Play Shool and Enid Blyton's Bedtime, Illustrating little girls and boys is a precise art. One freelance artist regularly had their heads replaced with a 'prettier' version by in-house artists.

How do you feel the annual market has changed over the last 20 years?
There's a greater emphasis on photographic content with an increase in quality of printing. I'd say the one area that's suffered is the boys' adventure annual. They've more or less disappeared. Great titles like Valiant and Lion haven't been replaced. Pedigree, who, in my opinion, currently produce the best annuals on the market, publish Action Man which classifies as an adventure title. But I can't think of others. The annuals based on U.S. series have also suffered in recent years. I'd love to see a return to annuals featuring top U.S. shows.

How do you see the annual market progressing in the future?
It's foolish to predict future trends in today's society. A few years back everyone was predicting that computer games and the internet would herald the end of printed books. I think they've have had some effect on sales in the short-term. But fads change constantly and computer games don't hold the same fascination they did five years ago. It would be great to see more dynamic titles both in comics and annuals.

Do you still produce any artwork today?
Yes. I produce two syndicated features, SHOWBIZ TEASER and TV CULTS for Knight Features in London. I created these

features a few years ago mainly because I wanted more control over my work. I also sell my work via eBay and the UK Collectibles website. A particular thrill recently was finding out that the person who bid on my portrait of Bob Denver from Gilligan's Island was none other than the actor Bob Denver!!

What made you decide to write Green's Guide? What do you hope to achieve by producing this guide?
My first ambition was simply to gather as much information about various titles as I could. But the list kept growing by the day. I was literally discovering new titles all the time. And to a lesser extent I still am. The U.S

Overstreet Comic Book Price Guide was a major inspiration. I remember buying the guide for the first time in the 1970s and spending hours looking through all the titles. I want the reader to share that same enthusiasm about annuals. My aim in producing Green's Guide is to stimulate interest in the market. The internet, and particularly the auction sites, have opened up new trading opportunities and created new markets. Many U.S. customers are seeing these annuals for the first time. In the UK we've been buying their comics since the 1950's but our annuals were never distributed outside the Commonwealth countries. My aim is to inform, educate and entertain.

 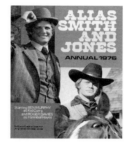 

A selection of annuals and covers by Paul Green

ONLINE AUCTIONS

BY LAURA TAYLOR

hopping on the net is still a relatively new experience, especially in the UK and many would say it is still in its infancy, but for the Annual collector it's a blessing in disguise.

You've probably spent hours trailing around book shops and collectors fairs trying to find that elusive title to complete your collection. Now you can just log on to one of the many auction websites on the net and search for whatever title you're looking for. Better than that, you'll often find editions of your favourite annuals that you didn't even know existed!

By far one of the largest auction sites and probably the most highly recommended is eBay! Its an ever growing population of buyers and sellers, where over 4,400,000 items are listed every day.

The majority of the market is based in the USA, but the UK eBay community is growing and there are separate sites for other countries.

http://www.ebay.com - USA residents
http://www.ebay.co.uk - UK residents
http://www.ebay.com.au - Australian residents
http://www.ebay.com/canada - Canadian residents
http://www.ebay.de - German residents
http://www.ebayjapan.co.jp - Japan residents

For those of you who are new to online auctions here are some hints and tips that should help ease your way into the world of Online Auctions. If you thought it was going to be plain sailing from here on in, think again.

Auction lots can in fact often be likened to having to push yourself in front of that old Granny who's giving you the evil eye as she rushes to get hold of the 1996 Boyzone Annual before you at the local market!

As they say, all's fair in love and war! You have to learn the tactics to make sure you're successful. First you have to search for the items your looking for. One of the main things to be aware of is the language barrier. If for example you go to the US website for eBay and do a search for the word annual you will come up with 1,000's of items (most of which will probably be related to Bergonias!)

However, if you enter the UK eBay website, and do a search for the word annual, you'll have more success, as this almost always exclusively lists the UK Annual! Now the fun really begins....

Another good tip when searching for a specific annual. Simply type, for example, Dukes +annual and this will show a list of all the Dukes of Hazzard annuals, or blue +annual which will show a list of all the blue peter titles! Its always good to check completed items as well (although at the time of writing this type of search can only be performed on ebay.com) but it can be particularly interesting to see what kind of prices annuals are selling for.

Before Bidding

Check. Check. Check.. Make sure you are fully aware of all the relevant information before placing your bid.

Check the sellers feedback rating
Check the shipping costs of your item
Check the condition of the annual

If you are unsure of any of these details email the seller and ask the questions.

Ready to Place Your bid!

Once you are ready to place your bid, decide the highest price you would be prepared to pay for the item and take advantage of the automatic incremental feature which is relevant to most big online auction sites. For example, if the item you are after already has a bid of £5.00 on it, and you feel that you are prepared to pay £10.00 for the item, you can automatically place your bid for £10.00. This doesn't mean that your bid will automatically shoot up to £10.00. You will simpy become the highest bidder. The highest bid price will go up to for example £5.50 (unless of course the previous bidder has placed a higher bid in which case it will go up to the next highest bid). The good thing about this is the fact that you will still remain the highest bidder even if somebody bids, for example, £6.00. It also saves you from having to keep rebidding on the auction!

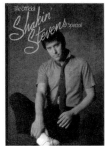

There is a lot of competition on the auctions and many hardened bidders will come along in the last few seconds of the auction to steal away what you thought was your winning lot! I have seen it happen many a time, and often the other person has only outbid you by 50p! At least if you have left a higher bid on the item than the current bid price, if they try to outbid you in the last few seconds, it is less likely. By the time they realise that you have in fact placed a higher bid, it will be too late and the auction will be over and you will have secured your lot!!!

After the Auction

Okay so now you've fought the battle and won.. What happens next? Generally buyer and seller should contact each other within 3 days (these are the rules of eBay). If you haven't heard from your buyer within 3 days, simply contact eBay and inform them and they will take it from there.

Once you and the seller have exchanged address and payment it should be only a matter of time before your postman delivers your sought after annual!

Let the World Know

One of the most important and often overlooked parts of eBay is feedback. Its just as important to let people know

when things go well as it is to let them know when things don't! If you're happy with the transaction then leave positive feedback. This helps others know that your seller/buyer is a trusted member of the eBay community. It's always a good idea to try one final email before leaving negative feedback. If they still fail to reply then you'll have no alternative but to leave your negative comment.!

Summary

At the end of the day, with the net at your fingertips you should be able to find many elusive annual titles. In the expanding world of e-commerce, online auctions are definitely a collectors haven for the future.

OTHER ONLINE AUCTIONS

Although eBay is one of the best known online auction sites, there are others worth checking it:

www.amazon.co.uk/auctions
www.auctionaddict.com
www.auctionrover.com
www.auctions.com
www.auctionuniverse.com
www.auctionwatch.com
www.biddersedge.com
www.bidhit.com/auction
www.boxlot.com
www.butterfields.com/index2.html
www.christies.com
www.dealdeal.com
www.digibid.com

www.ehammer.com
www.finelot.com
www.firstauction.com
www.gavelnet.com
www.haggle.com
www.leftbid.com
www.onsale.com
www.priceradar.com
www.qxl.co.uk
www.underthehammer.com
www.whatamibid.com
www.yahoo.co.uk

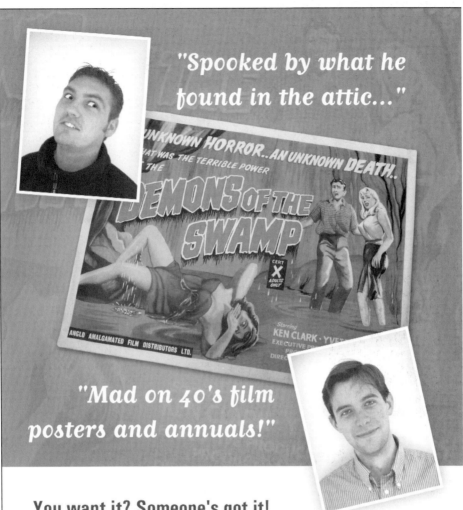

"Spooked by what he found in the attic..."

"Mad on 40's film posters and annuals!"

You want it? Someone's got it!

At eBay.co.uk you'll find thousands of TV, film, music and comic book annuals as well as film, TV and music memorabilia and collectables. All of the items for sale have been listed by other members of the eBay community, so if you want it, someone's bound to have it, and if you want to sell, there's no shortage of people looking to buy. Bidding is open 24 hours a day, and all you need to register is an email address, so don't get left behind, visit us today!

Find us at www.ebay.co.uk *Still got a question?* ukenquiries@ebay.com

ELUSIVE TITLES

BY PAUL GREEN

One of the great frustrations of collecting annuals is searching for a title that doesn't appear to exist. On the other hand one of the great joys of collecting annuals can be the discovery of that elusive title. Some titles never graduated to their own annual but can be found in comic or TV annuals.

Hidden Titles

All Stars Television
Steptoe and Son, Tightrope

ATV Show/TV Star Book:
I Love Lucy, 87th Precinct, The Deputy

TV Crimebusters:
Dixon of Dock Green, 77 Sunset Strip, Hawaiian Eye

TV Century 21
My Favourite Martian, The Munsters, Get Smart

ITV Annual for Girls & Boys
77 Sunset Strip, Hawaiian Eye

Look-In Television/Comedy
On the Buses, Bless This House, Benny Hill, Please Sir!, Man About the House, Doctor on the Go

Countdown
Hawaii Five-O, Secret Service

Thunderbirds
Department S

TV Detectives
Cannon, Columbo, McCloud, Rockford Files, McMillan & Wife, Harry O, Serpico

TV Favourites
Dynasty, Blue Thunder

TV Tornado/Mighty Warriors
Magnus, Robot Fighter (see the Cross Reference for full listings)

Missing Titles that never appeared in any annual

Comedy:
Dick Van Dyke Show, Petticoat Junction, Green Acres, Brady Bunch, Gilligan's Island, The Addams Family, Rowan and Martin's Laugh In, Hogan's Heroes, Porridge,

Little & Large, Are you Being Served?, Absolutely Fabulous, Black Adder, Mr Bean, Fawlty Towers, Lovejoy, The Fresh Prince of Bel Air, The Mary Tyler Moore Show, Police Squad, Rising Damp, Only Fools and Horses, Last of the Summer Wine, The Love Boat, Taxi, MASH, Cheers, The Golden Girls, The Cosby Show, Roseanne, The Simpsons, Northern Exposure,

Soaps:
Peyton Place, Falcon Crest, Flamingo Road, Knots Landing, The Waltons, Triangle, Upstairs Downstairs, Emmerdale, Dawsons Creek

Childrens:
Flipper, Noggin the Nog, Saved by the Bell, The Demon Headmaster, Animorphs, Sabrina the Teenage Witch

Medical:
Marcus Welby MD, General Hospital, Casualty, ER, Chicago Hope

Westerns:
The Virginian, Casey Jones, The Rifleman, Branded, The Big Valley, The Wild Wild West, Cade's County, Little House on the Prairie

War/Adventure:
Combat, Garrison's Gorillas, The Onedin Line

Police/Crime/Mystery:
Dragnet, Perry Mason, The Untouchables, The Baron, Man in a Suitcase, Callan, Softly Softly, Route 66, The Fugitive, Honey West, Mannix, Adam 12, I-Spy, Quincy, Bergerac, Juliet Bravo, Police Woman, Randall & Hopkirk (Deceased), Shaft, Special Branch, The Streets of San Francisco, Twin Peaks, Hill Street Blues, Prisoner Cell Block H, Cagney & Lacey, Miami Vice, Moonlighting, L A Law, Inspector Morse, Murder She Wrote, Hadleigh

Sci Fi/Horror:
The Time Tunnel, Wonder Woman (Lynda Carter), The Invaders, Kolchak: The Night Stalker, Quantam Leap, Red Dwarf, Alien Nation, X Files, Buffy the Vampire Slayer

Certain very popular TV series appear to be lost in annual limbo. We welcome any feedback from readers who own or come across any of the following titles, either in their own annuals or hidden away in other titles. Acknowledgements will be featured in the next edition. You can always email us at sales@ukcollectibles.co.uk

COLLECTORS CORNER

WITH GARY GRAHAM

How long have you been collecting Annuals?
I've been collecting annuals for about 10 years. Myself as well as most children during their childhood received annuals as 'Gift-Books' mainly at Christmas and on birthdays, but with time many were discarded. Mine however were not. This is where I believe my interest stemmed from and influenced me years later to start collecting.

What types of Annuals do you collect?
When I first started collecting annuals I only collected titles relating to my favourite T.V shows e.g, Six Million Dollar Man, Dr Who, Star Trek, The Sweeney, The Professionals and Minder. Before long I was bitten by the annual collecting bug and began collecting as many 60s, 70s and 80s T.V show related annuals as I could lay my hands on. Since then my interests have branched into different genres, namely, Pop music, Marvel superheroes, sci-fi and cartoon. I am always on the look out for new and undiscovered titles especially, but anything I come across sporting the word annual will be snapped up immediately and be given a loving home in my collection.

Why do you like collecting them?
There are so many annuals out there covering different interests and titles but there is one thing they all have in common. The subject of the annual and the material

contained within it all relates to whatever year that particular annual represents. Some annuals contain such varied features and information they are like a snap shot in time that the reader can look back on. They remind us of our childhood, the way things used to be and how time has changed. It's the nostalgia trip I experience which is responsible for why I

like collecting annuals.

Do you recall buying your first annual?
The first annual I ever bought was a 1978 Professionals annual produced by Brown & Watson. I purchased it from a second-hand bookshop whilst on holiday in Weymouth in 1990.

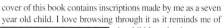

What is your favourite Annual and why?
My favourite annual has got to be my Look In Annual from 1977. This was the first annual my parents bought me as a child. There are loads of features within it that were of great interest to me at that time and still are. Also the inside front cover of this book contains inscriptions made by me as a seven year old child. I love browsing through it as it reminds me of the child I used to be.

> *They remind us of our childhood, the way things used to be and how time has changed. It's the nostalgia trip I experience which is responsible for why I like collecting annuals"*

Where do you find them?
I have obtained my annuals from many different sources in the past, mainly second-hand shops and collectors fairs. I have also obtained them from jumble sales and charity shops but I have found these to be an unreliable source for quality collectable annuals. Nowadays I surf the net for annuals. eBay is my personal favourite for its variety of choice and quality of product.

What's the most you have ever paid for an Annual?
The most I have ever paid for an annual is £25 for a 1965 Dr Who Annual featuring William Hartnell.

DAMAGE, STORAGE & GRADING

BY PAUL GREEN

It's a sad fact of life that the majority of vintage annuals have been mishandled to varying degrees. This is quite understandable given the fact that they were given as Christmas gifts to youngsters. A collector can take some comfort in the fact that a soiled or damaged annual reached that state due, in part, to continued reading. Like a tattered teddy bear a damaged annual can actually be seen as a sign of the affection it held for the young owner.

We first approach the unpleasant subject of damage caused by 'environmental' elements. Chief among these being the insect. The most common and well known devourer of annuals, or any books for that matter, is the book louse aka dustlouse, belonging to an order (Psocoptera) of approximately 1600 species! These insects (1-7mm in length) proliferate in damp conditions and feed on cloth, organic glue, silk, leather, starch, lichens and mould.
The nocturnal silverfish aka fish moth (Lepisma saccharina) is approx 12mm in length. They delight in feeding on starchy materials and cellulose. Easily recognised by their fast movement and silvery-scaled bodies they love warm, dark, damp areas.

Wood boring beetles come in a variety of species. Annual and book lovers should be wary of the reddish-brown furniture beetles (Coleoptera). The infamous book worms include the larvae of these insects. Upon hatching the larvae will bore their way through page upon page of your beloved book. Board backed annuals are no barrier to these determined book-worms. Once hatched, and if undetected, they can continue burrowing into your books for up to five years!

House moths (Lepidoptera-Oecophoridae) are a similar menace to the furniture beetle in that the cocoons can lay dormant and undetected in the pages of a book before they begin their path of destruction as they eat at the starch and glue. A simple solution to help eradicate insect infestation is to store your annuals in dark, cool areas.

Lighting is another major 'environmental' factor in the damage of annuals. We've all seen the faded colours of old books and magazines in shop windows. The ultra-violet light from the sun is the culprit. Annuals should always be stored away from any prolonged exposure to bright light, including flourescent lighting.

High temperatures are also to be avoided. Apart from the obvious effects of leaving an annual in bright sunlight annuals should always be stored away from radiators, pipes and insulated attics or roof areas. Moulds and fungus will occur under these conditions with the subsequent attraction for various insects. The ideal temperature is 40-50°F or less with a relative humidity of 50 percent.

One of the most common forms of 'non-environmental' damage to annuals is a torn spine. This is nearly always the result of poor handling. The top of the spine is usually used to pull the annual from bookshelves. The result, after repeated mishandling, is a torn spine. A book should always be removed from a shelf by placing the hands in the middle of the spine. Given the poor construction of certain 'modern' annuals even this can cause damage to the spine. In this case the best method is to place the hands on the front and back covers although this can prove difficult in tightly packed shelves. Which conveniently leads to my next point. Always avoid placing annuals tightly together. Apart from the obvious difficulties of removing individual annuals tight packing can result in misshapen books.

Stacking books on top of each other creates more problems. The sheer weight will cause annuals near the bottom of the pile to be damaged and misshapen. Leaving individual annuals on a carpeted floor can also encourage insect infestation. Even the cleanest of carpets harbours various mites.

Storage in boxes will almost always cause acid damage. Browning and brittle pages will occur. Acid free boxes are therefore essential. Annuals can also be stored in plastic bags to protect them from all the damaging elements previously mentioned. Plastic bags also contain damaging acids and should be replaced every 2-3 years.

GRADING

One aspect of collecting that causes the most controversy is grading. Unscrupulous dealers will often place a high grade on a title to ensure a greater financial return. Annuals should be inspected carefully before agreeing on a price. A VF cover does not guarantee VF contents. Another common practise is the removing or clipping of the price which is often displayed in the bottom right hand corner of the endpaper. This will drop a VF copy by one full grade. Avoid dealers who claim to have Mint condition copies. Near Mint is the highest grade, but very scarce in vintage annuals. The same rules that apply to the grading of comics apply to annuals. Exceptions include the hardback covers, which often show the most common wear, especially on the spine and the tendency to write dedications or complete puzzles in the contents.

Look for the following when grading annuals -
1) Yellowing pages
2) Signs of wear to the spine or corners of the cover

3) Indentations or marks on the covers. People often use annuals as surfaces to write letters or notes on.
4) Scribbling or writing on the pages
5) Creased pages and turned over corners
6) Water damage resulting in rippled or stained pages
7) Cut or torn pages

Low grade copies are self evident. They will include one or all of the following -
1) Cover detached from contents
2) Heavily taped spine or contents
3) Brown and brittle pages. Mould may be evident
4) Heavy scribbling including use of felt tip pen or markers
5) Crudely coloured b/w pages
6) Badly torn or missing pages

REPAIR & RESTORATION
Annual or book repair and restoration are specialised areas and shouldn't be attempted by the amateur. Any sign of repair will reduce the value of the annual. While it may look better in your collection the fact is, it won't be in it's original form. Any collector wishing to follow this path is advised to contact a professional restorer. But they must never attempt to sell the restored annual as a genuine Near Mint item. This is deception and greatly undermines the market. A restored annual should be valued at the price of an unrestored annual in VG condition.

GRADING

MINT (M)
Perfect, new copy. Rarely exists unless it is an untouched, uncirculated copy kept on file by the publishers.
NEAR MINT (NM)
As new. Very few faults. Extremely rare grade for older annuals. Some dealers grade NM copies as NM+ or NM- depending on the condition. If in doubt it is preferable to grade as VF.
VERY FINE (VF)
Very slight wear, but still an excellent copy. May have minimal spine or cover corner damage caused by storage.
FINE(F)
The basic desirable grade. Shows signs of wear but nothing that defaces the copy in a serious way.
VERY GOOD (VG)
Obviously second-hand. May contain writing, spine and cover wear or moderately creased or turned over pages.
GOOD (G)
Well read copy. Will have a worn cover, spine or contents, but everything is still intact.
FAIR (F)
May contain clipped panels, tears and heavy creases. The spine may have small portions missing and the cover may be slightly defaced. This is still a moderate collectable copy. If in doubt grade it Poor.
POOR (P)
Heavily soiled and damaged. May have portions of cover(s), spine or pages missing. Heavy taping, stains or excessive scribbling all contribute to a poor grade copy. Usually only very rare titles are collected in this grade.

WHO YA GONNA CALL?

THE REAL GHOSTBUSTERS
BY PAUL GREEN

Sharp-witted Peter Venkman, eccentric Egon Spengler, mechanically minded Ray Stantz, practical Winston Zeddmore, sarcastic Janine Melnitz and ever hungry Slimer made the transistion from live action movie adventures to animation courtesy of DIC studios and the American ABC network on 13th September 1986. Named 'The Real Ghostbusters' due to the rights of the name 'Ghostbusters' being granted to rival animation studio Filmation, the DIC version soon became the viewer's favourite.

Merchandising spin-offs followed as the show went into syndication, combining the spin-off series 'Slimer!' with the original 'Real Ghostbusters', under the title 'Slimer! and the Real Ghostbusters'. In the UK 'The Real Ghostbusters' was broadcast on the Children's ITV network and quickly gained a popular following.

The first UK annual was produced by Chad Valley (1988/89) and featured a mixture of comic strips and illustrated text stories. Marvel UK then took over publication of the annual which it published alongside it's monthly comic.

The annual boasted some excellent artwork from Phil Gascoine, Kevin Hopgood, Anthony Williams, Andy Lanning, Andy Wildman and Brian Williamson among others. Regular writers included John Carnell, Ian Rimmer and Dan Abnett.

The first published annual comic strip was a two-part Ian Rimmer story 'The Spook From Outer Space' involving an alien poltergeist who feeds on proton particles. 'Monster Movie' from the same Chad Valley annual cleverly provides continuity with the 1984 live action 'Ghostbusters' film. Making a film about busting ghosts is even harder than busting ghosts in real life", comments Ray Stantz

As the team take a break from filming their latest scene for 'Ghostbusters' they encounter a re-animated Mummy. They learn that monster maker Boris Carloft is haunting the studios and bringing his creations back to 'life' in anger at not being credited for his work when alive. To make him happy Venkman decides to finally give Boris the credit he's longed for. He stars as Stay-Puft in 'The Ghostbusters'!

John Carnell's inventive story and Anthony Williams and Paul Marshall's detailed artwork make this a memorable five page strip.

By 1992 the series had run its course and the annual and comic ceased publication. A 1997 'next generation' animated series 'Extreme Ghostbusters' made little impact on the UK market and 'The Real Ghostbusters' remains the most sought after collectable outside of the movie franchise.

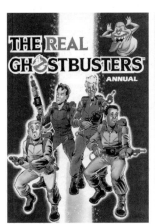

1989

1990

1991

ROY OF THE ROVERS

BY MARK TOWERS

Roy Race - 2000
(Drawn by Barrie Mitchell)

Roy Race, soccer star, first appeared in Amalgamated Press' new sports and adventure comic, Tiger, in September 1954. The first issue showed Roy playing for Milton Youth Club in a local cup-tie. In true storybook fashion the score was still 0-0 with only minutes to go, but Roy, tireless and still on his toes, pounced on a loose ball, pushed it past a lunging defender and ripped a shot towards the goal from the edge of the six yard box, which flew past the visitor's goalkeeper. Watching the match was Alf Leeds, Chief Scout for the famous Melchester Rovers. Spotting a potentially great talent, Alf invited Roy to join the First Division side's youth team. And so began a marriage made in alliterative heaven.

Frank Pepper, creator of Roy of the Rovers, had previously written 'Danny of the Dazzlers' for the Champion comic. He was asked to produce a more realistic football strip for Amalgamated's latest title. His brief was to show an ordinary lad with talent, joining a top-class club of long tradition, as a very humble junior who gradually makes his way up the ladder, until he becomes a star. The editor's were looking for a character the young readers could identify with and ultimately aspire to. Frank Pepper quit after only four issues (returning again in the 1960's). Frank's work schedule had become overloaded with various stories including the space-faring comic strip adventures of 'Captain Condor'. Roy of the Rovers artist Joe Colquhoun, adopted the pseudonym Stewart Colwyn, and scripted the story for four-and-a-half years. This included work in the excellent first Roy of the Rovers Annual in 1958. A year that also saw Roy become captain of Melchester Rovers.

During the latter part of Stewart Colwyn's stint as writer, Derek Burnage, the sub-editor (later editor) on Tiger wrote the majority of the scripts. In February 1960 the front page of the Tiger weekly comic blazed with the news that real-life Manchester United and England soccer hero Bobby Charlton was writing Roy's adventures. Unknown to the

readers it was in fact Derek Burnage. Under Bobby Charlton's (Burnage's) direction Roy led Melchester Rovers to FA Cup glory in 1961.

In the early 1960's Paul Trevillion illustrated the story. Paul has been rightly acclaimed as one of the finest sports artists in Europe. In the Roy of the Rovers 2000 Annual, Paul says, "I always felt the weight of Roy's many fans who expected so much from the artwork. It is a stage in my career I look back on with a great deal of affection." Paul's international career has taken him around the world and his high quality artwork has appeared in books, magazines and newspapers. His range of sports artwork includes basketball, American Football and golf.

Tom Tully was the last and longest running writer for Roy of the Rovers. He began scripting the story in the late 1960's and continued writing his adventures until the closure of the comic in 1993. Tom also wrote the Nipper comic strip, which appeared in both the Tiger and Roy of the Rovers comics. Tom was responsible for giving Roy a life outside of football. Roy married his secretary Penny (nee Laine!) in 1976; had twins Roy and Melinda and later another daughter named Diana.

Roy of the Rovers across the decades. (1950 to 2000). These images show how different artists have drawn "Roy of the Rovers" over the generations starting with Joe Colquhoun from the left and Barrie Mitchell's new "Roy" of the Rovers at the far right.

He briefly managed England in 1978, and in 1981 crazed TV actor Elton Blake shot him "JR Ewing style". This was also the year that Melchester Rovers were relegated from the old Division One (Premier League). Roy recovered from the shooting, quit the Rovers and joined Walford Rovers in 1983, only to return and rebuild his team after a terrorist bomb tore through the tour bus killing many of Roy's long standing team-mates. An earthquake ripped through the pitch at Mel Park in 1988, forcing Rovers to move their home games to Wembley, long before Arsenal had the idea!

David Sque had illustrated the story in the early 1980's but when the comic was revamped in 1990 credits were finally given to contributing artists and writers. Mike White became the first artist to be credited. Mike drew the Roy story from August 1986 to October 1992. He is one of the best known illustrators of "Roy of the Rovers". One of his most popular covers was for the book "Roy of the Rovers - The Playing Years". He has more recently designed one of the four new Royal Mail Millennium stamps, issued in June 1999. The 26p First Class stamp, number 27, "World Cup" celebrates England's 1966 win and surely one of the most memorable days of the 20th century for any England fan.

Another memorable day of the footballing 20th century was 20th March 1993. However, this day was memorable for different reasons. Roy Race had a tragic helicopter accident ending with the loss of his left foot and the closure of the Roy of the Rovers comic. The last regular annual was produced in 1994 and the story temporarily survived for a turbulent 18 issues in the Roy of the Rovers monthly. Roy came back to the fore in May 1997 as part of the launch of the Match of the Day Magazine. Sadly his wife Penny remained absent. Mystery still surrounds the exact circumstances of her death.

The story is still produced monthly for the magazine and has gained a new audience and increased popularity. Roy's son Roy junior (nicknamed Rocky) now wears the famous number 9 shirt, under the guidance of his father, the club's non playing manager. Ian Rimmer currently writes the story. Ian's ability as a writer is shown by the way he skilfully brings the story to life and covers a number of issues, which are intrinsic to the storyline each month. Current readers are pleased to have Barrie Mitchell drawing the storyline again. Barrie drew the strip for the last six months of the comic and he has made a welcome return in the Match of the Day magazine.

Barry and Ian are to be applauded for their part in the year 2000 Annual. This was produced to celebrate the Millennium and is full of interesting facts and details from the Roy of the Rovers story across the years and includes a new feature length storyline. Roy has also hit the net with his own official website at www.royoftherovers.com. There is information, nostalgic and new, and lots of topical football comment.

Roy player managing England in 1978 flanked by Trevor Francis (left) and Malcolm MacDonald (right). Drawn by David Sque.

Roy Race as drawn by Mike White 1991.

Roy Race as drawn by Mike White early 1990's.

Roy and some of the Rovers - Late 1970's

Roy as he first appeared in the Tiger comic in September 1954. Drawn by Joe Colquhoun.

See how Roy's hit the Net at

www.royoftherovers.com

Buy and sell your old annuals and comics in the Collectors Corner.

Catch up on Roy's stories old and new and check out the characters in the Who's Who.

These are just some of the many things which are available for you!

GREEN'S GUIDE

1950-2001

All prices quoted are intended as a guide and are not definitive values. Average current values are listed.

All prices are for strictly graded annuals in Very Fine condition.

NM = + 20-25% to VF value
VF = Value shown in Guide
F = -33% from VF
VG = - 50% from VF
G = -66% from VF
Price clipped annuals = one full grade of condition less

Grading guidelines can be found in the 'Storage of Your Annuals' section

The years listed in bold under each title indicate the years of publication of the annual.

The copyright symbol before each date indicates the year wasn't printed on the cover. As all UK annuals are published the year before the cover date, for example, a ©1999 annual will in fact be the 2000 annual.

Abbreviations used within the Price Guide -

© = copyright	N/D = not dated	fc = full-colour
tc = two-colour	bw = black & white	lw = line & wash
pg = pages	dj = dustjacket	

In listing the annuals the following is an example of the abbreviations used -

80pg fc/tc/bw = 80 pages featuring full-colour, two-colour and black & white content.

In listing the comic strips and features the following is an example of the abbreviation used -

2x4fc= features two, four page comic strips in full-colour

SELECTED 2001 ANNUALS

Art Attack	Dandy	Rupert
Action Man	DC Annual	Sesame Street
Animal Hospital	Digimon	Shoot
Bagpuss	Disney & Me	Sindy
Barbie	Disney Princess	Smart
Barney	Fireman Sam	Steps
Bash Street Kids	Girl Talk	Thomas Tank
Beano	Letterland	Thunderbirds Top Secret
Beezer	Looney Tunes	Tigger
Blue Peter	Marvel Comics	Tweenies
Bob the Builder	Match of the Day	Twinkle
Boyzone	Max Steel	Walking with Dinosaurs
Britney Spears	Mickey Mouse	Westlife
Brownie	Noddy	Winnie the Pooh
Cartoon Network	Pokemon	WCW
Childrens ITV	Postman Pat	World Wildlife Fund
Cub & Beaver Scout	Ricky Martin	

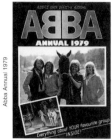

All prices are for strictly graded annuals in Very Fine condition.

ABBA (Stafford Pemberton)
1977-1983 (48pg)
1977 - 'Abba Gift Book' £12 $19
1978 (48pg) £10 $16
Features: The Abba Story, Stig Anderson, Profiles and pin ups
1979-1983 £8 $13
1979 (48pg)
Features: Profiles, Dinner with Abba, Pin ups and Quizzes
1980 (48pg)
Features: Abba - The Story Goes On, Abba Grub, On the Road, Baby Abbas, Stockholm, Discography, Have An Abba Christmas, Abba A-Z
1981 (48pg)
Features: Stig Anderson, pin ups, Abba Solo, Fleetwood Mac, The Eagles, Unicef Concert, The Bee Gees
Photo Covers
Based on the Swedish pop group

ACE REPORTS (World)
1982 £5 $8
©1981 (64pg)
Features: Wayne Laryea Q&A, Wildfowl Trust, Go Karting, Sharon Davies Swimmer, BMX, An Unusual Theatre, Future in Space, Torville & Dean, Lark Hill Place, History of Toys
Text Story: The Tenth Planet, Writer: Bill Price
Based on the Childrens ITV show

ACTION (IPC)
1977-1985
1977-1979 £8 $13
1978 (144pg) (fc/tc/bw)
Comic Strips: Flying Fortress (26fc/bw), Hook Jaw (8bw), Dredger (6bw), Nero Cortez Emperor of Crime (13bw), Dredger (8tc), Double Dynamite (8tc), Look out for Lefty! (8bw), Hell's Highway (5bw), Rory Macduff and the Phantom Legion (15bw)
1979 (128pg)
Comic Strips: Dredger (8tc), The Fat Man (4tc), Rory Macduff and the Whispering Menace (11bw), Cliff Hanger (3bw), The Suicide Club (3x3bw), Spinball (8fc), Look out for Lefty (8bw), Cliff Hanger (3bw), Hook Jaw (8fc), Code Name - Barracuda (8bw), Cliff Hanger (3bw), Simon Test and the Islands of Peril (13bw)
1980-1985 £6 $10
1981 (128pg)
Comic Strips: The Man with the Dollar Brand (7tc), Dredger in the Agent Vanishes (8tc), Look out for Lefty (8bw), Thunder Bill (10bw), Hook Jaw (8fc), Flying Ace Battler Briton and the Secret Weapon (4bw), Spinball (8tc), The Coffin Sub (6bw), Hellman of Hammer Force (15bw)
1982 (128pg) (fc/tc/bw)
Comic Strips: The Knight From Nowhere (3), Menace of the Stormtroopers (10), The Haunted Ship (20), Piracy on Satellite Seven (9), Rough Justice (8fc), Tobruk (13), The Smugglers (2fc), The Ton-Up Trio (13), Black Dragon's Perilous Quest (10)
Text stories include: Dredger of D.I.6 in Dead Man's Secret and 4 Minutes to Die
1983 (128pg)
Comic Strips: The Jailbird Commandos (8bw), Creatures of Fire (6bw), The Slithering Menace (8bw), Magnificent Mounties (3bw), Battleship Buster (8tc), Cap'n Codsmouth (7tc), Experiment X (6bw), The Quest for the Diamond Egg (8fc) The Legend of Benkei (5bw), The Space Freighters (8bw), The Gallant Six Hundred (6bw)

ACTION BOOK FOR BOYS (Purnell)
1968 £8 $13
ACTION BOOK FOR GIRLS (Purnell)
1968 £8 $13
©1967
Comic Strips (bw): Journey Into Danger (10) Caroline Baker in The Case of the Forged Rembrandt (6)
Text Stories (bw): The Mascot of St. Mary's by Daphne Dublane, The Happy Failure by Winifred Norling, A Riddle at Charters by Bertha Leonard, Sylvie in Skye by Mabel E. Allen Trouble for Tessa by G. E. Breary, The Tiger Tulip by Susan Groom, A Nice Time on the River by A. E. Seymour

ACTION FORCE (Marvel)
1985-1989
1985 £8 $13
1986 -1989 £6 $10
©1987 (64pg)
Comic Strips (2x22fc):
Cobra Island (Part 1) Hydrofoil - Writer: Larry Hama, Pencils: Rod Whigham, Inks: Andy Mushynsky
Cobra Island (Part 2) Strategic Diplomacy - Writer: Larry Hama, Pencils: Rod Whigham, Inks: Williams
Text Stories: Night Fighting, Writer: Steve Alan, Art: Kev Hopgood
©1988 (64pg)
Comic Strips (2x22fc):
The Old Switcheroo - Writer: Larry Hama, Art: Herb Trimpe,
Words of Honour - Writer: Larry Hama, Art: Herb Trimpe
Text Story: Havoc in the Outback! - Story: Dan Abnett, Art: Jerry Paris

'G.I. JOE - THE ACTION FORCE'
1990-1991 £8 $13
1991 (64pg) (fc)
Cover Art/ Endpaper: Robin Smith, Editor: Steve White, Design: Andy Seddon
Comic Strips: Mexican Holiday (22), Writer: Michael Fleisher, Pencils: Javier Saltares, Inks; Jose Marzan
Piece Of The Action (10), Writers: Stan Abnett, Steve White, Art: Stewart Johnson
Text Story: Action Of The "Tiger!", Writer: Dan Abnett, Art: Stewart Johnson

ACTION MAN (Stafford Pemberton/IPC/Pedigree)
1979-1985, 1996-Present
1979 (Stafford Pemberton) (64pg) (fc) £10 $16
Comic Strips: Below Zero (6), Ransom - Five Million Pounds (4)
Text Stories: The Ghost Pagoda, Force 136, Up Periscopes
1980-1985 £7 $11
1980 (Stafford Pemberton)
Comic Strips (fc): The French Connection, Death in the Mountains
1996-2000 £5 $8
1996 (Pedigree) - Bumper Annual (48pg) (fc)
Comic Strips (fc): Combat - The Mission (10)
Combat - Amazonia Adventure (9)
Text Story: Tokyo Terror
1998 (Pedigree) (112pg) (fc)
Comic Strips: The Omega Mission (112pg)
Mission Omega (70pg) (3 Chapters)
2000 (Pedigree) (112pg) (fc)
Comic Strips: Millenium Crisis, Maximum Velocity, Paws For Thought, Netscape, Mega Bite

ADAM ADAMANT
1968 £15 $24
Based on the BBC fantasy series
ADAM & THE ANTS (Stafford Pemberton)
1983 (48pg) (fc/bw) £6 $10
Features: Message from Adam, Adam's Progress, Adam's Mentors,
First Lines, Image and Lifestyle Influences, Adam's Name, Videos,
Ant Family Tree, Ants Past and Present, Discography, Adam's
Views, Ant-icipations
Photo Cover
Based on the UK pop group
ADVENTURE (Boardman)
1953 £15 $24
Features: Swift Morgan, Roy Carson Art: Denis McLoughlin
ADVENTURES IN THE DC UNIVERSE (Pedigree)
1999-2000
2000 (112pg) (fc) £5 $8
Comic Strips: Batman: All Hellgrammite Breaks Loose! (22)
Script: Stan Vance, Pencils: John Delaney, Inks: Ron Boyd
Aquaman: Battle Royal (10)
Script: Stan Vance, Art: Delaney & Cooper
The JLA in Cipher Rules!
Script: Stan Vance, Pencils: John Delaney, Inks: Ron Boyd
Superboy & The Flash: Not Always to the Swift... (15)
Script: Steve Vance, Pencils: John Delaney, Inks: Ron Boyd & Ray
Kryssing - Reprints #14
Wonder Woman & Catwoman: The Truth About Cats And Gods!
(22)
Script: Stan Vance, Pencils: John Delaney, Inks: Ron Boyd
First published in Adventures in the DC Universe comic book
THE ADVENTURES OF ROBIN HOOD (Adprint)
1956-1960's
1956 (No.1) £20 $32
1957-1959 £15 $24
1960 on £10 $16
© 1959 - (96pg) Annual No. 4 - Adapted by Harold Ramsey
Art: R.S. Embleton
Comic Strips (2x4bw): The Haunted Abbey, The Tunnel
fc & bw illus text stories
Based on the TV series starring Richard Greene
THE ADVENTURES OF SIR LANCELOT (Adprint)
1957-1958
No.1- © 1957 £20 $32
No.2 - © 1958 £15 $24
Art: Ron Embleton
Based on the TV series starring William Russell
The AERONAUTS (World)
1973 (96pg) (fc) £10 $16
Comic Strip: Writer: Jean-Michel Charlier, Art: Jijé, Translations:
Charles A Pemberton
Based on the French comic strip and TV series
A-HA Special (Grandreams)
1987-1988 £6 $10
©1986 (64pg)
Cover photographs by Duncan Raban - Text by John Kercher
Features: The Aha Story, pin ups, Did you know..., Morten Harket,
Starsigns, Magne Furuholmen, The Aha Quiz, Pal Waaktaar, A
Week in the life of Aha

©1987 (64pg)
Features: Aha Story, Aha on Aha, Morten Harket, Feelings on
Fashion, The Aha Quiz, Pal Waaktaar, Love Match, Family Facts,
30 Things to Know, Magne Furuholmen, The Boys & Britain, The
World Tour, Questions & Answers, Record Review, A Day in the Life
of Aha
Photo Covers
Based on the Norwegian pop group
AIRWOLF (World)
1980's £7 $11
1986 (64pg) (fc)
Text Stories: A Hostage to the Storm, Shotgun Doublecross, Desert
Death Trap, Flames Over the Water, Border Incident, In the Shadow
of the Wolverine, Day of the Hunter,
Comic Strip (fc): Snow to Eskimos (6)
Based on the TV action adventure series
AJAX ADVENTURE (Popular Press)
1950's £20 $32
ALADDIN Disneys (Fleetway)
©**1993** (64pg) (fc) £6 $10
Based on the Walt Disney animated movie
ALF- 'No Problem!' (World)
1989-1990 £6 $10
1989 (64pg)
Text Stories: Summer Camp Adventure (20)
Writer: Harry Coe Verr, Art: Eldon Doty
The Great Alfonso (17)
Writer: Roxanne Ruth-Stephens, Art: Eldon Doty
A Day At The Fair (18)
Writer: Johnson Hill, Art: Eldon Doty
Stories previously published by Checkerboard Press, New York
Based on the TV comedy series
ALIAS SMITH & JONES (World)
1976-1977
1976 £10 $16
Endpaper: Glenn Rix
Comic Strips (featuring Murphy and Davies):
Ride For Freedom (6fc), Art: Martin Asbury
Smokescreen (10tc), Art: Martin Asbury (uncredited),
Fight For Freedom (10fc) - Photo Finish (6tc)
Stories and feature art: A Fair Day's Pay, The Winner, Alias Kid
Curry, Art: Paul Crompton,
Wild Wild Women, They Helped..., Songs of the Outlaw, Quickdraw
Quips, Life on the Western Frontier - Art: Paul Green
Starring Ben Murphy as Kid Curry and Roger Davies as Hannibal
Heyes
Note: Roger Davies' surname is mis-spelt on the cover credits
Photo Cover featuring Ben Murphy, Roger Davies
1977 £8 $13
Cover art: Paul Crompton
Based on the TV Western comedy series
ALI CAT (Stafford Pemberton)
1979 (64pg) (fc) £4 $7
Artwork by Mostyn
Features: Magic Tricks, Ali's Magic Trip Game
Comic Strips: Ali Fools a Thief (4), Skateboard Crazy (6), Icy
Business (6)
Text Stories: Putting on a Show, Broom Boogie, Ali on the Carpet,
Ali Magic

Allo Allo 1989

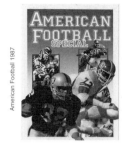

American Football 1987

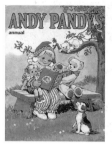

Andy Pandy 1975

Based on the childrens HTV puppet series
ALL CREATURES GREAT & SMALL (Stafford Pemberton)
1980's £7 $11
1982 (80pg) (fc/tc/bw)
Editor: Eve Sumner
Art: Graham Fryer, Edgar Hodges
Features: Herriot's Yorkshire, Christopher Timothy profile, The Milk on your Doorstep, A Year in the Life of a Shepherd, Robert Hardy profile, Follow the Vets game, Working Dogs, Peter Davison profile, Feathered Friends, A Litter of Piglets, Keeping a Pony, Rabbits, The People Who Care, Carol Drinkwater profile, The County Show
Photo Cover
Based on the BBC vetinary TV series

ALLO ALLO (Grandreams)
1989 (64pg) £8 $13
Comic Strips (2x8) - Art: Andy Hunt
Text Story: Message Understood, Come Fly With Me!,
Interviews: Gorden Kaye, Carmen Silvera
Profiles: Vicki Michelle, Richard Marner, Arthur Bostrom, Richard Gibson, Guy Siner, Kim Hartman, Jack Haig, Rose Hill profile, Gavin Richards, Sue Hodge
Pin Up: Rose Hill
Photo Cover
Based on the BBC comedy series

ALL SAINTS Totally Unofficial 100% Special (Grandreams)
©1998 (64pg) (fc) £4 $7
Written & designed by Teresa Maughan
Based on the UK girl band

ALL STARS FOOTBALL BOOK (World)
1968-1975
1968-1970 £7 $11
©1969 (124pg) (bw)
Editor: Jimmy Armfield
Features: Billy Bremner, Colin Bell, Tony Green, Howard Kendall, Alex Stepney, Colin Suggett, Willie Wallace, Les Barrett, Stan Mortensen
1971-1975 £5 $8
1975 (96pg) (bw)
Editor: Colin Todd

ALL STARS TELEVISION ANNUAL (Panda)
1973 (96pg) £12 $19
Features: Magpie, Harry Secombe, Tightrope, Follyfoot, Catweazle, Roger Moore, Steptoe and Son, Jack Wild, Top of the Pops
Comic Strips: Scooby-Doo , Harlem Globetrotters, Steptoe and Son, Banana Splits

ALPHABET ZOO (ITV Books)
1984 (64pg) (fc) £4 $7
Art: Valerie Pye & David Clark - Stories by Frances Kennett
Based on the childrens TV series starring Nerys Hughes and Ralph McTell

AMERICAN FOOTBALL Special (Grandreams/Marvel)
1988-1990 £4 $7
©1987 (Grandreams) (64pg)
©1988 (Grandreams) (64pg)
©1989 (Marvel) (64pg)

ANDY PANDY's Annual (Purnell)
1960's-1970's
1960's £12 $19

©1967 (80pg)
Picture Strips: The Budgerigar (2fc), The Birthday Cake (2bw), Teddy The Piano Tuner (1tc), The Weather Man (2), Teddy's Bead Belt (2), Teddy's New Tie (2fc)
Text Stories: Andy Pandy's Wigwam, The Farmyard, Teddy's Feather, Looby Loo and the Goat, The Greedy Geese, The Cat and the Mouse, The Rescue
©1968 (80pg) - Art: J. Malone
1970's £8 $13
©1974 (60pg) - Art: Phil Gascoine
Picture Strips: Washing Up, Teddy's Drum, The Melting Igloo
Text Stories: Andy 's Carrying Box, Rags and The Nodding Dog, Looby Loo and the Doves, The Little Horse
Based on the childrens BBC TV puppet series

ANGELS (World)
1977-1978 £7 $11
1977 (78pg)
Art: Edgar Hodges
Profiles: Erin Geraghy, Clare Elizabeth Clifford, Karan David, Julie Dawn Cole, Fiona Fullerton, Lesley Dunlop, Angela Bruce, Faith Brook, Ron Craddock
Features: How Angels was Born, The Lady with the Lamp, The Changing Face of Nursing, Script
Text Story: A Night To Remember, Rules and Regulations,
Photo Cover
1978 (64pg) (fc/tc/bw)
Art: Melvyn Powell, Glenn Rix, Jo Berriman, Paul Green, David Hart
Profiles: Julie Dawn Cole, Angela Bruce, Erin Geraghty, Clare Elizabeth Clifford
Features: Community Nursing, Albert Schweitzer
Text Story: The Red Cross, A Diet of Daffodils, Maureens Problem Patient, A Hectic Life, The Goodwill Errand
Photo Cover
Based on BBC medical drama

ANGELS (City)
1967 (Scarce) £25 $40
Based on Captain Scarlet characters

ANGLERS MAIL (Fleetway)
1970's-1980s
1970's £6 $10
1980's (96pg) (bw) £5 $8
Editor: John Ingham
Based on the fishing magazine

ANIMAL HOSPITAL (EgmontWorld)
1999-present £3 $6
Writer: Michelle O'Connell, Art: Rachel B Stevens
Photo Cover
BBC factual vet series with Rolf Harris

ANIMALS OF FARTHING WOOD (World)
1990's £5 $8
1995 (64pg) (fc)
Picture Strips: The Picnic (4), The Fair (4), Danger! (2), Amazed (4)
Text Stories: The Story of Farthing Wood, Home from Home, The Cut, The Tip, Nearly There....
1996 (64pg) (fc)
Picture Strips: Spring (4), Rescue! (3), The Bonfire (5), The Lost Sheep (2), Writer: Brenda Apsley, Art: Jane Swift
Based on the novels by Colin Dann
Based on the TV animated series

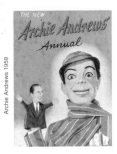

Archie Andrews 1959

The Avengers 1977

Avengers 1970

ANNIE (Marvel/Grandreams)
Not Dated **(Estimate)** 1982 (64pg) £6 $10
Comic Strip Movie adaptation (46fc)
Writer/Artist: Leonard Starr
Features: Profiles on Aileen Quinn, Albert Finney, Carol Burnett,
Bernadette Peters, Tim Curry, Ann Reinking, Ray Stark, John
Huston (includes filmography), Leonard Starr
Photo Cover
Based on the movie

ARCHIE ANDREWS (Preview)
1950's (tc) £25 $40
Edited by Robert Tredinnick and Drawn by Ian Scott

New ARCHIE ANDREWS (Thames Publishing)
1950's £20 $32
©1958 (128pg)
Picture Strips (tc/bw): Archie's Shadow Chase (2tc), Buster's
Slimming Bath (1bw), Archie Scoresa Bully's Eye (1bw)
Text Stories: Fishy Business, Friendly Ponies of the New Forest,
Beware of the Bull, Archie's Fireworks, Archie Andrews Anecdotes,
Rough on Pigs, Pigeon Post, Archie the Music Maker, Archie's
Beanstalks, Ducking for Two, Bath Time for Archie, The Waxwork
Show, Before the Royal Family by Peter Brough, The Great Tie Up,
Brough's Carol Party, Message by Smoke, Archie the Artist, Parrot
Talk, Nettled, Archie's Yule Log
Art: G. Higham

ARNOLD SCHWARZENEGGER Special (Grandreams)
1993
©1992 (48pg) (fc) £5 $8
Layout and Design: Louise Ivimy, Writer: John Kercher
Photo Features: The Early Days, The Films, Red Sonja,
Commando, Predator, The Running Man, Red Heat, Twins, Total
Recall, Kindergarten Cop, Terminator I and II, Anrie Off Duty
Based on the Movie Star

ARTHUR (Grandreams)
2000 (64pg) (fc) £4 $7
Comic Strips: Lemonade Anyone?, Too Many Sweets!, Peace and
Quiet! , Writer: Lynne Gibbs, Art: Chris Russell
Based on the childrens animated TV series

A-TEAM (World)
1985-1988, 1991
©1984 (64pg) (fc) £8 $13
Pin Ups: Hannibal, B.A, Murdock, Face,
Text Stories: Swamp Wreck, When the War Came Back, Seizure at
Sneekerville, Down at the Day Care Centre, The Scuzzball Diamond
Set-To
Comic Strips: ...Buried Alive! (6), ...Bring Him Back Alive! (6)
Strip artwork by Glenn Rix - Photo cover
1986 (64pg) (fc) £6 $10
Art: Walter Howarth, Glenn Rix
Pin Ups: B.A., Hannibal, Murdoch, Face
Text Stories: The Mild Mannered Murderer, Bad Day in the Battle
Zone, In Search of the Seven Golden Orchids, Exit the Dragon, Fast
Train to Medicine Bend, Tarzan of the Farmyard, Some Kind of
Doublecross
Comic Strips (fc): The Night the Face Turned Traitor (6), Jungle
Nightmare (6)
Photo Cover
1987 (64pg) (fc) £5 $8
Pin Ups: B.A., Hannibal, Murdoch, Face

Text Stories: Working the High Steal, The Fall of the Mean
Musketeer, White Water Warriors, The Vengeance of Johnny Cruel
Shoes, 'Gator Bait, The Wrecking of Estaban's Dream. The Storm
Comic Strips (6x2): Idol Talk!, High Sea Hijack - Art: Walter Howarth
1988 (64pg) (fc) £5 $8
Art: Walter Howarth
Text Stories: Carve-Up In No Man's Land, The Princers' Grip, The
Letter, Nukes Jukes and Compulsory Sunglasses, The Prisoner of
the Two Cockatoos
Comic Strips (fc): The Luckiest Punks in the Universe (6) Night of
the Renegades (6)
1991 (Marvel) (64pg) (fc) £6 $10
Profiles: Hannibal, Face, B.A, Murdock
Comic Strips: The Flight of the Redbird! (22) - Script & Inks: Alan
Kupperberg, Inks: Brian Moore
Who Kidnapped Kuramoto (22fc) - Script: Jim Salicrup, Pencils: Jim
Mooney, Inks: Joe Giella
Photo Cover
Based on the action adventure TV series

ATOM ANT (Atlas)
1968 (64pg) (Scarce) £20 $32
Comic Strips featuring Atom Ant, Top Cat, Secret Squirrel and
Quickdraw Mcgraw
Hanna Barbera Title

ATV SHOW BOOK (L.T.A. Robinson/Purnell)
1950's-1960's
1950's £15 $24
1960's £12 $19
Later titled 'ATV Television Show/Star Book'
Number One (not dated)
Features: I Love Lucy, Liberace, My Hero, My Little Margie, Cloak
and Dagger Heroes, Roy Rogers, Sunday Night at the Palladium,
Situation Comedy, The Young Stars, The Gimmick Shows, The
Play's the Thing - bw
©1962 - 'ATV Television Show Book'
'With all the Top Pop Stars' - Features: Lulu and The Saint etc.
Helen Shapiro full colour photo cover
©1962 (80pg bw) 'ATV Television Star Book'
Features: Billy Fury, Bobby Rydell, Joe Brown, Adam Faith, Marty
Wilde, Petula Clark, Susan Maughan,Neil Sedaka, Danny Williams,
Bruce Forsyth, Kenny Ball, Frank Ifield, John Barry, Tommy Steele,
Angela Bracewell, Emergency Ward 10, Ghost Squad, Broadway
Goes Latin, 87th Precint, The Saint (Roger Moore), Westerns
(Bonanza, Outlaws, Cheyenne)
Photo Cover features Billy Fury

AVENGERS (Souvenir/Atlas)
1966-1970
1966 (Thorpe & Porter) £25 $40
1967 (Atlas) - Diana Rigg £20 $32
1968 - Linda Thorson £15 $24
©1969 (Atlas) (76pg) (fc/tc/bw) (Scarce) £20 $32
Comic Strips: Good Guys and Bad Guys (9tc), May I Have This
Trance? (12tc),Thou'rt an Interfering Letter Mr. Steed (8tc)
Text Stories: Don't Go Down the Mine Dad (Mother's Already
There), Come On In the Water's Deadly, What's a Ghoul like you
doing in a Place Like This?
Features: Off-Set with The Avengers, The Avengers Change Gear,
Going Home to Mother
Features: Linda Thorson

Bananaman 1985

Banana Splits 1971

Barbapapa 1977

	£	$		£	$

Cover art by Chantrell
Based on the TV show starring Patrick McNee
The AVENGERS (World)

1975-1978	£10	$16

1977 (80pg) (fc)
Comic Strips: Chapter 1 - Nuklo... The Invader that Time Forgot
(16), Chapter 2 - The Child is Father to The Fiend! (12), Chapter 3 -
What Hell Hath Joined Together (6)
Also Features: Thor & Mantis, Captain America, Iron Man
Writer/Editor: Roy Thomas, Artist: Rich Buckler
Conan The Barbarian - The Dragon from the Inland Sea (19)
Author/Editor: Roy Thomas, Artist: John Buscema
The Mighty Avengers - Right between the Eons (14)
Words & Pictures: Steve Englehart & George Perez, Inks: Sam
Grainger
Cover Art: Gil Kane & Frank Giacoia, Editor: Jim Salicrup
Marvel Comics Characters
BABAR (BBC/Odhams)

1971	£10	$16

Based on the animated TV series
BABY'S OWN Annual (Fleetway)

1982-1983	£5	$8

1982 (48pg) (fc)
Picture Strips: Three Pretty Playful Kittens, Woodland Friends, Little
Boy Blue, Mickey the Mischievous Monkey, The Tidy Pixies, Winkie
the Imp, Gregory Grasshopper and his Friends, Painting Pixie, The
Broken Bridge
1983 (48pg) (fc)
Picture Strips: Sammy the Squirrel, Fairyland Tennis, The Playful
Otter, Gregory Grasshopper, Katie Country Mouse, The Dirty Home,
Three Playful Happy Kittens, Leo and the Fireflies, Playing Hide and
Seek with Rabbit
BABY'S OWN Colour Annual (IPC)

1972	£4	$7

BACKSTREET BOYS 100% Unofficial Special (Grandrams)
1999
©1998 (64pg) (fc) £5 $8
Design by Joanna Davies - Photo features (fc)
Based on the US boy band
BACK TO THE FUTURE (Marvel)
1991
©1990 (64pg) (fc) £6 $10
Editor: John Freeman
Designer: Gary Gilbert
Writers: David Bishop, Randall D. Larson, John Freeman
Photo Features: Profiles on Michael J Fox, Christopher Lloyd, Lea
Thompson
Photo Cover
Based on the Movie
BAGPUSS (BBC)

1974-1975, 2001	£10	$16

1974
Story: Ship in a bottle
Features: How to make Madeleine's Sugar Mice, Madeleine's Finger
puppet mice, A Bagpuss Pyjama Case, the great cheese race game
1975
Story: Owls of Athens
Features: How to make Chocolate Obols, A Lavender Madeleine,
Toad's Treasure Hunt game

Based on the BBC puppet character
BAILEY'S BIRD (Purnell)
1980
©1979 £5 $8
Writer: Stephen Holt
The Wreck on Shark Reefs
Contain complete story split into text chapters and fc/b/w comic
strips
Based on the Australian TV series
BANANAS IN PYJAMAS (World)
1997 (64pg) (fc) £4 $7
Writer: Brenda Apsley and Vicki Adams
Edited by Nina Filipek, Designed and Art: Geoff Ball
Picture Strips: Munchy Honey Cakes Time!, Treasure Ahoy!,
Morgan's Surprise
BANANAMAN (D.C. Thomson)
1980's £8 $13
1985 (96pg) (fc)
Comic Strip:General Blight's Jelly Babies (21), Jungle Fever (12),
Bank Blunders (4), Meets the Mad Magician (12), Aunties Antics
(16), Stormy Weather (11)
Based on the animated TV series
BANANAMAN Storybook Based on the TV Series (St Michael)
1985
©1984 (78pg) £10 $16
Features illustrated stories - Art: Peter Campbell
BANANA SPLITS Hanna Barbera's (World/Atlas)
1970-1971
©1969 (Atlas) (Scarce) £20 $32
©1970 (World) (96pg) (fc) £15 $24
Comic Strips: How to be a Former Farmer (7), Sub-A-Dub-Dub (14),
The Proud Loud Crowd (4), Riddle Me Another (1)
Gold Key Reprints
Text Stories: Twangs a Lot, Showboat Blues, Saddle My Guitar, Dig
That Note!, The Banana Splits, Quit Bugging Me, What A Circus!
Photo Cover
BARBARA WOODHOUSE Animal Annual (Grandreams)
1985 (64pg) (fc/bw) £4 $7
Editor: John Barraclough, Layout & Design: Nigel I Money
Photo cover
Based on the animal trainer
BARBAPAPA (World)
1976-1977 £10 $16
1977 (80pg) (fc)
Based on the BBC TV animated series
BARBIE (Fleetway/Marvel/World/Grandreams/Pedigree)
1984-present
1984 £10 $16
1985-1989 £8 $16
1985 (Fleetway)
Comic Strips: Barbie Works Out (5bw), Skipper Scents Trouble!
(4bw), A Bouquet for Barbie (8bw), The Perfect Picnic (5bw),
Skipper Saves the Day (5bw), Barbie's Greek Adventure (5bw)
Pin Ups: Musical Youth, Limahl, Duran Duran
1986 (Fleetway) (60pg) (fc/bw)
Comic Strips: Barbie Wins Through (5bw), The Smell of Success
(4bw), Barbie's Double Trouble (8bw), Skipper Goes Skiing (5bw),
Skipper's Puppy Love! (5bw), A Birthday to Remember (5bw)

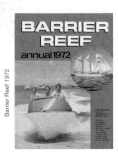

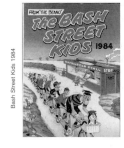

Features: Limahl, Tracey Ullman, Simon Le Bon & John Taylor
Pin Ups: Spandau Ballet, Duran Duran, Wham
1987 (Fleetway) (80pg) (fc/bw)
Comic Strips (bw): Out West With Barbie, Superstar Ken!, Skipper's
Animal Adventure - My Giddy Goat!, The Ruined Christmas, The
Haunting at Kingsville Manor, Spooky Special, The Fairy's Promise,
Debbie's Dearest Friend, Girl of the Forest
Features and Pin Ups: Shakin Stevens, U2, Wham, Lloyd Cole &
The Commotions, Thompson Twins, Tears for Fears, Spandau Ballet
plus Barbie doll layouts
1989 (World) (64pg) (fc)
Comic Strips: That's What Friends are For (6fc), The Surprise Party
(6fc)
1990 - present   £5 $8
©1993 (Marvel) (64pg) (fc)
Comic Strips: Jump for Joy (20), The Big New York Adventure (20)
Text Story: Queen of the Jungle by John Gatehouse, Art: Mario
Capaldi
1995 (Marvel) (96pg) (fc)
Comic Strips (fc): Mystery Mansion (37), Skipper in the Sound of
Music (10), The Fashion Show Must Go On (6)
Photo Strips: Drama in the Snow (5), Barbie's Big Beach Adventure
(5), Ride into Danger (5),
©1995 (Marvel) (64pg) (fc)
Comic Strips (fc): Sweet Sixteen Snowstorm, What Goes Up Must
Come Down (3 part)
1997 (Marvel) (64pg) (tc)
Editor: Jen Wackett
Comic Strips (fc): A Romance to Remember (10)
Photo Story: A Snack for Nibbles (5)
©1997 (Grandreams) (64pg) (fc)
Writer: Caroline Brook
Photo Stories & Features
©1998 (Grandreams) (64pg) (fc)
Writer: Caroline Brook
Photo Stories & Features
2000 (Pedigree)

BARETTA (Brown Watson)
1977   £8 $13
Based on the TV detective series starring Robert Blake

BARNABY (Stafford Pemberton)
1976   £6 $10

BARNEY (World)
1990 (64pg) (fc)   £4 $7
Writer: Peter Bonnici, Art: Edgar Hodges
Comic Strips (3x1): Strike it Lucky, Roger's Regular Excercise, The
Safari
From an original idea by Shirley-Anne Lewis
From characters created by Lisa Kopper
Based on the childrens animated TV series

BARNEY (Grandreams)
2000   £4 $7
Based on the childrens TV series

BARNEY BEAR and DROOPY (World)
1974   £10 $16
Based on the MGM cartoon characters

BARRIER REEF (World)
1972-1973   £7 $13
1972 (80pg) (fc/tc)

Comic Strips: Peril Below (6fc), Shark Ho (6tc)
Text Stories: Stranglehold, Pirates Deep, The Lido and the Lady,
Treachery under the Reef, Mermaid of the Reef, Killer Weed
Photo Cover
1973 (80pg)
Comic Strips: Underwater Peril (8fc), Cave of Gold (8tc)
Text Stories: Blow the Man Down, Phantom in the Mist, No Escape,
Fury from the Deep, Guardian of the Relics
Based on the Australian childrens TV series starring Joe James

BARRY MANILOW Special (Grandreams)
1983
©1982   £8 $13
Photo cover

BASH STREET KIDS Book (D.C.Thomson)
1979-present
1979   £15 $24
1980   £12 $19
1982   £10 $16
1984   £8 $13
1986   £8 $13
1989   £7 $11
1990 - present   £5 $8
Bi-annual in the eighties - Characters from 'The Beano' comic

BASIL BRUSH (World)
1972-1980's   £10 $16
1972 (80pg) (fc/tc)
Comic Strips: The Loch Brush Monster (4fc), Basil Super Salesman
(4tc)
Photo Cover
1974 (80pg) (fc/tc)
Art: John Leeder
Comic Strips: Cooking with Basil (4fc), Basil of the Bugle (4tc)
Photo Cover
1976 (64pg) (fc/tc)
Art: John Leeder
Comic Strips (2x4fc) The Hungry Horse, Hob-Knobbing with No-
Toes
Photo Cover
1977 (80pg) (fc/tc)
Art: John Leeder
Comic Strips (2x4fc): Suitable Suitor, The Missing Money
Photo Cover
1978 (64pg) (fc/tc)
Comic Strips (2x4): Ali Basil and the Portly Thieves (tc), Fobbery
Robbery (fc) - Art: Edgar Hodges
Based on the BBC puppet character

BATMAN ADVENTURES (World)
1996-1997   £6 $10
1996 (64pg) (fc)
Cover Art: Dev Madan
Comic Strips: Good Face Bad Face (22), Writer: Kelley Puckett,
Pencils: Mike Parobeck, Inks: Rick B.
The Joker in Laughter After Midnight (10), Writer: Paul Dini, Pencils:
John Byrne, Inks: Rick Burchett
Toxic Shock (22), Writer: Kelley Puckett, Pencils: Mike Parobeck,
Inks: Rick B
1997 (64pg) (fc)
Based on Batman: The Animated Series

BATMAN (Atlas/Top Sellers/Egmont/ London)

Batman 1989

Battle Picture Weekly 1977

Battlestar Storybook 1979

£ $ £ $

Editions/World/Fleetway/Grandreams)
1950s-1995

	£	$
1960-1961 (Scarce)	£100	$160
1961-1962	£60	$96
1962-1963	£40	$65
1963-1964	£30	$48
1964-1965	£25	$40
1965-1967	£20	$32
1968 (Atlas) Adam West photo cover	£25	$40
1969	£20	$32
1970-1971	£15	$24

1972 - 'Batman and Robin Annual No. 1'
(Brown Watson) - Neal Adams art   £15 $24
1973-1979   £10 $16
1980-1989   £8 $13
1980 (Egmont) (64pg) (fc)
Cover Art: Paul Green
Comic Strips: Batman and Metal Men in The 50-Storey Killer! (20)
Story: Bob Haney, Art: Jim Aparo
... And Be A Villain! (18) - Featuring The Creeper
Story: Denny O'Neill, Art: Irv Novick & Dick Giordano, Editor: Julius
Schwartz, Robin the Boy Wonder in Danger in the Hall of Trophies!
(6), Golden Age classic, I Died A Thousand Deaths (13)
Writer: Frank Robbins, Art: Bob Brown and Joe Giella
1989 (London Editions) (64pg) (fc)
Comic Strips: The Scarecrow's Trail of Fear (18), Editor: Julius
Schwartz, Writer: Denny O'Neil, Art: Ernie Chua and Dick Giordano
The Jokers Playground of Peril, Writer: Denny O'Neil, Assisted by
Julie Schwartz and E Nelson Bridwell, Art: Irv Novick and Bob
Wiacek
The Last Laugh - Editor: Denny O'Neil, Writer: Mike W Barr, Artists:
Alan Davis and Paul Neary
1990's   £6 $10
1991 (World) (64pg) (fc)
Comic Strips: Bat-Mites New York Adventure (6)
Writer: Bob Rozakis, Pencils: Michael Golden, Inks: Bob Smith
The Deadshot Ricochet (17), The Laughing Fish (17), Sign of the
Joker (17)
Writer: Steve Englehart, Pencils: Marshall Rogers, Inks: Terry Austin
1993 (Fleetway Editions)
Comic Strips: While The City Sleeps (12), Artist: Dick Sprang
Sisters In Arms (2 part) (44)
Writer: Alan Grant, Pencils: Norm Breyfogle, Inks: Tim Sale (Part 1),
Steve Mitchell (Part 2), Editor: Dennis O'Neil
©1993 (Ravette)
Comic Strip (fc): Double Image - Art: Jim Baikie
BATMAN & ROBIN (World)
1997 (64pg) (fc)   £5 $8
Comic Strips:Two Timer - Writer: Paul Dini, Pencils: Ty Templeton,
Inks: Rick Burchett, Editor: Scott Peterson
Secret Origin of the Batman (6) - Writer: Kelley Puckett, Pencils:
Mike Parobeck, Inks: Rick Burchett, Editor: Scott Peterson
Trial Run (6) - Writer: Kelly Puckett, Pencils: Mike Parobeck
Inks: Rich Burchett, Editor: Charles Kochman
Reprints from Batman Adventures (DC)
Based on the animated TV series
BATMAN & ROBIN (Grandreams)
1997 (64pg)   £5 $8
Originally published in a different format by Landoll Inc

Photo story
Based on the movie starring George Clooney
BATTLE BEASTS (World)
1988 (64pg) (fc)   £6 $10
Cover Art: Paul Green and Glenn Rix
Endpaper: Paul Crompton
Comic Strips: Trial By Combat (6), Art: Paul Green and Glenn Rix
Feature Art: Paul Crompton, Paul Green, Glenn Rix and Alan
Lindsell
Based on the toy range
BATTLE OF THE PLANETS
1980   £7 $13
Based on the animated TV series
BATTLE PICTURE WEEKLY (Fleetway/IPC)
1976-1988
1976-1979   £8 $10
1977 (144pg)
Comic Strips: Rat Pack (7fc), Lofty's One Man Luftwaffe (8bw),
Sudden Death (24bw), Return of the Eagle (6bw), Rat Pack (9tc),
Desert Hawks (8bw), Dangerous Driving in E-Boat Alley (3bw), The
Battling Butler (17bw), Sergeant Without Stripes (4bw)
Text Stories: Destroy the Dry-Dock!, Blind Alley, Bombers Revenge
1979 (128pg)
Comic Strips: Major Eazy (fc), Wolves, Lofty's One Man Luftwaffe,
Panzer G-Man, Sergeant Rock Special Air Service, D Day Dawson,
The Bootneck Boy, The Flight of Golden Hinde, Pegasus Bridge (tc),
Rat Pack (tc/bw), Johnny Red, The Sarge
1980-1988   £5 $8
1980 (128pg)
Comic Strips: Johnny Red (7fc), Sergeant Without Stripes (4bw),
Day of the Eagle (26), Major Eazy (8bw), Crazy Keller (8bw), Rat
Pack (10tc), The Boy who took the Suicide Express (2bw)
1982 (128pg)
Comic Strips: Charley's War (7fc), Death Squad (6bw), Revenge of
the Eagle (6bw), Johnny Red (8bw), Cowards Brand on Bradley
(34bw), Fighting Mann (6bw), Pipes of Glory(2tc), Rat Pack (6tc),
Desert Dane (3bw), Knights Cross (4bw)
1984 - 'Battle Annual'
1985 - 'Battle Action Force Annual'
1985 - (IPC) (128pg)
Comic Strips: Operation Ironblood (Action Man) (7fc), Charleys War
(8bw), Ambush (Action Man) (8bw), The Bootneck Boy (17bw),
Johnny Red (7bw), The Fortrose Falcon (3bw), The Hunters (8bw),
Hellman of Hammer Force (4bw), Crossfire (Action Man) (10tc), Rat
Pack (6tc), Merrill's Marauders (3bw), Bootneck Boy (Part II) (16bw),
The Forgotten War (4bw), Panic Under Fire (3bw)
Features: Action Force Toys Supplement
1987 - 'Battle Action Force Annual'
1988 - 'Battle Annual'
BATTLESTAR GALACTICA (Grandreams)
1979   £10 $16
©1978 (64pg)
Comic Strips: Battlestar Galactica (3 bw), Chess Players of Space
(4 fc), Bane of Baal Farr (6 fc), Amazons of Space (6 bw)
Art: John Higgins
Includes text stories and colour photo features on Special Effects
guru John Dykstra, Cylons, and the show's main stars
Based on the sci-fi TV series
BATTLESTAR GALACTICA Storybook (Brown Watson)

1979 £10 $16
©1978 (96pg) (fc)
Based on the Movie
BAY CITY ROLLERS (World/Stafford Pemberton)
1975-1977 £12 $19
1976 (Stafford Pemberton) (72pg) (fc/bw)
'Facts, Photo's And Features Of The Fabulous Rollers'
Photographs (fc): David Golumb
Includes profiles of band members, quizzes and pin ups
Based on the UK boy band
BAY CITY ROLLERS ON TOUR (World)
1976
©1975 (48pg) (fc/bw) £12 $19
Cover Art: Paul Crompton
Annual type publication
BAYWATCH (Grandreams)
1996 £5 $8
©1995 (fc)
Writer: Melanie J Clayden, Design by Louise Ivimy
Photo features
Based on the TV series starring David Hasselhoff
BEANO BOOK (D.C.Thomson)
1940 - present
©1939 £1500 $2400
1943-1950 - 'The Magic Beano Book'
1950 £300 $480
1951 - Beano Book £250 $400
1952-1955 £150 $240
1956-1959 £100 $160
1960-1965 £60 $96
1966 - Ist dated cover £60 $96
1967-1970 £40 $60
1971-1975 £20 $32
1976-1980 £15 $24
1981-1989 £12 $19
1990 -present £6 $10
Classic characters featured include:
Dennis the Menace, The Bash Street Kids, Minnie the Minx, Pansy
Potter, The 3 Bears, Lord Snooty, Roger the Dodger and General
Jumbo
Based on the UK comic
BEAVER Annual (Fairhaven Books)
1960's
©1962 (80pg) (fc/bw) (Scarce) £20 $32
Comic Strips (fc): Yogi Bear in No Escape (4), Huckleberry Hound in
The Gorilla Grabber (5), Cowardly K-9 (1), The Flintstones in Four
Alarm Fizzle (5 pg), Toll Crossing (1), Pixie, Dixie and Mr Jinks in
Something Fishy (5), Yogi Bear in Bearly Beat (3)
Picture Strip (5 fc): The Adventures of Billy Beaver
Editor: Nancy Spain, Art: W. S. Greenhalgh
Features articles from Matt Busby, Nancy Spain, Charlie Drake, Cliff
Richard, Tony Warren, Gwen Farran, Eileen Sheridan, Johnny
Leach, Robert Harbin, Jane Dorling, Tom Pugh, Harry Carlisle and
Sheila Van Damm
BEAVIS and BUTTHEAD
1996 £5 $8
Based on the NTV animated characters
BEETLEJUICE (Marvel)
1993 £5 $8

©1992 (64pg)
Cover Art: Brian Williamson, Stephen Baskerville and John Burns
Endpaper: Andy Lannings and John Burns
Editor/Designer: Peri Godbold, Writer: John Carnell
Comic Strips (UK fc): Night Fever (5), Art: Andy Lanning and Lesley
Dalton, Blind Date! (1), Art: Bambos, Fast Food Freak-Out! (5),
Horrible Hobby! (4), Pharoah 'Nuff (5), Art: Anthony Williams and
Lesley Dalton
Based on the animated series
BEEZER BOOK (D.C.Thomson)
1958 - present
©1957 £150 $240
©1958 £70 $110
©1959 £50 $80
©1960-1964 £30 $48
1966 - first dated cover £25 $40
1967-1970 £15 $24
1971-1979 £10 $16
1980-1989 £8 $13
1990-present £5 $8
Classic characters features include: Ginger, Pop Dick and Harry,
The Banana Bunch, Young Sid, The Badd Lads, Baby Crockett,
Little Mo, Colonel Blink, The Numskulls, The Hillys and the Billys
Based on the UK comic
BEHIND THE BIKE SHEDS (Purnell)
1985 (48pg) (fc) £4 $7
Photo Cover
Based on the childrens TV series
BEN CASEY (World)
1963 £12 $19
Based on the US medical drama
BERTHA (Polystyle)
1986 £4 $7
Based on the childrens TV series
BERYL THE PERIL Book (D.C.Thomson)
1958-1990's
©1958 £150 $240
©1960 £70 $110
©1962 £50 $80
©1964 £30 $48
1967-1969 - first dated cover £15 $24
1971-1979 £10 $16
1980-1988 £8 $13
Bi-annual to 1979 then irregular
Based on the DC Thomson character
BEVERLY HILLBILLIES (World)
1960s £15 $24
©1965 (96pg)
Comic Strips (fc): Treasure Hunt, Granny Goes Hunting, Jethro Digs
In, Elly's Turn, End Of The Hunt, Holiday Havoc, The Show Must Go
On, Hillbilly Hands, The Big Night
Photo cover
Based on the TV comedy series
BEVERLY HILLS 90210 Official Annual (World)
1993-1994 £7 $11
1993 (64pg) (fc)
Editor: Dick Wallis, Writer: Lucy Etherington
Features: Series Pilot, Growing Up, The Real Beverly Hills,
Factfiles: Jason Priestley, Shannen Doherty, Jennie Garth, Brian

The Bill 1990

Billy the Kid 1959

Bionic Six 1987

BI

Austin Green, Gabrielle Carteris, Luke Perry, Ian Ziering, Tori Spelling
1994 (64pg) (fc)
Editor: Dick Wallis, Writer: Lucy Etherington
Features: Jason Priestley, After Hours, Shannen Doherty, School's Out, Brian Austin Green, Other Side of the Camera, The Script, Brotherly Love, Luke Perry, Jennie Garth, Downtown, Ian Ziering, Tori Spelling, Heart to Heart, Gabrielle Carteris, Happy Families, Coping with Success
Full colour photo features
Based on the US teen drama

BEWITCHED (World)
1966-1967
©1966 £30 $48
©1967 (96pg) (fc) £25 $40
Text stories: I Married A Witch, Selling Witchcraft!, Hook That Crook!, Mediterranean Magic, Debut For A Witch, A Flying Finish, All's Well
Cover art R.W. Smethurst
Based on the TV comedy series starring Elizabeth Montgomery

BEWITCHED Totally 100% Unofficial Special (Grandreams)
2000 £4 $7
©1999
Based on the Irish girl band

BIG BATTLE ANNUAL (World)
N/D (1960's) (96pg) (fc) £8 $13
War strips and features

BIG COMIC Book (Fleetway/IPC/World)
1980s-1990s
1980s £6 $10
1988 (255pg)
1990s £4 $7
1992 (Fleetway) (256pg) (bw)
Comic Strips include: The Krazy Gang, Robert's Robot, Jack Pott, Toy Boy, Sherlock Jnr, Frankie Stein, The Spooktacular 7, Lazy Bones, Dads as Lads, Sammy Shrink, Calculator Kid, Richie Wraggs, Timothy Tester, Mustapha Mi££ion
1994 (World) (224pg) (bw)
Whizzer & Chips, Whoopee! and Buster comic strip reprints

BIG DADDY
1984 (80pg) (fc/bw) £4 $7
Based on the UK wrestler

BIGGLES (World)
1981 £8 $13
Art: Paul Crompton
©1980 (64pg) (fc/bw)
Picture Strips (2x6fc): Biggles Seeks Revenge, Spitfire Squadron 666 - Includes text stories and single page feature on Biggles' creator Capt. W. E. Johns

BIG SHOW (Hanna Barbera's) (Brown Watson)
1973 £12 $19
©1972 (80pg) - No. 1 (scarce)
Comic Strips: Quick Draw McGraw: The Boothill Brigade (5), Three Times as Bad! (4), I'll Drink Tuh That! (4), After You Ma'm (4), 6 Guns Sam (5), The Build-Up (2) - By J. Gill & G. Wildman, Boss Cat: - The Hopeless Case (4), The Brain Drain (4), A Friend In Need (4), Dibble's Double Duty (8)
Text stories (tc): Quick Draw McGraw in The Taming of 'Shorty' Warty, The Jail-Breakers Boss Cat in Dogs of War, All at Sea

'Featuring Boss Cat & Quick Draw McGraw'
Based on the Hanna Barbera characters

BIKER MICE FROM MARS (World)
1995 (64pg) £8 $13
Comic Strips: Bikes Twice (6fc), The Night When all the Lights Went Off (7fc), Charleys Day Off (4fc)
Written: Margaret McCarthy, Art: : Rob Sharp
Based on the animated series

The BILL (Grandreams)
1990
©1989 (64pg) (fc) £5 $8
Writer: Tony Lynch, Layout/Design: Louise Ivimy
Based on the ITV police series

BILL & BEN
1970's £12 $19
Based on the BBC puppet characters

BILL BOYD Western Comic Annual (L. Miller & Co.)
1957-1960
No.1 £20 $32
No.2-5 £15 $24
©1959 (No.4)
'Explosive Action on the Trails of the Wild and Wooly West'
(bw) comic strips

BILLY BUNTER'S HOLIDAY Annual (Odhams)
1967 £15 $24

BILLY THE KID Western Annual (World)
1950s
©1953 £20 $32
©1954-58 £15 $24
©1953
Features full colour single-page photo of Rex Allen plus bw comic strips
©1958 (96pg) (tc)
Comic Strips: Billy the Kid (2x8), The Brand of Justice, Double Crossing Bandit Reprints U.S. comic, Red Mask (2x6 pg), Death at Split Mesa!, The Man Who Rescued Red Mask - Art: Frank Bolle
Reprints Red Mask comic by Magazine Enterprises
Originally published as 3-D strips
Text Stories: The Black Rider of Sunset Pass, A Bandit for Breakfast by Tex Bland, The End of Red Mask by Hart Cooper, The Sun Swallower by Jay Laurence, The Ransom of Little Bear by Dirk Saxon - Cover art: Walter Howarth
Based on the Western Outlaw

BILLY THE KID Book of Picture Stories
1950s £20 $32

BIMBO Book (D.C. Thomson)
1963-1980s
©1962 £15 $24
©1963-1969 £12 $19
1970's £8 $16
1980's £5 $8

BIONIC SIX (Grandreams)
1987-1988 £5 $8
©1986
Text stories and factfiles
Based on the animated TV series

BIONIC WOMAN (Brown Watson)
1978-1979 £10 $16

Black Hole 1981

Blakes 7 1980

Blue Jeans 1980

©1977 (64pg)
Art: Ian Gibson
Comic Strips: Kidnappers Strike! (5fc), The Heavy Mob (6fc), Secret of the Mountains (6fc)
Photo Cover
©1978 (64pg)
Art: Ian Gibson
Featuring Maximillian the Bionic Dog
Photo Cover
Based on the TV Series starring Lindsay Wagner

BIRTHDAY BOOK FOR GIRLS (Fleetway)

1970s	£8	$13

1972 (128pg)
Incorporating June, School Friend, Princess Tina & Tammy

BJ & THE BEAR (Grandreams)

1981-1982	£7	$11

©1980 (64pg)
Comic Strips: Peak of Imperfection (8bw), Magic Night (8fc), A Bonus for Bear (8bw)
Photo Cover
©1981 (64pg)
Comic Strips: Wheels of Fear (8tc), Diner for Two (8tc), Phantom of the Freeway (8tc)
Photo Cover
Based on TV Series starring Greg Evigan

BLACK BEAUTY (World)

1975-1977	£8	$16

1975 (80pg) (fc/tc/bw)
Endpaper: Glenn Rix
Photo Text Stories:
Photo Cover
1976 (64pg) (fc/tc/bw)
Endpaper: Glenn Rix, Art: Glenn Rix, David Hart, Susan Aspey
Photo Text Stories:
Photo cover
1977 (80pg) (fc/tc/bw)
Cover Art: Glenn Rix
Art: Glenn Rix, Susan Aspey, John Millington, David Hart, Paul Green
Based on the Childrens ITV series

BLACK BEAUTY (World)

1978-1980	£6	$10

1978 (64pg)
Cover art: Glenn Rix
Art: Glenn Rix, David Hart, Paul Green, Susan Aspey
1979 (64pg)
Art: Glenn Rix, Susan Aspey & John Millington
1980 (64pg) (fc/tc)
Cover Art: Glenn Rix, Endpaper: Glenn Rix
Art: Glenn Rix, Susan Aspey, Annabel Spenceley
Based on the characters created by Anna Sewell

BLACK BEAUTY (Opal Quill)

1985	£5	$8

Adaptation of the book by Anna Sewell

BLACK BOB Book (D.C. Thomson)
1950-1965
Not published every year. All oblong format except 1965
Picture strips of a British sheepdog

©1949	£100	$160

1st story -'The Bravery of Bob'

1950	£80	$150
1952	£60	$95
1954	£45	$65
1956	£40	$60
1958	£30	$48
1960	£20	$32
1964	£15	$24

BLACK HOLE (Stafford Pemberton)

1981 (64pg) (fc):	£8	$13

Comic Strips : Beyond the Black Hole (24), Whitman Black Hole #3 reprint, The Virlights (24), Art: Dan Spiegle
Includes full-colour photo features of the movie and star profiles
Cover features production art and photos
Based on Walt Disney movie

BLAKE'S SEVEN (World)
1979-1981

1979-1980	£10	$16

1980 (64pg) (fc/tc)
Art: Melvyn Powell
Text Stories: Planet of No Escape, Museum Piece, Sabotage!, A Task for Bondor, Red for Danger

1981	£12	$19

Based on BBC TV sci-fi series

BLADE RUNNER (Marvel/Grandreams)
1983

©1982	£8	$13

Penciled by Al Williamson and Carlos Garzon
Inked by Al Williamson, Dan Green and Ralph Reese
Editor Jim Salicrup
Includes fc photo album from the sci-fi movie and Behind the Comics adaptation feature with full-colour staff photo of Archie Goodwin, Al Williamson and Carlos Garzon and reproduction of the original Marvel comics Jim Steranko cover minus logo and cover blurbs.- Photo Cover
Official Comic Strip adaptation by Archie Goodwin

BLEEP & BOOSTER

1969	£10	$16

Based on the comic strip characters from Blue Peter

BLOCKBUSTERS (World)

1989 (64pg) (fc)	£4	$7

Editor: John Malam
Art: Nick Payne & Walter Howarth
Based on ITV student quiz show

BLONDIE (R&L-Locker)

1951 (fc)	£25	$40

Reprints the mid-forties U.S. newspaper strip by Chic Young

BLUE JEANS Annual (DC Thomson)
1980-1990s

1980's	£6	$11

1980 (96pg)
Comic Strip (3x4bw): Trapped in the Dark, Who's this guy Dick Turpin?, The Love Forecast
Feature: Leslie Ash
Small Features: Bob Geldof, Johnny Fingers, Debbie Harry, Olivia Newton John, Kate Bush, Bjorn of Abba, Dennis Waterman, Liz Mitchell of Boney M, Keith Atack of Child, Lewis Collins, Jimmy Pursey of Sham 69, John Travolta, Debbie Harry, Tina Charles, Anna of Abba, Frida of Abba, Julie Covington, Mary Tamm, Olivia

Blue Peter Fourth Book 1968

Blue Peter Seventh Book 1971

Blue Peter Tenth Book 1974

Newton John, Poly Styrene of X Ray Spex, Lena Zavaroni, Suzi Quatro
Photo Cover: Leslie Ash
1981 (96pg)
Comic Strip (4x4bw): Get the Picture, Leave it to Fate, Recipe for Love
Small Features: David Essex, Jimmy Pursey, Bob Geldof, Pauline Black, Debbie Harry, Shakin Stevens, Sting, Paul Weller, Patrick Duffy, Suzi Quatro, Amii Stewart
1982 (96pg)
Comic Strip (4x4bw): There's No Future in it!, The Perfect Wedding Dress
Text stories by Sue Papworth
Small Features: Toyah Wilcox, Debbie Harry, Fay Fife of The Revillos, Chrissie Hynde, Thereze Bazar of Dollar, Annie Lennox, Pauline Black of The Selecter, Lene Lovich, Wendy Wu of The Photos, Rita Ray of the Darts, Andy Summers of The Police, Feargal Sharkey, Cliff Richard, Dave Bartram of Showaddywaddy, Sheena Easton, Jimmy Pursey, Paul Weller of The Jam, Paul Di'Anno of Iron Maiden, Bob Geldof
1983 (96pg)
Comic Strip: Love is Like a Butterfly (4bw), A Previous Engagement (4bw)
Text stories by Hazel Martell, Mary Hooper
Small Features: Mike Read, Simon Le Bon, Damian O'Neill of The Undertones, Todd Carty, Chas Smash of Madness, Thereze Bazaar of Dollar, Toyah, Robin Campbell of UB40, Louis Alphonso of Bad Manners, Suzi Quatro, Debbie Harry, David Sylvian of Japan, Kim Wilde, David Van Day of Dollar
1984 (96pg)
Small Features: Marc Almond, Sting, Bruno of Fame, Nick Heyward, Steve Strange, Kevin Rowland, John Taylor, Dave Gahan of Depeche Mode, Simon Le Bon, Buster Bloodvessel, Kim Wilde, Mick Jagger, Midge Ure, Olivia Newton John, Martin Fry of ABC, Shakin Stevens, Sheena Easton, Simon Le Bon,
1985 (96pg)
Text stories by Helen Emerson, Kate Lee, Sue Papworth, Don Wright
1986 (96pg)
Pin up: George Michael
1987 (96pg)
Features: Paul Young, excellent 4 page feature on Duran Duran, The Escape Club, Eastenders feature
Text stories by Mark Roberts, Jo Hardy
1988 (96pg)
Feature: Curiosity Killed the Cat
Small Features: Five Star, Emilio Estevez, Matt Dillon, Ralph Macchio, Sean and Chris Penn, Andrew McCarthy, Rob Lowe, Thomas Howell, Michael J Fox, Tom Cruise,
Pin Up: Morten Harket, Nick Berry, Rob Lowe
1990's £4 $7
1990 (96pg)
Features: Tanita Tikaram, Kylie Minogue, Lisa Marie Presley, Kim Wilde, Brother Beyond, Pet Shop Boys, Whitney Houston, UK Soaps, The Brat Pack
Pin Ups: Brother Beyond, Rick Astley, Pet Shop Boys, Bros, Phillip Schofield
Text stories by Elaine Hatton, Sheila Benton,
1993 (96pg)
Features: The Beatles, Wham, Donny Osmond, Bros, Jason

Donovan, Winona Ryder, Christian Slater, Julia Roberts,
Pin Ups: Kevin Costner (bw), Matt Dillow (bw), River Phoenix (fc)
Based on the Girls comic
BLUE JEANS PHOTO STORY (DC Thomson)
1984 (96pg) £5 $8
Art: Graham P Williams
Text stories by Roy Lennox, Barbara Jacobs, Mary Hooper, Sue Marshall
BLUE PETER (BBC/Ringpress/World)
1965-present
Writers: Biddy Baxter, Edward Barnes and Rosemary Gill
1965 £90 $144
©1964 (Scarce) First Book
Valerie Singleton, Christopher Trace and Petra photo cover
1966 £50 $80
©1965 Second Book
Valerie Singleton, Christopher Trace, Petra and Jason photo cover
1967 £30 $48
©1966 - Third Book
1968-1970 £20 $32
©1967 (80pg) Fourth Book
Jason, Petra and Jason photo cover
Picture Strip: Bengo by Tim (4fc/tc)
Text Stories: Bleep & Booster (4fc), Paddington Gets the Bird (6bw), Writer: Michael Bond, Art: 'Hargreaves'
©1968 (80pg) Fifth Book
Valerie Singleton, John Noakes and Peter Purves photo cover
Picture Strip: Bengo by Tim (4fc), The Best Christmas Tree Of All (3), Father David's Deer (3), Art: Robert Broomfield
Text Story: Bleep & Booster (4fc)
© 1969 (80pg) - Sixth Book
Valerie Singleton, John Noakes, Peter Purvis, Petra and Mini Moke on cover
1971-1980 £10 $16
©1970 (80pg) Seventh Book
Valerie Singleton, John Noakes, Peter Purvis and Autogyro
Features: Dressing an Action Man Doll, Crufts Dogshow, Autogyro
Picture Strips: The Man in White (4fc), Art: Bob Broomfield, Bengo (1fc) by Tim
Text Strip: Bleep & Booster (4fc) by Tim
©1971 (80pg) (fc) Eighth Book
John Noakes & Peter Purves and Blue Peter train photo cover
Art: Robert Broomfield
Features: Valerie Singleton, John Noakes and Peter Purves
Text Story: Bleep & Booster (4), Paddington Weighs In (5tc), Writer: Michael Bond, Art: 'Hargreaves'
Picture Strips: Bengo by Tim (1), Aztecs (2), Marie Antoinette Queen and Shepherdess (3)
©1972 (80pg) Ninth Book
John Noakes & Shep photo cover
Valerie Singleton, John Noakes, Peter Purvis and Lesley Judd
Picture Story: John Noakes and the Mystery Picture by Tim
Text stories: The Cornish Adventure & Roman Reporter, Writer: Dorothy Smith, The Eddystone Light and Rahere, Art: Robert Bloomfield, Bleep & Booster, The Case of the Missing Link, Art: Bernard Blatch, Roman Reporter, Art: Mark Peppe
©1974 Eleventh Book
John Noakes skydiving photo cover

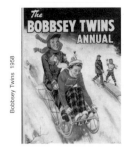

Blue Peter Twenty Eight 1999

Bobbsey Twins 1958

Bobo Bunny 1975

Features: Valerie Singleton, Peter Purves, John Noakes and Lesley Judd
Picture Strip: Tolpuddle Martyrs (3fc), Art: Robert Broomfield
Text Story: Bleep & Booster, Art: Tim (4)
©1975 (80pg) Twelth Book
Petra, Jason & Shep photo cover
Picture Strip: The Runaways, Art: Robert Broomfield
Text Story: The House of Secrets, Writer: Dorothy Smith
Paddington Clocks In - Writer: Michael Bond, Art: 'Hargreaves'
Bleep and Booster, Art: Tim
The Case of the Maltese Cross, Art: Bernard Blatch
©1976 (80pg) Thirteenth Book
Lesley Judd, John Noakes, Peter Pervis photo cover
Picture Strip: Bengo (1tc)
Text Story: Paddington in the Hot Seat - Writer: Michael Bond, Art: 'Hargreaves', Bleep & Booster, Art: 'Tim', The Eglinton Tournament Art: Robert Bloomfield
Features: Generation Game with Bruce Forsythe
©1978 (80pg) Fifteenth Book
John Noakes, Peter Purvis and Leslie Judd circus cover
©1979 (80pg) Sixteenth Book
Simon Groom & Goldie photo cover
Features: Simon Groom, Tina Heath, Lesley Judd and Chris
Picture Strip: The Tale of the Red Indian Princess, Art: Robert Broomfield
Text Story: Paddington Takes a Cut - Writer: Michael Bond, Art: 'Hargreaves'
Features: 20th birthday reunion of Blue Peter featuring previous presenters
1981-1989   £8 $13
©1980 (80pg) Seventeenth Book
Simon Groom, Tina Heath and Chris photo cover
Features: First appearance of Sarah Greene
Picture Strip: The Story of Joey the Clown - Here we are again! (3fc) Art: Robert Broomfield
Text Story: Paddington's Christmas Treasure Hunt - Writer: Michael Bond - Art: 'Hargreaves'
Feature: Bob Broomfield the illustrator
©1981 (80pg) Eighteenth Book
Sarah Greene and Goldie photo cover
Endpapers: All the animals who have appeared on Blue Peter
Picture Strip: Who Stole the Stone, Art: Robert Broomfield
Features: Rupert Bear, Grange Hill, Doctor Who
©1982 (80pg) Nineteenth Book
Simon Groom, Sarah Greene, Peter Duncan, Goldie, Jack and Jill photo cover
Features: Morph, Ventriloquism
©1983 (80pg) Twenty Book
Simon Groom, Sarah Greene, Peter Duncan celebrating 25 years of Blue Peter photo cover
©1984 (80pg) Twenty One Book
Simon Groom, Peter Duncan and Janet Ellis photo cover
Features: Shakin Stevens, Colin Baker
©1985 (80pg) Twenty Two Book
Simon Groom, Janet Ellis photo cover
©1988 (Ringpress) (80pg) 24th
Mark Curry, Caron Keating and Yvette Fielding in Moscow photo cover
30 Years 1958-1988 back cover
1990-present   £5 $8

©1989 (Ringpress) (64pg) 25th
Yvette Fielding and Bonnie
1991 (World) (64pg) 26th
John Leslie, Yvette Fielding and Diane Jordan photo cover
©1992 - 27th Book
Diane Jordan and John Leslie photo cover
Yvette Fielding on back cover
Feature: Thunderbirds (2pg)
©1998 (World) (64pg) - 28th Book
Katy Hill and Stuart Miles photo cover
Writer: Oliver Macfarlane, John Comerford and Anne Dixon - This annual was removed from distribution and existing copies recalled following the sacking of presenter Richard Bacon
Front cover: Katy Hill and Stuart Miles
Back cover: Konnie Huq and Richard Bacon
©1999 (Egmont World) (64pg) 29th
Katy Hill, Konnie Huq, Simon Thomas, Mabel, Lucy photo cover
Also features: Matt Baker
Writer: Steve Hocking, Anne Dixon and Bridget Caldwell
Profiles: Simon Thomas and Matt Baker
Features: Interview with Steps the pop band, Bye Bye Bonnie
Based on long-running BBC children's TV series

BLUE PETER STAMP ANNUAL (Yellow Submarine)
1998 (72pg)   £4 $7
Katy Hill, Stuart Miles, Romana, Richard Bacon
Special issue about collecting stamps - Art:Jody Winger

BMX Special (Grandreams)
N/D (64pg) Cover Price - £2.95   £3 $5
Writer: John Kercher

BOB THE BUILDER (EgmontWorld)
2000   £3 $5
Based on ITV puppet animation show

BOBBSEY TWINS (World)
1957-1960   £10 $16
©1957 (112pg) (bw) (dj)
Writer: Laura Lee Hope
Picture Stories: An Adventure in the Air (8), New Years Day Mystery (10)
Text Stories: The Secret of the Green Lady, Monty the Mystery Dog, Monsieur Quatre Doigts Du Pied, Ship Ahoy Monkey!, African Hunt, Hollywood Surprise
©1959 (112pg) (bw)
Writer: Laura Lee Hope
Picture Strips: The Phantom Island Adventure (9bw), A Circus Mystery (8bw)
Text Stories: The Mexican Silver Horse, The Snow Cat Rescue, A Yachting Adventure, The Mystery of the Polka-Dot Kite, The Talking Fish, Chib-San's Secret
Based on the novels by Laura Lee Hope

BOBBY BEAR'S Annual (Dean)
1920-1969
1950's-1955   £20 $32
1956-1959   £15 $24
1960-1965   £12 $19
1966-1969   £10 $16

BOB WILSON TV SPORTS (Brown Watson)
1979   £5 $8

BOBO BUNNY (Fleetway)
1970's   £5 $8

Bonanaza 1965

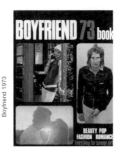

Boyfriend 1973

Boys & Girls Cinema Club - Not Dated

1975 (80pg) (fc)
Published in Holland
BONANZA (World/Purnell)
1962-1969
1962-1963   £20   £32
1964-1966   £15 $24
©1962 (Purnell) (96pg) (bw)
Writer: John Challis
Art: Leo Rawlings and Simonetti
Comic Strips: Tumbleweed (9), The Indian Fighter (8), Border Feud (7)
Text Stories: The Double Take, Stampede, The Paint Horse, Stage from Red Bluffs, The Scapegoat, War Party, Coyote Canyon, Siege at Twelve Tree Hill
Lorne Greene, Dan Blocker, Michael Landon, Pernell Roberts
Pernell Roberts
©1964 (Purnell) (96pg) (bw)
Writer: Basil Deakin
Art: R Walker
Comic Strips: Looting at the Ponderosa (8), Robbery at the Rodeo (8), The Redskins is A-Comin' (8)
Text Stories: The Treble Bush-whack, The Prairie Race, Battle on the Prairie, Almost a Broken Promise, Hard Learning for Hoss, The Prisoner of River Bend, Stampede, The Redskins is A-coming, The Forgotten Birthday, Hop Sing's Lynch Party.
Lorne Greene, Dan Blocker, Michael Landon, Pernell Roberts photo cover
©1964 (World) (96pg) (fc)
Comic Strips include: Blood Debt, Black Day at Virginia City, The Miser - Dell reprints
Lorne Greene, Dan Blocker, Michael Landon, Pernell Roberts illustrated cover
©1965 (World) (96pg) (fc)
Comic Strips (fc): The Hatchet Man (14), The Convict (13), Ride A Wild Hope (14), The Mestenera (13), Bull of the Woods (14), Bedrock Barnes, Prospector in The Claim Jumper (4), The Living Nightmare (13)
Lorne Greene, Dan Blocker, Michael Landon, Pernell Roberts illustrated cover
1967-1969   £10 $16
©1968 (World) (96pg) (fc)
Comic Strips (fc): Indians on Horseback (1), House of Refuge (15), Bedrock Barnes, Prospector in The Gold Trap (4), The Witch's Curse (9)
Lorne Greene, Michael Landon, Dan Blocker illustrated cover
Based on the TV western series
BONNIE (Fleetway)
1970s   £8 $13
1977 (80pg) (fc/tc)
Picture Strips: Jenny and the Gingerbread Boy, Dougal (Magic Roundabout), Sally and Jake, The Dolly Girls, Florence (Magic Roundabout), Leo the Merry Lion, Meet the Beans, The Missing Buttons, The Enchanted Book, Daffy and Dilly, At the end of the Rainbow, Polly Perkins
BONNY (Swan)
1951-1956   £20 $32
BONZO'S Annual (Dean)
1940s-1950s
1950's   £20 $32

BOYFRIEND (City Magazines/World)
1961-1970s
1961-1965   £15 $24
1966-1969   £12 $19
1968 (128pg)
Comic Strips: She's Kind of Special he Said (3bw), Keeping the Mind on the Job (4bw), With the Passing of Time (3bw), It Started as a Dream (6bw), I'll Force Him to Care (3bw), That Second Chance (3bw), It Could be a Mistake (3bw), Dreams Have to Follow Through (3bw), That Love Hate Relationship (3bw), Searching for the Steady Type (6bw), Unapproachable Man (3bw)
Features: The Monkees
Small Features: Bruce Johnston, Dave Dee, Cat Stevens, Stevie Windood, Scott Engel, Mike D'Abo, Paul McCartney, Mike Jagger, Wayne Fontana, The Troggs, Adam Faith, The Nashville Teens
Pin Ups: Paul Jones, Donovan, The Mindbenders, Cliff Richard, The Beach Boys, Tom Jones, Patrick McGoohan, Mick Jagger, Alan Price, Cat Stevens, Michael Caine, Stevie Winwood, Michael Crawford, Georgie Fame, The Walker Brothers
1970's   £8 $13
1971 (City Magazines) (128p) (fc/bw)
Comic Strips (bw): It Happened in Spain (7), The Greatest Fall of All (4), Romance Ahoy! (7), Too Tough to Love (5), I Wanted to be Free (6), Portrait of My Love (6)
Features: Bob Dylan, Donovan Leitch, Andy Brown, Emperor Rosko, Maurice Gibb, Marc Bolan, Eric Clapton, Herman, Peter Sarstedt, Steve Ellis, Jim Morrison, Tom Jones, The Beatles, The Moody Blues, Family Dogg
Pin Ups: P P Arnold, The Marmalade, Lulu, The Move, Bobbie Gentry, Bee Gee Barry, Carl Wayne, The Beatles, Joe Dolan, Hermans Hermits, Status Quo, The Hollies, Clodagh Rodgers, Mama Cass, Peter Sarstedt
1973 (104pg) (fc/bw)
Comic Strips: Summer Love (8), Lost Happiness (6), Living Model (7), Dream Lover (8), The Timid Doctor Midly (7)
Features: Elton John, Lulu, Cliff Richard, Everly Brothers, Olivia Newton John, John Farrar, Wings, Elvis, George Best, Alan Hudson
Pin Ups (fc): Jethro Tull, Frank Zappa, Slade, Tony Blackburn, Alvin Lee, Noel Edmonds, Pink Floyd, Gianni
Pin Ups (bw): Neil Diamond
1974 (80pg) (fc/tc) (World)
Romance comic strips (tc), pop and fashion features
Includes features and pin ups of: Johnny Nash, Rod Stewart, David Bowie, The Beach Boys, the Osmonds, Marc Bolan, The Jacksons, Slade - Photo cover features David Cassidy
BOY'S AND GIRLS' CINEMA CLUBS (Juvenille)
1950's-1960s
1950s   £20 $32
N/D (estimate 1950s) (64pg) (tc)
Editor: Robert Moss
Features: Walt Disney, Roy Rogers, Bells of St Trinians, Greer Garson, Knights of the Round Table, King Richard and the Crusaders, Heidi
Michael Chipan, Eileen Janssen photo cover
1960s   £15 $24
BOY'S HEROES OF THE SEA
1950's   £12 $19
BOY'S OWN (Purnell)
1879-1970s

Boys' World 1967

Boyzone 1997

Bread 1991

1950's	£20	$32
1960's	£15	$24
1970's	£12	$19

1971 (128pg) (bw)
Editor: Jack Cox
Text Stories: Noondi by Charles Webster, Art: James MacIntyre
Leader of Men by John Bancroft, Art: Tom Taylor
Last Noel by Leonard Gribble, Art: John Jarvis
Five Eyes by Charles Webster, Art: Laszlo Acs
The Fairhills Stag by Tom Turner, Art: Eileen A. Soper
The Riddle of the Marie Celeste by Trevor Holloway, Art: Tom Taylor
The Caretaker by John Wingate, Art: Kenneth Bayley
Night Flight to Kupang by Charles Pittock, Art: Glenn Steward
1972 (128pg) (bw)
Editor: Jack Cox
Text Stories: Lost Lagoon by Charles Webster, Art: Glenn Steward
The Sun Path by Gerald Wyatt, Art: Laszlo Acs
Six Shooter Fish by John Bancroft, Art: Jean De Lemos
The Bullwhackers by Jeff Jeffries, Art: John Jarvis
Black Panther by C M Graham, Art: Gavin Rowe
Pony Express by Jeff Jeffries, Art: John Jarvies
Man in the Shadow by Geoffrey Morgan, Art: Jane Kirk
1976 (80pg) (bw)
Editor Jack Cox
Text Stories: Death in the Grass by Keith Horan, Art: Raymond Sheppard
The Ferry by C. Harcourt Robertson, Art: Gordon Nicoll
Viva el Football! by John Davies, Art: Bowyer
The Ambush by John Marsh, Art: Roland Davies
Circumstantial Evidence by Group Captain SC George, Art: Berto

BOY'S WORLD (Odhams)
1963-1971

1963-1964	£15	$24
1965-1966	£10	$24
1967-1971	£8	$13

1967 (128pg)
Comic Strips: The Bridge that Collapsed (4tc), Pony Express (4bw), Slumberjack (2bw), Wrath of the Gods (8fc), Art: John Burns, Night Flight (4bw), Merlo the Magician in Man Overboard (4bw), Pinch and Mcnab (2bw), Men Out of Time (8fc), Raff Regan and the Glory Hunter (4bw), Death at Midnight (4tc)
Text Stories: The Hunter and the Hunted!, Snowfall!, Jungle Green, The Big Race, The Listening Trees, Art: Ron Embelton, A Case of Vital Importance, Duggie's Dinosaur, Art: Edgar Spencerly, Just Sam
1970 (116pg)
Comic Strips: Harry the Hairy Hunter (9tc), Cannon Ball King (7bw), Return of the Raiders (5bw), The Cruise of the Gay Gordon (5bw), Lancelot Knight (5fc), O'Rourke to the Rescue (5bw), Art: John Burns, Davy Collins (6tc)
Text Stories: The Relief, Art: Eric Kincaid, Mountain Rescue, Jeremy Starbuck, Hunters Lance, Art: Ron Embelton, Simon & Sharkfin, Johnny Boyland and the Clonmel Code, Ghosts Stalk our Mountains, Flame Head
Based on the UK comic

BOYS WORLD FISHING Annual (Odhams)

| 1964 | £5 | $8 |

BOYZONE Official Annual (Grandreams)
1997- present

| 1997- present | £7 | $11 |

©1996 Special (48pg)

Writer: Mike Hrano, with Shane, Stephen, Mikey, Keith & Ronan
Design by Louise Ivimy, Susan Bartram and Joanna Davies
©1997 (64pg) (fc)
Writers: Eddie Rowley, Kathryn Rogers-Design: Jason Bazini
©1998 (64pg) (fc)
Writers: Leslie Rowley, Katherine Rogers-Design: Joanna Davies
©1999 (64pg)
Writer: Eddie Rowley, Designed by Jason Bazini
Based on the Irish boy band

BRAVESTARR (World)

| 1988-1990 | £7 | $11 |

1988 (fc)
Comic Strip: Desert Ordeal (6)
Text stories: Welcome to New Texas!, The Kerium Connection, Small Guy...Tall Tales, Into the Hexagon!, Night of the Storm, Sea of Fog, Underground Lawman - 64 pg
Based on Filmation animated TV series

BREAD (Grandreams)

| 1990-1991 | £5 | $8 |

©1989 (64pg)
Editors: John Barraclough, Melanie J Clayden
Writer: John Kercher
Design & Layout: Louise Ivimy
©1990 (64pg)
Editors: Kesta Desmond
Writer: John Kercher
Design & Layout: Louise Ivimy
Features: Jean Boht, Carla Lane, Giles Watling, Melanie Hill, Graham Bickley, John Hearn, Ronald Forfar, Vic McGuire, Nick Conway, Kenneth Waller, Jonathon Morris
Full colour photo features on the stars
Based on the popular BBC TV sitcom

BRING 'EM BACK ALIVE (Grandreams)

| 1982 | £8 | $13 |

Based on the TV action adventure series starring Bruce Boxleitner

BRONCO LAYNE (World)
1959-1964

| 1959 | £15 | $24 |
| 1960-1964 | £12 | $19 |

©1963 (96pg)
Art: Walter Howarth
Text Stories (fc)
Based on Western TV series starring Ty Hardin

THE BROONS (D.C. Thomson)
1940-present - bi-annual

1940	£800	$1280
1942	£550	$850
1948	£450	$720
1952	£350	$560
1954	£250	$400
1956	£150	$240
1958	£100	$160
1960	£80	$128
1962	£70	$110
1964	£60	$96
1966-1970	£40	$60
1972-1980	£20	$32
1980 - last Dudley Watkins		
1982-1990	£10	$16

Brownie 1978

Buck Rogers 1984

Bugs Bunny 1972

1992-present £6 $10
BROS Special (Grandreams/World)
1989-1991 £4 $7
1989 (World) (64pg)
Editor & Writer: J. Donnelly, L. Antony & T. Nicholson
1990 (World) (60pg)
Edited and Writer: Alex Kadis
Contributors: William Shaw and Sylvia Patterson
©1990 Special (Grandreams) (64pg)
Based on the UK pop band
BROTHER BEYOND
1990 (64pg) £3 $5
Editor and Writers: Chris Heath and Brother Beyond
Based on the pop band
BROWNIE (Purnell/AP/Guide Association)
1960s-present
1960's £7 $11
1970's £5 $8
1978 (Purnell) (96pg)
Editor: Robert Moss
Comic Strips: The Treasure of Wildwater adapted by Robert Moss
from a story by C. Cartlidge, The Lost Key
Text stories: The Snowmen That Came to Life by Tilly Wingrave
Lisa's Sticky Day by Nora Windridge, Wendy in a Temper by
Barbara Laming, The Butterfly Venture by Edna Gilbert, The Lost
Letter by Jean Dixon, The Naughty New Recruit by Brenda Morton
1980's £4 $7
1990's £3 $5
1995 (World) (64pg)
Text Stories: Summer Special by Gillian Ellis, Art: Paula Martyr
Concert Time by Gillian Ellis - Art: by Lisa Berkshire
A New Start for Lucy?, Writer: Heather Welford - Art: Celia Chester
Emily brings greetings from Kenya, Writer: Lynda Neilands - Art:
Jenny Norton Aunt Rose's Special Cake - Writer: Heather Gorst Art:
Kate Simpson
1996 (APL) (96pg) (fc)
Editor: Chris Maynard
The BRUNS (Polystyle)
1980s £5 $8
Based on the childrens puppet TV series
BRYAN ROBSON'S Soccer Annual (Hamlyn)
1989 (64pg) (fc)
Editor: Tom Tyrell
Features: Bryan's Soccer Diary 1987-1988 season, Five for the
Future, Paul Gasgoigne, Nigel Clough, Gary Pallister, David
Rocastle, Paul Lake
Based on the soccer star
The BUBBLIES (Grandreams)
1980 £4 $7
BUCK JONES (Amalgamated Press)
1957-1958 £10 $19
BUCK ROGERS in the 25th CENTURY
(Stafford Pemberton)
1981-1984 £8 $13
1981 (64pg) (fc)
Cover Art: Edgar Hodges - Endpaper Art: Paul Green
Comic Strips: The Space Slavers (32), Buck Rogers #1 reprint
The Missing Element (22), Writer: Paul S Newman

Art: Al McWilliams, Buck Rogers #5 reprint
Feature: Buck Rogers - A Short History, Writer/Art: Paul Green
1982 (80pg) (fc)
Cover Art: Edgar Hodges
Comic Strips (fc): The Hostage (22) - Writer: Paul S Newman, Art: Al
McWilliams, The Trial (22), The Battle over Planet Earth (21)
Writer: Michael Teitelbaum, Art: Al McWilliams
1983 (64pg) (fc)
Cover Art: Edgar Hodges
Comic Strips: From Ersta... with Hate! (22), S'ashi! (22)
Writer J. M. Dematteis, Art: Al McWilliams
1984 (Scarce) £10 $16
Comic Strips: That Which Seems to be (23fc), Writer: B S Watson,
Art: Mike Roy
10 Levels of Death (9fc), Writer: B S Watson, Art: Mike Roy
Olympiad (22fc), Writer: B S Watson, Art: Mike Roy
All comic strips were originally published by Gold Key/Whitman
Based on the sci-fi TV series
BUFFALO BILL WILD WEST (Popular/Dean)
1950-1962
©1949 (1st) (177pg) £25 $40
Writer: Arthur Groom, Art: Denis McLoughlin
Comic Strips: Enter Buffalo Bill (8 tc), The Round-Up (4bw),
Calamity Jane (5tc), The Lessons of Buffalo Bill (3bw), Wild Bill's
First Killing (6bw), Chief White Owl (6bw)
1950-1955 £20 $32
©1950 (196pg)
Writer: Arthur Groom, Art: Denis McLoughlin
Comic Strips: The Fight (10tc), The Camp (6tc), Red Men of the
West (14tc), The Historical Wanderers (4bw combined text/strip)
Bad Men (13tc), They Brought Law To The West (4bw combined
text/strip), Curiosities Of The West! (4bw)
1956-1961 £15 $24
Based on the UK comic
BUGS BUNNY (World)
1960's-1980's
1960's £12 $19
©1968 (96pg)
Comic Strips (fc): Bubble Trouble, Spirit Rock, The Rabbitfields and
the Coys, Idle Idol Emeralds, A Case of Weepies, Visitor Invasion,
The Carrot Touch, A Flood of Fun, Mystery at Mouldy Mansion,
Mutiny on the Bunny, Aqua Antics, The Teacher Teacher, The Last
Straw
1970's £8 $13
©1970
Comic Strips (fc): Bugs Bunny in Rabbitson Crusoe, Damp Diggings,
The Rocketing Radish, Binky Bunny's Visit, The Genie with the Light
Grey Hare, Unlucky to be Lucky, From Bugs to Riches, Daffy Duck
in Tornado Chaser, The Flighty Fellow
1976 (64pg)
Comic Strips (fc): Bugs Bunny in A Trip To Mars, Telegraph Pole
Capers, Monkey Mischief, Bunny and Claude, Kangaroo Antics,
Bugs Bunny, The Irate Pirate, Cousin Cuthbert, Adventure with an
Octopus
1980's £6 $10
'Bugs Bunny Cartoon Annual' - 1980
©1980 (80pg)
Comic Strips (fc/bw): Seeing Double, A Small Matter, The Bear
Facts, Tenny the Wonder Horse, A Helping Hand, Big Beat Bunny,

Bunty 1965

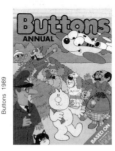

Buttons 1989

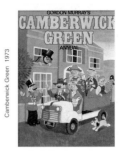

Camberwick Green 1973

The Lobster Trap, Trapped in Wonderland, Camera Sly
©1982 (64pg)
Comic Strips (fc): Dilemma in Dead End, Far Out Visitor, The
Cannonball Caper, Power of Pizazz
All annuals contain US comic strip reprints
Based on the Warner Brothers cartoon character

BUNTY for Girls (D.C.Thomson)
1960 - Present
Early annuals have dust jacket

©1959	£40	$60
1961-1966	£30	$48
1967-1970	£20	$32
1970-1979	£10	$19

1976 (128pg)
Comic Strips: Freda's in Fashion, The Four Marys, Mighty Mo,
Watson the Wonder Dog, Horse-Shy Shona, Abby-Jo Hill Billy a-go-
go!, Patty's 'Grew-Some' Plant, Miss Merlin, The Broomstick
Brigade, Think Thin Thelma, Quackers, The Hee-Haw Hero, Stella
the Star Gazer, There's Magic in Her Needles!, The Face That Did
Not Fit, The Cheddar Mob, Hairway to the Stars

1980-1989	£6	$10

1982 (128pg)
Comic Strips (fc/tc): Maid Marian, Girl Friday, Wendy's Wonder
Horse, Dear Dad..., Little Queen Bea, Mojo the Milky Way Dog,
Princess Pain-in-the-Neck, The Four Marys, Tillie the Trier, Belle of
the Ball, Her Gran's the Greatest, Meggie's Magic Book, Catch the
Cat!, Toots, The Three Imps, Haggis, Try-It-Out Terry, Rambling
Rose and The No-Good Gnome
Photo Story (bw): Ever Had That Shrinking Feeling?
1983 (128pg)
Comic Strips (tc/fc): The Four Mary's (8), Haggis (2), Dolwyn's Dolls
(8), Wanderer - The Story of a Foal ((5), The Flights of Flopear (9),
Belle of the Ball (5), The Three Imps (9), Kate Must Skate (6), Maid
Marian (8), Wonderwoofa (7), The Faith & Hope of Charity Brown
(7), The Incredibe Adventures of Mini Mum (8), The Wonder of
Grace (8), Goosey Goosey Gander (8)
©1987
Comic Strips: The Comp, Fear of the Future, Love Thy Neighbour,
Who's Next Door, Prefect's Pet, The Four Marys, The Comp,
Pennys Place, Lizzie's New Life, Pretend Friends, The Four Marys

1990-present	£5	$8

1990
Comic Strips (fc/tc): Bonnie & Claude, The Wilde Bunch, The
Necklace, Life with Bunty, Toots, Bike Rider, The Four Marys,
Haggis, Dream Pony
Pin Ups (fc sp): Kylie Minogue, Whitney Houston, Tiffany, Sinitta
Includes fc feature on the production of a Photo Story
1992
Comic Strips: The Four Marys, The Four Marys' Mums, Bonnie and
Claude, Robina Hood, Bea-witched!, Grappling Gertie, Backstreet
Hospital, Haggis, Toots, Maisie Mercury, Bunty - A Girl Like You,
Star Pets
Photo Story (fc): Birthday Surprise!
1997 (128pg)
Comic Strips (fc/tc): The Four Mary's (6), The Lies about Lucy (7),
Wendy's Three Wishes (7), The Blue Bonnet (9), The Girl in the
Mirror (7), The Four Marys (10), The Comp (6), No Dogs Allowed
(6), The New Girls (9), The Prisoners (4), Magnum the Magnificent
(5), The Seeker (5), The Comp (5), Clumsy Claudia (6)
2000 (128pg)

Comic Strips (fc) The Comp (12), The Four Marys (5), Bugsy (2),
Creeper Creatures (5), Room 13 (5), Fay's Future (5), Girl Zone (2),
Seeing Stars (5), The Four Marys (6), Penny's Place (5)
Based on the UK girls comic

BURKE'S LAW (World)

1965 (96pg) (fc)		£12	$19

Comic Strips (3x32): Who Killed The Curious Crew? Who Killed
Harry Dare? A Dead Helping Hand
Dell Comic Reprints
Based on the TV crime series starring Gene Barry

BUSTER Book (Fleetway)
1962-1994

1962	£60	$90
1963	£40	$60
1964-1965	£25	$40
1966-1969	£15	$24
1970-1973	£12	$19
1974-1979	£10	$16
1980-1994	£8	$13

1986 (112pg) (fc/tc/bw)
Comic Strips: Ivor Lott and Tony Broke, Gums, Good Guy, X Ray
Specs, Mummys Boy, School Belle, The School Team, Milly O'Naire
and Penny Less, Chalky, Strawbelly, Faceache, Young Arfur, The
Winners, Wonder Wellies, Jack Pott, The Leopard from Lime Street

BUTTONS (Polystyle)

1980s	£6	$10

©1987 (64pg) (fc)
Comic Strips: Bertha, Henry's Cat and friends, Jimbo and the Jet-
Set, Mop and Smiff, Pigeon Street, King Rollo, The Flumps,
Postman Pat
©1988 (64pg) (fc)
Comic Strips: Henry's Cat, The Flumps, Postman Pat, Pigeon
Street, Jimbo Jet Set, King Rollo, Bertha, Mop & Smiff
Based on pre-school childrens BBC TV programmes

BUZBY (Brown Watson)

1980	£6	$10

©1979
Comic Strips by Mevin

BYKER GROVE (Grandreams)

1990	£8	$13

©1989 (64pg) (fc)
Editor: John Barraclough
Writer: Tony Lynch, Designer: Louise Ivimy
Features: Ant McPartlin and Declan Donnelly profiles
Photo features
Based on the Childrens BBC TV series

CALLING NURSE ABBOT (Longacre Press)

1963 (112pg)	£8	$13

Picture Strips: Famous Overnight! (8fc), The Playground (8fc), Edith
Cavell (1bw), Marie Curie (1bw), Helen Keller (1bw), Elsie Inglis
(1bw)
From the publishers of GIRL Comic

CAMBERWICK GREEN Gordon Murray's (Purnell)
1960's-1970's

1960's	£20	$32

1968
Stories and Play pages by Janice Godfrey, Art: Reg Hoye

1970's	£10	$16

©1971

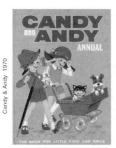

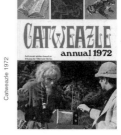

Candy & Andy 1970

Captain Scarlet 1968

Catweazle 1972

Writer: Muriel Ray, Art: Brick and Woody Ink
Features text stories and puzzles
©1973 (includes photo stories)   £15 $24
Writer/Art: Woody Ink
Features photo and text stories
Based on the Childrens BBC TV puppet series
CANDY and ANDY (Century 21/City)
1968-1970
©1967   £12 $19
©1968-©1969   £8 $13
Based on the childrens characters
CANDY and ANDY Story Book (Century 21)
1969   £8 $13
©1968
CANNON & BALL (World)
1983 (64pg) (tc)   £6 $10
Comic Strips (2x2): Touch Wood!, Posh Nosh, Art: Bill Titcombe
Writers: Glynis Langley, Norman Leaver
Based on the UK comedians
CAPTAIN AMERICA (Marvel)
1981   £15 $24
Marvel Comics character
CAPTAIN BEAKY (Stafford Pemberton)
1981 (64pg) (fc/bw)   £6 $10
Features: The Making of Captain Beaky including Twiggy, Harry
Secombe, Peter Sellers, Keith Michell
Based on the animated series by Jeremy Lloyd
CAPTAIN BRITAIN (Marvel)
1978   £10 $16
Marvel Comics character
CAPTAIN PLANET AND THE PLANETEERS (World)
1993 (64pg) (fc)   £7 $11
Editor: Peter Nicholls
Endpaper: Tim Perkins
Writer: Philip Caveney, Art: Tim Perkins,
Comic Strips (2x6): Lake Fear, Ghost Mine
Based on the animated TV series
CAPTAIN POWER
1989   £5 $8
CAPTAIN PUGWASH (World)
1976 (64pg)   £8 $13
Comic Strips: Potted Pirates (4fc), A Fight tooth the End (4tc), The
Buried Treasure (4tc), The Hot Cargo (4tc)
Based on the Childrens BBC TV animated series
CAPTAIN SCARLET (City Magazines)
1968-1969
©1967 (96pg)   £25 $40
Comic Strip: Hamed Mohamed Will Destory New Baghdad at Noon
(5fc), The World Government Space Administrator Will Die
Tomorrow (4fc), Technoburg is to be Destroyed (4fc), President
Juma will Die.... (5fc), We Are the Mysterons in Six Hours We
Destroy the Indian Aqua City (8fc), In Twenty Four Hours An
Epidemic of Nerve Fever Will Cripple Birmingham (6fc), The Portillo
Project is Doomed. We The Mysterons Will Destroy It (4fc), The
Director of Economic Affairs Will Be Assassinated (5fc)
©1968   £20 $32
Based on the Gerry Anderson TV Series
CAPTAIN SCARLET & THUNDERBIRDS (City Magazines)

1970
©1969   £25 $40
Based on the Gerry Anderson TV Series
CAPTAIN SCARLET & MYSTERONS (Grandreams)
1994-1995   £5 $8
©1993 (48pg) (fc)
Comic Strips: The World Government Space Administrator Will Die
Tomorrow (4), The Portillo Project Is Doomed (4), President Juma
Will Die... (5)
Captain Scarlet Annual ©1967 Comic Strip Reprints
©1994 (48pg) (fc)
Comic Strip: Treble Cross (8)
Art: Arkadia
Based on the Gerry Anderson TV series
Based on the Gerry Anderson TV Series
CAPTAIN SPACE KINGLEY Adventures of
1950's
1952 - No. 1   £30 $48
CARE BEARS (Grandreams/Marvel)
1987-1994   £7 $11
©1986 (64pg) (fc)
Editor: Etta Saunders
Comic Strips: Care Bears, Forest Trouble, Hugs and Tugs, Care
Bears, Hugs and Tugs
©1987 (64pg) (Marvel)
Editor: Diana Barton
Comic Strips: Grumpy gets Going!, Around the World, Hugs and
Tugs and the Chestnuts, Memories
©1989 (64pg) (fc) (Marvel)
Editor: Diana Barton, Art: Harry Papadopoulos
Comic Strips: The Great Word Ocean, Christmas Highlights, The
Circus, It's Hugs and Tugs, Back to School, A Caring Christmas
1990 (Marvel) (64pg) (fc)
Editor: Cartwright Roper, Art: Alan O'Keefe
Comic Strips (5x5): A Knight to Remember, Snow, On the Move,
Hugs and Tugs (2), Care Bears, Snowballs
1991 (64pg) (fc)
Editor: Alan O'Keefe, Art: Dave Boyle
Comic Strips: Care Bears Stolen Stare, Owlie, Best of Friends,
Magic World, Thunder
Based on the animated TV series
CARTOON NETWORK (Pedigree)
1998-present   £6 $10
2000 (112pg) (fc)
Writer: Michael Kraiger, Frank Strom, Sam Henderson and Matt
Wayne
Artists: Vince Deporter, Gary Fields, Sean Taggart & Tim Harkins
Comic Strips: The Flintstones, Hong Kong Phooey, Cow and
Chicken, The Jetsons, Wacky Races
Also featuring: Scooby Doo, Tom and Jerry, Dexter's Laboratory, Top
Cat and Johnny Bravo
CASPER GHOSTLAND (Brown & Watson)
1974   £12 $19
©1973 (80pg) (fc/tc)
Havey Comics reprints
CASPER (Grandreams)
1996   £5 $8
©1995 (48pg) (fc)
Editor: Melanie J Clayden, Writer: Tony Lynch

Charlies Angels 1980

Charlie Chaplin 1975

Cherry Ames 1964

Based on the moving starring Christina Ricci and Bill Pullman

CATWEAZLE
1970-1972   £10 $16
Based on the Childrens ITV fantasy series

CELTIC Football Club (Inglis Allen)
1991-1997
1997-No.7 (56pg) (fc/bw)   £5 $8
Editor: John C. Traynor, Writer: Douglas G. Russell
Photo features

CENTURIONS 'PowerXtreme' (World)
1987-1988   £7 $11
1987 (64pg) (fc)
Art: Paul Green, Glenn Rix
1988 (64pg) (fc)
Art: Graham Kennedy
Based on the animated TV series

CHAMPION Annual For Boys (Fleetway House)
1924-1956 - Later 'Book For Boys'
1950-1956   £10 $19
CHAMPION THE WONDER HORSE (Daily Mirror/World/
Purnell)
1953-1962
1953   £20 $32
1954-1959   £15 $24
©1957 (128pg) (Daily Mirror)
Writer: Arthur Groom, Art: John Pollack
Text stories (tc) - Painted full colour frontpiece
©1958 (128pg) (Daily Mirror)
Writer: Arthur Groom, Art: John Burns
Text Stories (tc) - Painted full colour frontpiece by J.M.B.
©1959 (128pg) (Daily Mirror)
Writer: Arthur Groom, Art: Michael Godfrey
Text stories: (tc) - Painted full colour frontpiece J McConnell
1960-1962   £12 $19
World version known as 'Champion The Wonder Horse Comic
Annual'
©1960 (128pg) (Daily Mirror)
Writer: Arthur Groom, Art: Michael Godfrey
Text stories (tc)
Based on the TV series

CHARLES BUCHAN'S SOCCER Gift Book
(Charles Buchan/IPC)
1953/4-1970s
1950's   £15 $24
1960's   £10 $16
1970's   £8 $13
Early years have dustjacket (162pg)

CHARLIE'S ANGELS (Stafford Pemberton)
1978-1981   £12 $19
1978 (64pg) (fc)
Comic Strips: Past the Post (6)
Text Stories: Fair Shares for All (8), Your Very Good Health (8), Get
it on Tape (6)
Features: Full-colour photo profiles of Kate Jackson, Farrah
Fawcett-Majors, Jaclyn Smith
Photo Cover
1979 (64pg) (fc)
Comic Strip: New York Clean-Up (6)
Features: Full-colour photo profiles of Jaclyn Smith, Kate Jackson

and Cheryl Ladd
Photo cover
1980 (64pg) (fc)
Comic Strips: Twin Trouble (7), Back from the Dead (6), Where
there's a Will (6)
Text Stories (8x3): Sabrina Could Have Died, For Love of a Lady,
The Cut-Throat Affair
Features: Full-colour photo profiles of Jaclyn Smith, Kate Jackson
and Cheryl Ladd
Photo cover
Based on the TV detective series

CHARLIE CHALK (World)
1992 (64pg) (fc)   £3 $5
Writer: Geoffrey Cowan, Sue Pearson, Art: Ray and Christine
Mutimer
Picture strips previously appeared in 'Buttons' comic

CHARLIE CHAPLIN (Brown & Watson)
1975   £8 $13
©1974
Comic Strips: Scene Stealer! (5fc), Safari So Good (6fc), Sleep
Walking (5fc), Classroom Capers (5fc), Super Salesman (5fc), Self
Defence (12fc), On the Farm (5fc), Odd Job Man (5fc)
Art: Torre Grosa
Text Stories: Calling the Tune, A Race Against Time
Features: Charlie Chaplin (bw)
Based on the movie character

CHEEKY (Fleetway)
1980's   £5 $8
CHATTERBOX (Wells Gardner, Darton & Co Limited/Dean)
1894-1950s
1950's   £20 $32
CHEGGERS (Stafford Pemberton)
1980 (64pg)   £8 $13
Features: Wings, Grease, Brotherhood of Man, Smokie, Frankie
Miller, 10CC, David Essex, Blondie, Bee Gees, Elton John, Julie
Covington, Leo Sayer, Boney M, Donna Summer, Abba,
Commodores, Rod Stewart, Boomtown Rats
Based on the UK TV personality Keith Chegwin

CHERRY AMES Girls Annual (World)
1950s-1965   £20 $32
©1963 (128pg)
©1964 (128pg)
Fontispiece: Full colour
Text Stories:
A Cape Cod Tale by Helen Wells
The Second-best Bed by Agnes Booth
The Moonstone Ring by Sylvia Edwards
A Crown for a Princess by D M Priestley
The Hidden Room by Joyce Hiorns
The Taking of the Red One by Kay Farrell
A Test of Courage by Kay Fielding
Daddy Longlegs to the Rescue by Karen Frost
The Riddle of Devil's Mountain by Helen Wells
The Menkausus Affair by Diane Powell
The Case of the Lonely Girl by Mary Harvey
Nursing Today by Sylvia Edwards
Trouble in Hollywood by Trudi Arlen

CHEYENNE (World)
1960-1965

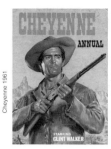

Cheyenne 1961

Circus Boy 1960

Clue Club 1979

1960	£20	$32
1961-1965	£15	$24

©1961 (96pg) (fc)
Writer: Joe Morrissey
Art: Walter Howarth
Comic Strips: The Loner (14), The Marked Witness (13)
Dell Comic reprints
©1963 (96pg) (fc)
Art: Walter Howarth
Comic Strips (2x12): The Medicine Buffalo, Gambling With A Noose, Small Bear in The War Dance (4)
Dell Comic reprints

CHEYENNE Adventure Stories (Adprint)

©1960 (96pg) (bw)	£12	$19

Writer: John Stanstead, Art: Desmond Walduck

CHEYENNE, A TELEVISION STORYBOOK (New Town Printers)

1961-1962	£10	$16

CHICKS' OWN (Amalgamated Press)

1924-1957

1950-1957	£20	$32

Early editions tabloid size

CHILDREN'S HOUR

1954	£25	$40

Features: Flowerpot Men etc.

CHILDREN'S TV (BBC)

2000 (62pg)	£5	$8

Features: BBC Presenters, Richard McCourt, Grange Hill, Linford's Record Breakers, The Really Wild Show, Kirsten O'Brien, Newsround, Chucklevision, Mark Speight, Live and Kicking, Blue Peter, Linford Christie, Smart, Rugrats, Rewind, Kate Sanderson, Short Change, Steve Wilson
Based on Childrens BBC TV Characters

"CHiPs" (World)

1980-1984	£8	$13

1980 (64pg) (fc/tc)
Art: Paul Crompton, Melvyn Powell
Text Stories: Delivery Boys, Monkey Business, Kidnapping with a Difference, Just like in the Movies, Highway Holiday, An Angel on the Freeway
Erik Estrada & Larry Wilcox photo cover
1981 (64pg) (fc/tc)
Art: Melvyn Powell
Text stories: CHiPs Boogie Blues, The Passing of a Meteor, When the Honeymoon's Over, Living in the Fast Lane, Jalopy Derby
Erik Estrada & Tom Reilly photo cover
1982 (64pg) (fc/tc)
Endpaper & Art: Paul Crompton
Text Stories: Fruits of Evil, Accidents will Happen, Watch the Skies!, Home Ground, Escort, The Drugs Run
1983 (64pg) (fc/tc)
Endpaper, Art: Paul Crompton, Paul Green
Text Stories: Daredevil Derby, The Grudge, A Fun Evening, Armed and Dangerous, Rip-Off and Lift-Off, Track Treachery
Erik Estrada & Larry Wilcox photo cover
©1984 (64pg) (fc/tc)
The Bomb Rider, One Day On The Ridge, When Ghosts Talk
Art: Glenn Rix
Erik Estrada & Tom Reilly photo cover (front)
Based on the California Highway Patrol TV series

CIRCUS BOY (Daily Mirror)

1958-1960	£15	$24

©1958 (130pg) (tc)
Writer: Dorothea J. Snow, Adapted by Gordon Grimsley
Art: John Pollack
Mickey Dolenz photo cover (fc)
Full-colour photo back cover features all the cast
Text stories with frontispiece (tc)
Based on the TV series

CLANGERS (Odhams/Polystyle)

1971-1973	£10	$16

Writers: Oliver Postgate and Peter Firmin
1972
Text Stories: The Freezing Froglets, The Hoots
Based on the BBC puppet series

CLEOPATRA (Grandreams)

1999	£3	$5

©1998 (64pg)
Writer: Michael Heatley, Designer: Jason Bazini
Based on the girl band

CLIPPER ANNUAL OF FOOTBALL FACTS

1970's	£5	$8

CLOPPA CASTLE (World)

1980 (64pg)	£6	$10

Custard Pie Ghosts, Beosweyne's Birthday, Sleeping Beauties, A Sticky End, Queen's Champion, The Moat Monster, Allbrite's Wonderful Lamp
Includes photos from the series
Based on the Children's TV puppet series

CLUE CLUB Hanna Barbera (World)

1979 (64pg) (fc/tc)	£10	$16

Text Stories: The Case of the Strange Sea Monster, The Mystery of the Missing Jewels, The Case of the Disappearing Dress, The Case of the Missing Racehorse, The Case of the Missing Marrow
Based on the animated TV series

COCKLESHELL BAY (World)

1980's	£6	$10

©1984
Photo features
Based on the Cosgrove Hall puppet series

COLLINS BOYS' Annual (Collins)

1930s - 1960s

1950-1960	£10	$16

©1966 (132pg)
Picture Strips: Red Radford and the Tangier Smugglers, The Menacing Asteroid, Ambush
Text Stories: The Ex Marshall by Gerry Wood
The Jaguar's Heart by Stuart Tresilian
The Cliffs of Tontire by E. Hood
Into a Hornets' Nest by R. A. Branton
Half Breed by G. W. Backhouse
The Hopewell's Lady by Geoffrey Whittam
Whistle by Moonlight by Neville Dear
Red Radford and the Killing Storm by R. A. Branton
The Unexplored Island by McConnell
Midnight Rendezvous by Roger Payne

COLLINS CHILDREN'S Annual (Collins)

1950's-1960s

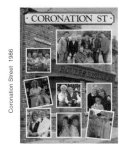
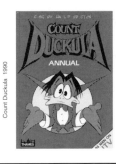

| 1950's | £15 | $24 |
| 1960's | £10 | $16 |

©1966 (96pg) (fc/tc/bw)
Picture Strips: Pinny's A Sharp Lad by Racey Helps
The Little Black Lamb by Madeleine Robinson
Kate and the Cows by Betty Golby
Text Stories: The March Hare's Tea Party by Tansy Baran
The Story of Abou-Hassan by Kris
The Sancastle by Grace Lodge
The Strange Gift by Esme Eve
The Dog without a Pedigree by Grace Lodge
The Rescue of Spring by Gladys Mason
The Woodcutter's Three Daughter's by Doreen Baxter
The Witch who Lost her Temper by Esme Eve
The Secret by Joan Calvert
Shamrocks by E. Osborn Corbett

COLLINS GIRLS' Annual (Collins)
1950s-1960s

| 1950's | £15 | $24 |

©1955 (132pg) (fc/bw)
Frontispiece: Valerie Sweet
Picture Strips: The Kidnapped Star by Valerie Sweet
Mandy and Carol
Text Stories: Beetle, Writer: P M Warner by Valerie Sweet
Half-Term Hold Up, Writer ECR Lorac by Raw
The Madadh Ruadh, Writer: David Stephen by Len Fullerton
The Wilsons Wont Mind!, Writer: Jane Shaw by R A Branton
Betsy's Escapade, Writer: Jean Matheson by Arnold Beauvais
Guest Star, Writer: Mollie Chappell by Kris
My Great-Aunt Honoria, Writer: Edward Boyd by D L Wynne
Beware of Uncles, Writer: Anne Barrett by Gilbert Dunlop
The Laurence Boy, Writer: Louisa M Alcott by S. Van Abbe

| 1960's | £10 | $16 |

COMBAT Picture Annual (G.M. Smith)

| 1962 | £15 | $24 |

COMICOLOUR (Swan)

| 1947-1955 | £20 | $32 |

COMMANDER Boys Annual
1956-1960s

| 1956-1959 | £15 | $24 |
| 1960's | £12 | $19 |

COMPACT (World)

| 1964 | £20 | $32 |

©1963 (Scarce) (112pg) (bw)
Photo Cover
Based on the BBC TV series by Hazel Adair and Peter Ling

CONAN THE BARBARIAN (Marvel/Grandreams)

| N/D - Cover Price £2.50 (64pg) (fc) | £8 | $13 |

Art: John Buscema
Marvel comic strip adaptation (48fc)
Features: John Milius, Arnold Schwarzenegger, Ron Cobb, James
Earl Jones
Photo Cover
Based on the film starring Arnold Schwarzenegger

CONAN THE DESTROYER (Marvel/Grandreams)

| 1985 | £8 | $13 |

©1984 (64pg)
Photo Cover

Based on the film starring Arnold Schwarzenegger

COR!! (Fleetway)
1972-1986

| 1970's | £8 | $13 |
| 1980's | £6 | $10 |

Based on the UK comic

CORONATION STREET (Grandreams/World)
1986, 1997

| ©1985 (64pg) (Grandreams) | £7 | $11 |
| 1997 (64pg) (World) | £5 | $8 |

Design: Rob Sharp
Based on the UK soap set in Manchester

COUNTDOWN (Polystyle)
1972-1973

| 1972 | £15 | $24 |

©1971
Photo endpapers feature UFO craft
Comic Strips: UFO in The Circus (7fc), Dastardley and Muttley
(2x2tc), Thunderbirds in Terror at Torreba (6tc), Captain Scarlet
(5fc), Art: John Cooper, The Secret Service (6tc), Dr. Who (8fc)-Art:
Jim Baikie, features Jon Pertwee
Text Stories: UFO: The Defenders-Emergency Red Alert (photo
story fc), Dangerous Friend (fc), Joe 90 Resigns (fc)
Includes photo feature: A Day With Dr. Who- behind the scenes on
the filming of a Dr. Who (Jon Pertwee) episode
Pin-Up (fc): Jon Pertwee
Photo cover features UFO, Dr. Who (Pertwee), Thunderbirds,
Captain Scarlet

| 1973 | £10 | $16 |

©1972 (80pg) (fc/tc) - 'Countdown for TV Action'
Photo endpaper features Dr. Who (Pertwee)
Art: Frank Langford
Comic Strips: Gerry Anderson's UFO - Smash and Grab (8fc), The
Haunted Mine (6fc), Thunderbirds - The Collector (7tc), Captain
Scarlet - Wheels Of Destruction (7tc)
Hanna Barbera's Dastardly and Muttley (2tc), Hanna Barbera's
Autocat and Motormouse (2tc), Dr. Who - Ride To Nowhere (7fc),
features Jon Pertwee
Photo Text Story (fc): The Persuaders in By Person or Person's
Unknown! (8)
Also includes double-page cutaway of a UFO Interceptor and profile
of Ed Bishop (fc)
Photo cover
Based on the UK comic

COUNT DUCKULA (Marvel/World)
1989-1990s

| 1989 (64pg) (fc) (Marvel) | £6 | $10 |

Writer: Joyce McAleer, John Broadhead, Art: Alan Case
Comic Strips: Adventurous Spirit, Art: Brian Williamson, Inks: Tim
Perkins
A Duck of Sports, Art: Arthur Ranson, Inks: Dave Hine
Nanny, Art: Andy Lanning, Inks: Tim Perkins
Transylvanian Modern, Art: Anthony Williams, Inks: Liam Sharp
Compiled and Editor Nicholas Abadzis, Art & Design: Helen Stone

| 1990 (64pg) (fc) (World) | £6 | $10 |

Duckula In Space, Messing About On A Boat, The Duckwagon Train
Based on the Cosgrove Hall animated TV series

COUNTRY MUSIC

| 1976 | £8 | $13 |

Crackerjack ©1970

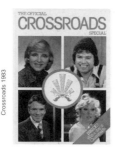

Crossroads 1983

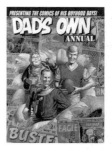

Dad's Own 1993

COWBOY COMIC

1960's £12 $19
No 1-3

CRACKERJACK (Daily Mirro/Atlas/World)

1960s-1980s
1960's-1965 £20 $32
©1962 (128pg) (tc)
"The Eamonn Andrews Crackerjack Book"
Pin Ups: Cliff Richard, Lonnie Donegan, The Shadows, Billy Fury, Russ Conway, Teddy Johnson & Pearl Carr, Dickie Valentine, Frank Ifield, Bert Weedon, Shirley Bassey, Craig Douglas, Danny Williams, Kenny Ball, Bob Wallis, June Christy, Helen Shapiro, Brenda Lee, Elvis Presley, Sandy Nelson, Mr Ackerbilk, Chris Barber, Terry Lightfoot
Eamonn Andrews photo cover
1966-1969 £15 $24
1970s £10 $16
©1969 (Atlas) (80pg)
Michael Aspel illustrated cover
Comic Strips: Peter's 'New' Old Car (7tc), Rod buys a Yacht (7tc)
Photo Strip: Rod Saves the Day (8fc/bw)
Features: The Troggs, Love Affair, The Small Faces, The Hollies, Amen Corner
©1970 (World) (80pg) (No. 2)
Features: The Bachelors, Roy Orbison, Tom Jones, Georgie Fame, Alan Price, The Who, Peter Sarstedt, Englebert Humperdinck, Cliff Richard, Glenn Campbell, Stevie Wonder, Jose Feliciano, Cilla Black, Sandy Shaw, Lulu, The Tremloes, The Marmalade, Hermans Hermits, The Foundations
1980s £6 $10
Based on the Childrens BBC TV variety show

CRACKERJACK For Boys

1950's £20 $32
©1958 - Includes Jennings and Space adventures

CRACKERJACK GIRLS OWN Book (Children's Press)

1960s £10 $16
N/D
Frontispiece: Branton
Comic Strip: Sandra and June in the Cave Adventure Written and drawn by G C Robinson, Blue Ribbon Barb Written and drawn by Reg Hicks
Text Stories: Susan's School Play by Jane Shaw by R A Branton
A Good Neighbour, Writer: Carol Ann Pearce by Veronica Fryer
The Uninvited Ghost Writer: Anne Bradley by Joan Thompson
Flash's Last Round Up - Writer and by Valerie Sweet
A Bit of Mystery Writer: Frances Cowen by Gilbert Dunlop
Volunteer Nurse Writer: Margaret Ruthin by R A Branton
The Little Snob Writer: Valerie Winterton by Geoffrey Fletcher
The Minstrel's Quest Writer: Violet Needham by John Wood
The Lost - Chance Writer: Frances B Clark by J B Long
The Rubies of Hkun Mung Writer: Hugh Paterson by Malcolm Tompkins
The Midnight Picnic Writer: Carol Ann Pearce by R A Branton
Features: At the Sign of the Long Bow by Trevor Holloway
The University of the Footlights Writer: Kay Weston by Valerie Sweet

CRACKERJACK WESTERN Book

1950s £15 $24

CROSSROADS Special (Grandreams)

1980's £8 $13

©1979 (64pg) (fc/tc)
Writers: Glynis Langley, Alison Spenceley, Hilda Young
Photo Features and Photo Cover
©1982 (64pg) (fc)
Photo features and Photo Cover
Based on the UK soap

CUB SCOUT (World /Pedigree)

1970s - present
1970's £8 $13
1980's £6 $10
1990's £4 $6
1973 (104pg) (tc) (World)
Editor: Ron Jeffries
Text stories: Adventure for Three Cubs by Heather Gorst, Cattle Drive by Richard Ringley, The New Boy by Tony Oldfield, Cage Me a Cat by Kevin McGarry, The Friends by Kevin McGarry, The Drowned Graveyard by Sydney Bounds, Reggie and Ozzletwishes by Valerie Barton, Snap by David Harwood.
Picture Stories: Baden-Powell House and The Story of Gilwell by Brenda Uttley
1992 (64pg) (World)
Comic Strip: Space Explorer (4fc), Art: Steve Harman
Text Stories: Billy and the Friendly Ghost by Neil Williams, Fudging the Truth, Zack and the Time Machine, Art: Caroline
Feature: Micro Machines

CULTURE CLUB (Grandreams)

1984 (64pg) (fc/bw) £8 $13
Pop band featuring 'Boy George'

CUTE FUN ALBUM

1947-1956 £30 $48

DAD'S ARMY (World)

1973-1978 £12 $19
1973-1975
1975 - Cover Art: Edgar Hodges
1976-1978
1976 (64pg)
Comic Strips: Fishy Business (6tc), The Document (6fc)
Cover art: Edgar Hodges, Art: Edgar Hodges and Paul Crompton
1978 - Cover Art: Edgar Hodges
Based on the BBC TV comedy series

DAD'S OWN (Fleetway)

1994
©1993 (64pg) (fc/bw) £8 $13
'Presenting The Comics Of His Boyhood Days!'
Covers and sample contents include: Eagle, Film Fun, Jack and Jill, Look and Learn, Swift, Ranger, Knockout, Tiger, Comic Cuts, Buster, Playhour, Tiny Tots, Mickey Mouse Weekly

DAILY EXPRESS SCIENCE (Beaverbrook)

1960's £12 $19

DAILY MAIL ADVENTURE

1950's £15 $24
N/D - Davy Crockett cover

DAILY MAIL BOYS' ANNUAL

1950-1960's
1950's £15 $24
1960's £12 $24

DAILY MAIL For Boy's and Girls Annual

1940's -1950's

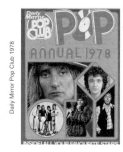

1950's	£15	$24

DAILY MAIL Annual For Girls

1950's-1960's

1950's	£15	$24
1960's	£12	$16

DAILY MAIL TEDDY TAIL Annual

See: TEDDY TAIL

DAILY MIRROR Book for Boys (Mirror/Hamlyn)

1970-1980's

1970's	£15	$24

1970 (96pg) (fc/bw)

Comic Strips: Garth in Space - Writer: Ken Roscoe, Art: Steve Dowling and John Allard

River of Revenge - Writer: Pat Taylor and Art: Gerry Embleton, Race for life - no credits

Undersea Agent - Writer: Geoff Kemp - Art: Keith Watson and Eric Eden

The Colours of the Brancasters - no credits

Mission to Martuan - no credits

Text Story: A Good Snake, Writer: Maxwell Hunter, Art: Reg Gray

The Blind Messenger, Writer: Ernest Sharrard, Art: Reg Gray

Lake of Fear, Writer: S J Bounds, Art: Ron Embleton

Feature: Men on the Moon, Writer: John W R Taylor, Art: Gordon Davis

1980's	£8	$13

DAILY MIRROR Book for Boys and Girls (Mirror/Hamlyn)

1970-1980s	£15	$24

1981

Comic Strips: The Spectre of Stafford Grange (2bw), The Lost City of the Incas (6bw), Ghost of the Tideless Sea (8fc), Art: Don Lawrence, The Spirit of Nathan Sparr (3bw), Pancho Villa (10bw)

Features: Abba (2pg), Blondie (2pg), Dollar (2pg)

DAILY MIRROR Book for Girls (Mirror/Hamlyn)

1970-1980s	£15	$24

1972 (96pg)

Comic Strips: Secret of the Loch (4bw), The Small Woman (5fc), Nora's Ark (4bw), Sorry Sue, (4fc), The Long Walk (4bw), Not All Honey (4fc)

Text Story: The Third Child, Writer: Sue Kirkpatrick, Art: Boada

Bird's Eye View, Writer: Laurie Kuhrt, Art: Badia

Larder Beauty, Writer: Sally Cork, Art: Ferguson Dewar

The Pony She Wanted, Writer: Margaret May, Art: Harry Lindfield

You Never Had it So Good, Writer: Denise Cork, Art: McMarty, Art signed by Graham Allen

Fairy Flag of Dunvegan, Wrtier: Graeme Cook, Art: Exell

Features: The Railway Children by E. Nesbit - 6 pg (fc)

DAILY MIRROR POP CLUB (Stafford Pemberton)

1970s-1980s

1978 (72pg) (fc/tc/bw)	£10	$16

Features: Rod Stewart, Noel Edmonds, Leo Sayer, George Harrison, David Bowie, Black Sabbath, Bay City Rollers, Dennis Roussos, Abba, Carpenters, Mick Jagger, ELO

1982 (World)	£8	$13

Editor: Ken Irwin

Features: Dire Straits, Police, Status Quo, Sheena Easton, John Peel, Earth, Wind and Fire, Joan Armatrading, Olivia Newton John, Billy Joel, Barry Manilow, Neil Diamond, Kelly Marie, Kiss, Eurythmics, Air Supply, Barclay James Harvest, XTC, Hazel O'Connor, Don McLean, Elton John

Pin Ups (fc): Debbie Harry, Cliff Richard, Sad Cafe, Judas Priest, Thin Lizzy, The Blues Band, Rod Stewart, Leo Sayer, Kate Bush, Madness, Paul McCartney

DAILY SKETCH CHILDREN'S Annual

1960's	£15	$24

DAILY SKETCH MODERN BOYS' Annual

1960's	£15	$24

DAILY SKETCH MODERN GIRLS Annual

1960's - with dustjacket	£15	$24
without dj	£12	$16

n/d 1963 Priced 9/6 (200pg) (fc/tc)

Editor: Frances Rowan

Comic Strips: Dotty (4tc), The Children's Village (4bw)

Text Stories: With a Fringe on the Cuffs: Writer: H.P. Bonner, Art: Exell

Gymkhana: Writer: Arthur P. Jacobs, Art: Sheila Rose, House-Boat Adventure: Writer: Arthur P. Jacobs, Art: Terence Freeman

Accident and Design; Writer: Mollie Chappell, Art: Brian Nissen

Surprises For the Twins: Writer: Catherine Morris, Art: Lola Fielding, Where the Oyster-Catchers Call: Writer: Catherine Morris, Art: G.J. Galsworthy

The Ballad of the Ten Thousand Ants: Writer: Alex Potter, Art: Eve

This Little Pig: Writer: Maisie Sharman, Art: Terence Freeman

Elsa's Country Cousin: Writer: Betty E. Spence, Art: James Hunt

Aunt Cynthia's Methods: Writer: Frank Knight, Art: Will Nickless

A Bird in Hand: Writer: Claire Moore, Art: Sheila Rusby

Smuggler's Ruse: Writer: John Hynam, Art: Adrian Bailey, Princess of Cooks: Writer: John Hynam, Art: William McLaren

What Happened to the Captain's Gold: Writer: Colette Mancroft, Art: Teela Marus

Cobby's Night Out: Writer: Rosemary Weir, Art: Joan Thompson

The Sun Festival: Writer: Pauline Hamm, Art: Grace Huxtable

The Golden Horse: Writer: Joyce Stranger, Art: Juliette Palmer

Yellow Flower's Charm: Writer: Judith Nisbet, Art: Stuart Tresilian

Moonlight Ride: Writer: Kathleen MacKenzie, Art: Joanna Curzon

Feature Writers: Ian Wallace, Doreen Hinchcliffe, David Gunston, Jill Wilson, Joy M. Coleman, Kathleen D. Britten, J.S. Goodall, K.& M. Peyton, Meg Howarth

Feature Artists: H. C. McBeath, Nancy Catford, A. Burgess Sharrocks, Hickey, J. S. Goodall

DAKOTAS (Purnell)

1963-1964	£10	$16

Based on the TV Western series

DAKTARI (World)

1967-1971

©1967 (96pg) (fc/tc)	£12	$19

Cover Art: Ron Smethurst

Writers: Joe Morrissey, J H Pavey, Mae Broadley, Ken Denham, and J. W. Elliott-Art: Edgar Hodges, T. Nolan, David Brian

1968-1970	£10	$16

©1968 (96pg) (fc/tc)

Text Stories: Rogue on the Run, Voice of the Wild, Cry Death, The Tiger, Rival for Sacrifice, Beware Elephant!, Lion on the Loose, The Ghost White Hunter, All That Glitters, Dynamite for Judy

©1969 (96pg) (fc/tc)

Text Stories: Return of the Sorceress, Horn of Trouble, Jack and the Baboons, Crash Landing, Vengeance Trophy, In Tamest Africa, The White Gorilla, He-Who-Makes-Thunder

Based on the Ivan Tors' TV series starring Marshall Thompson

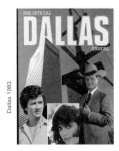

Dallas 1983

Dan Dare 1991

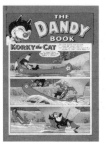

Dandy 1959

DALEK BOOK (Souvenir /Panther)
1964 (Very scarce) £80 $128
DALEK WORLD (Souvenir/Panther)
1965 (Scarce) £70 $110
DALEK OUTER SPACE BOOK (Souvenir/Panther)
1966 (Very scarce) £80 $128
DALEK Terry Nation's (World)
1976-1979 £12 $19
1977 (80pg)
Cover Art/Endpaper: Edgar Hodges
Comic Strips: The Envoys of Evil (8fc), The Menace of the
Monstrons (6fc), The Quest (6bw)
Strips originally published in TV Century 21 comic
Text story Art: Edgar Hodges
Feature pages Art: Paul Green and John Fasnacht
DALLAS (Grandreams)
1982-1983 £8 $13
©1981
©1982
Editor: John Barraclough
Colour/bw photo features
Based on the US soap starring Larry Hagman
DAN DARE (Fleetway)
1974-1991
1974 (Scarce) £20 $32
1979, 1980 £12 $19
1987, 1991 £10 $16
1987 (96pg fc)
Comic Strips: Dan Dare (15fc), Dan Dare (8bw), The Exterminator
(8bw), Dan Dare (8bw)
Features: Tribute to artists Frank Bellamy, Frank Hampson, Don
Harley, Harold Johns/Gretta Tomlinson, Keith Watson, Gerry
Embleton, Ian Kennedy, Carlos Cruz
1991(64pg)
Art: Keith Page
Comic Strips: Dan Dare Pilot of the Future (8fc), Digby (4bw),
Funfair of Death (8fc), Dan Dare Pilot of the Future (7fc)
Features: Tribute to artist Keith Watson
DAN DARE'S SPACEBOOK (Hulton)
1953 (Scarce) £80 $128
DAN DARE SPACE (Longacre)
1963 £30 $48
DANDY BOOK (D.C.Thomson)
1938-present
©1939 £1500 $2400
1939-1952 - 'The Dandy Monster Comic'
1950-1955 £150 $240
1953 - first 'The Dandy Book'
1956-1959 £80 $128
1960-1965 £50 $80
1966 - lst dated cover £50 $80
1967-1970 £30 $48
1971-1975 £20 $32
1976-1980 £15 $24
1981-1989 £12 $19
1990 -present £6 $10
DANGER MAN (Atlas/World)
1964-1967

1964 £20 $32
1965-1967 £15 $24
©1965 (World)
Cover art and text story Art:Walter Howarth
©1966 (World) (96pg)
Text Story: The Big Splash, No Medals For The General, The Silver
Ring, Smoked Out!, Smugglers' Cove, Countdown, Dead on Nine,
Payoff on the Frontier, Moses was the 1st Spy King!, Playback
'War Against Mafia', 'Kingdom of Fear'
Based on the TV series starring Patrick McGoohan
DANGER MAN TELEVISION STORYBOOK (PBS)
1965 £15 $24
DANGER MAN 'Top TV Series' (Young World)
1965 Hardback comic £12 $19
DANGER MOUSE (Stafford Pemberton/ITP)
1980's £8 $13
1983 (Stafford Pemberton) (48pg) (fc)
Comic Strips: A Sticky Problem, The Day It Rained Penfold and
Danger Mouse - Includes text stories
1984 (64pg) (fc)
Text Stories: Dracula? He's Bats!, The Bermuda Trombone, The
Fiendish Fun Fair!, A Model Colonel!,
1986 (64pg) (ITP)
Writer: Angus P. Allan
Art: Arthur Ranson and Dick Millington
Text stories and features
1987 (64pg)
Writer: Angus P. Allan, Art: Arthur Ranson
Picture Strips: The Case of the Dodgy Dinosaur, The Great Fish
Caper, A Better Better Mousetrap, The Toad from Uncle, Too Much
Monkey Business, The Crown Jewels Caper, An Old Old Story,
Coming on Strong, Mummy Mummy Where's the Treasure!
Based on the Cosgrove Hall animated TV series
DANGER MOUSE (St. Michael)
1982-1983
Limited distribution in Marks & Spencers stores
©1982 (orange cover) £8 $13
Art: Michael Wells Studio
Text Stories: The World of Machines, Custard, The Ghost Bus,The
Martian Misfit
©1983 (blue cover) £8 $13
Art: Michael Wells Studio
Text Stories:The Chicken Run, The Invasion of Colonel K, Demons
Aren't Dull, The Odd Ball Run A Round
©1984 (fc) (dark blue cover) £8 $13
Dangermouse to the Rescue
Text Stories: Tiptoe Through the Penfolds, Project Moon, Who Stole
the Bagpipes?, The Long Lost Crown Affair, Four Heads are Better
than Two
Art: Peter Campbell
Based on the Cosgrove Hall animated TV series
DANGER UXB (World)
1980
©1979 (64pg) (fc/tc) £10 $16
Art: Paul Crompton, David Fryer, Edgar Hodges, Melvyn Powell
Writer: Brenda Apsley, Paul Hunter, Alison Spenceley, Hilda Young
'Action-Packed Stories Of Men Who Diced With Death'
Based on the ITV drama series
DAREDEVIL (World)

David Soul Gift Book 1979

Dennis 1988

Diana 1967

1978 (78pg)	£5	$8

Features: Evel Knievel
Stuntmen & daring sports

DAVID BECKHAM Special (Grandreams)

1998-2000	£5	$8

Based on the UK soccer star

DAVID BELLAMY'S I SPY BOOK OF NATURE (Fleetway)

1986 (80pg) (fc/tc)	£5	$8

DAVID CASSIDY (World)

1974-1975	£12	$19

1974 (80pg) (fc/tc)
Endpaper/Art: Steve Livesey
Comic Strips: Wanted: A Friend (7tc) - Art: S Gumen
The Cassidy Collection (6tc)
Charlton Comics reprints
Photo Cover
Features: Partridge Family photos
1975 (80pg (tc/fc)
Comic Strips: David's Near Miss (6tc)
David's Date (6tc)
Features: Shirley Jones
Based on the actor/pop singer

DAVID COLEMANS WORLD OF FOOTBALL

1969	£7	$11

Based on the BBC TV sports present

DAVID ESSEX

1976-1978	£8	$13

1978 (64pg) (fc/bw)
Features: The Places I Work, Coming Home, Me and the Boys,
Dreams and Disappointments, What a Crazy Way to Earn a Living,
Behind the Scenes
Based on the UK pop star

DAVID SOUL Gift Book (Stafford Pemberton)

1979		

©1978 (48pg) (fc/bw) £10 $16
Features: The David Soul Story, Days When 'Starsky & Hutch'
Went On Strike, My Pal Paul, Singing For His Supper
Based on the actor/pop singer

DAVY CROCKETT Walt Disneys (Dean)

N/D	£20	$32

Cover Art: Ron Embleton
Based on the Disney TV series

DAY TO DAY DIARY (World)

1979
Art: Annabel Spenceley, Compiled by Pippa Little and Hilda Young
Day by Day news, people events and interests for 1979!

DC SUPER POWERS

1977	£8	$13

DEBBIE for Girls (DC Thomson)

1970's-1980's

1970s	£5	$8
1980s	£3	$5

1980 (128pg) (fc/tc/bw)
Comic Strips: Mary Brown's Schooldays, The Night Before
Christmas, Skip 'n' Rope, Meg of the Moors, Little Sis, Jo and Mo,
The House that Cared, My Pal Lou, Little Miss Featherfeet, If you
can Help Somebody, Trixie's Treasure Chest, The Bionic Horse, The
Flower Princess, Pollys Patches, London's Burning, Swan Song

Photo Stories: The Wishing Well, The Forbidden Garden
Features: Magpie Team, Legs and Co, The Dooleys, It's A Knockout
Baesd on the girls comic

DEFENDERS OF THE EARTH (Marvel)

1990 (64pg) (fc)	£7	$11

©1989
Comic strip 'Defenders of the Earth' (43pg) - no credits
Based on the animated TV series

DEMPSEY & MAKEPEACE (World)

1986-1987	£7	$11

1986 (64pg) (fc)
Art: Melvyn Powell
Comic Strip: Dead Man's Deal! (6)
Photo covers
1987 (64pg)
Endpaper/Text Story Art: Walter Howarth
Comic Strip: The Drop (6), Art: Glenn Rix
Based on ITV detective series

DENNIS (World)

1988 (64pg)	£7	$11

DENNIS THE MENACE Book (D.C.Thomson)

1955 - present

1955	£200	$320
1956-1959	£100	$160
1960-1965	£50	$80
1966-1970	£40	$60
1968 first dated cover		
1971-1979	£25	$40
1980-1990	£12	$19
1991-present	£6	$10

Bi-annual until 1970
Based on the Beano comic character

DEPUTY DAWG (World)

1970-1974 (80pg) (fc)	£10	$16

Cover/Text Story Art: David Fryer (uncredited)
Comic Strips feature: Deputy Dawg, Heckle and Jeckle and Silly
Sidney
US Reprints
Based on the animated TV series

DESPERATE DAN Book (D.C. Thomson)

1954 - present

©1953 Dudley Watkins art	£200	$320
1955-1959	£100	$160
1960-1965	£50	$80
1966-1970	£30	$48
1971-1979	£20	$32
1980-1990	£12	$19
1991-present	£6	$10

Based on the Dandy comic character

DIANA For Girls (D.C.Thomson)

1967-1980s

1967-1969 (with dj)	£15	$24
1967-1969 (without dj)	£10	$16

1967
Comic Strips (fc): Mystery Eagle Island, The Constant Tin Soldier
(Hans Christian Anderson), The Magic Mirror, The Girl Who Danced
in Her Sleep, Yum Yum in Switzerland, The Wonder Girl
1968
Front Endpaper 'Secret Agents' with bw photos of James Bond

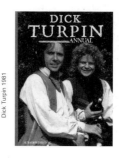

Diana 1985

Dick Barton Special Agent 1979

Dick Turpin 1981

(Sean Connery), Emma Peel (Diana Rigg), The Girl From U.N.C.L.E. (Stefanie Powers and Noel Harrison), The Man From U.N.C.L.E. (David McCallum), Danger Man (Patrick McGoohan) and The Baron (Steve Forrest) Back
Back Endpaper 'Pop Stars' includes two-colour photos of Cilla Black, Lulu, Gene Pitney, Dusty Springfield, Sandie Shaw, Andy Williams, Paul Jones, Rod Stewart and The Seekers.
Comic Strips (fc): The Girls From N.O.O.D.L.E.S., Starr of Wonderland, Babs of Butterfly Farm, Kitty's Concert Party, The Merry Mermaids, Emergency Nurse Gwen, A Christmas Miracle, The Magic Mirror, The First Punch and Judy Man
Feature (bw): On BBC TV Series Adam Adamant

1970-1979 (with dj)	£10	$16
1970-1979 (without dj)	£8	$13

1970
Comic Strips (fc): Mary Brown's Schooldays, Our Gang, Model Miss Jane, Starr of Wonderland, Night of the Witches, My Big Sister Billie, Afraid to tell the Truth, School for Penfriends, My Big Brother Marmaduke, Mactaggart of the Mounted Police, Clumsy Claudia, The Broken Ballerina, Nellie Bashem, Ingrid, Lorna on Stage,
1971
Comic Strips (fc): The Swiss Family Robinson, Countess Tolstoy, Countess of Airlie, Lorna in the Wild West, The Sacred Geese of Juno, Mister Magic's Last Trick, Little Yoo, My Big Brother Marmaduke, Mary Brown's Schooldays, Terrors from the Tiny Planet, School for Pen Friends, Secret of the White Rose, Sue of the Silver Arrow, Secret of the Mountain Dog, Ingrid and the Robot, Patsy O'Hara, Jane Model Miss, Starr of Wonderland
Features: Jean Simmons
1972
Comic Strips (fc): My Big Brother Marmaduke, Sara and the Singing Planet, Jane Model Miss, The Ghost in the Big Top, California - Here we Come, I'm Belle of the Ball, A Girl called Sarah, The Pony Who Liked Fun, Miranda's Mexican Ballet, Lucy and the Dog Next Door, The Boy Next Door, Patti's Pony Express, Slave of the Romans, Pride of St Petersburg, A Thin Time for Tessa, Willa the Witch, Rosie Red Riding Hood
1973 (128pg)
Comic Strips: Mary Brown's Schooldays, Up to Date Kate, Queen of the Planet of Flowers, Lorna in the Court of King Arthur, Maureen and the Boy Next Door, My Big Brother Marmaduke, Jane Model Miss, The Unlucky Horseshoe, Rosie, Letty Leads the Way!, Rusty's Frist Rosettes, The Day of the Dancing Dolls, A Penny for the Cornets, A Girl Called Sarah, Dear Little Elf, Shona's Faithful Friend
1979
Comic Strips (fc): Double Trouble For Samantha, Sixpence For A Broken Heart, For Love Of Leni..., The Raven, Menace By Moonlight, The Fair Maid Of Fouroaks (tc/bw), Charlotte Holmes 'n' Watson, Cinder Nellie
Features and pin ups: Abba, Rod Stewart, David Essex, Alvin Stardust, The Discoteers (painted group portrait of Radio One DJ's Kid Jensen, Simon Bates, Anie Nightingale, Dave Lee Travis, Noel Edmonds, Ed Stewart and Tony Blackburn

1980's	£6	$10

1981
Comic Strips (fc): Sam in the Heart of the Country, Flight From Versailles, The Good, The Bad and the Not So Ugly..., A Secret In Silver (A Man In Black Story), Five Days In August, Once Upon A Fancy Dress Ball..., Charlotte Holmes 'n' Watson

Features and pin ups: Ian Drury, Debbie Harry, Kid Jensen, Sapphire & Steel (Joanna Lumley interview with full-colour photos), Boomtown Rats (painted portrait), Manhattan Transfer
David Essex endpaper (back)
1982 (126pg)
Comic Strips (fc/tc): The Joker, Annas Story, Smith V Smythe, In An English Country Garden, Black Wedding Day, Village of Fear, When the Snow Lay Deep
Features and pin ups: Olivia Newton John, Elvis, Bjorn Borg, Sting, Cliff, Richard O'Sullivan, The Beatles, Trevor Eve, The Osmonds, Clint Eastwood, Lewis Collins, Bee Gees, Abba
1983
Comic Strips (fc): Sam in Search of Romance, To Kill A Queen, Green Grows The Ivy (A Man In Black Story), The Medusa Mission, Man-Trap! It's A Cat's Life!, The Tadcaster Twins (bw)
Features and pin ups: Toyah, Benedict Taylor, Adam and the Ants, Sue Barker, Sharron Davies, Goldie Hawn (painted 'Private Benjamin' portrait), The Jam, Buck's Fizz, Madness, Christopher Reeve (painted 'Superman' portrait), Stray Cats, Jane Fonda (painted 'Barbarella' portrait), Dollar, Robert De Niro (painted 'Raging Bull' portrait), Anne Kirkbride (Dierdre from 'Coronation Street'), Shakin' Stevens
1985 (128pg)
Comic Strips (fc): One Day in Camelot, Rubies of Revenge, Becky and Brock (bw), Yasmin's Mission of Mercy, Sam 2000, How Miss Puddlethorpe 1984 became Miss World 1985 (bw), Ghost Train, Features: Gone with the Wind, Star Wars, Jaws, Paul Daniels, Grease
Pin Ups: David Essex, Hart to Hart, Harrison Ford, Tom Selleck, Bucks Fizz
1986 (128pg)
Comic Strips: Jason & Mary, Sam at Hungry Hall, Amber Goes to War, Lord of the Red Eyes, Eye of the Tiger, The Puddlethorpe Curse, Jenny the Master,
Features and pin ups: Alvin Stardust, Ruth Madocs (Hi de Hi), Wham, Kim Wilde, Simon Le Bon, Princess Diana
Based on the girls comic
DIANA PRINCESS OF WALES (Grandreams)

1986	£10	$16

DICK BARTON

1950's	£25	$40

Based on the radio and film character
DICK BARTON SPECIAL AGENT (Brown Watson)

1980	£5	$8

©1979 (64pg) (tc)
Art: David Lloyd
Comic Strips: An Explosive Situation, Murder Mansion
Features photo profiles: Tony Vogel, Anthony Heaton, James Cosmo, Noël Johnson, History of Dick Barton
Photo Cover
Based on the TV series
DICKORY DOCK (Fleetway)
1980s (80pg) (fc/tc)
Picture Strips: Piggles the Postman, Ferdy Fox and Horace Hound, Happy the Helpful Hare, Duke of the Duckpond, Clever Dick and Silly Billy, Goggles and Giggles, Bananas Bunny, Sweet Sue and Big Brother
Based on the UK comic
DICK TURPIN (Grandreams)

Disco 81 - 1981

Disneyland 1973

Dr Kildare 1694

1980-1981   £5 $8
©1979 (64pg fc/bw)
Comic Strips: The Trap, The King's Shilling, Swiftnick's Folly
Includes text stories and photo features
Photo cover
©1980 (64pg) (fc/bw)
Comic Strips: Scourge of the Sea Dogs, Murder Mile
Based on ITV drama
DINO RIDERS (Marvel)
1990 (64pg)   £5 $8
Editor: Steve White and Euan Peters
Cover Art: Art Wetherell, Stephen Baskerville and John Burns
Comic Strip: Dino Riders - Script: George Carragone
Pencils; Kelley Jones, Inks: Danny Bulanadi
US Marvel Comic Strip Reprint
Based on the Tyco toy range
DISCO 45 (Stafford Pemberton)
1977-1978   £10 $16
1977 (72pg)
Features: Mud, Queen, Roxy Music, Jonathan King, Eagles, 10cc,
Slik, Hot Chocolate
Pin Ups: Mud, Abba, John Miles, Lol Creme, Smokie, Rod Stewart,
1978 (72pg)
Features: Cliff Richard, Leo Sayer, Status Quo, Rod Stewart, David
Soul, Paul McCartney & Wings, Elton John, Tina Charles, Thin
Lizzey, Abba, Stevie Wonder, Gladys Knight
Pin Ups: Paul McCartney, Peter Frampton, Abba, Kiki Dee, Billy
Ocean, Gallagher & Lyle
Based on the music magazine
DISCO 81
1981   £8 $13
Features: Chic, Boney M, Sister Sledge, The Jacksons, John
Travolta, Donna Summer, Eruption, The Three Degrees
DISNEY Annual (Fleetway/Pedigree)
1990s   £7 $11
1992 (64pg) (fc)
Editor: Mike Phipps
Comic Strips : Mickey Mouse, Goofy, Chip n Dale, Ducktales,
Clarabelle, Donald Duck
1993 (64pg) (fc)
Editor: Kathy Szeputi
Comic Strips: Mickey Mouse, Minnie Mouse, Uncle Scrooge, Pluto,
Donald Duck, Goofy, Li'l Bad Wolf
1997 (Pedigree) (112pg) (fc)
Strips and text stories are combined.
Comic Strips (4x20fc): Beauty and the Beast, Aladdin, The Lion
King, Pocahontas, Mickey Mouse strip/story to colour (4bw), 'Mickey
and the Runaway Brain'
Endpaper: Gatefold film poster celebrating 60 years of Disney -
Animated Classics
1998 (Pedigree) (112pg) (fc)
Toy Story (13), Hercules (11), The Little Mermaid (13), Mickey
Mouse in Runaway Brain (13), The Hunchback of Notre Dame (13)
101 Dalmations (13)
DISNEY & ME (EgmontWorld)
2000 (64pg) (fc)   £5 $8
Editor: Shaynie Morris
Features Mulan, Bugs, Lady and the Tramp, Tarzan, Ariel, Lion
King, Oliver and Peter Pan

DISNEYLAND (London Editions/Fleetway/World)
1960s-1990s
1960's   £12 $19
1970's   £10 $16
1973 (72pg) (fc)
Features: Donald Duck, Little Hiawatha, Pinocchio, Dumbo, Bambi,
Jungle Book, Alice in Wonderland, Mickey Mouse, Peter Pan,
Winnie Pooh and Tigger, Three Little Pigs, Snow White, Uncle
Scrooge, The Aristocats, Cinderella,
1976 (72pg)
Features: Mickey Mouse, Snow White & Seven Dwarfs, Brer Rabbit,
Huey Louie and Dewey, Mowgli, Pinocchio, Cinderella, Winnie the
Pooh, Hiawatha, Peter Pan, Alice in Wonderland, Three Little Pigs,
1978 (72pg) (fc)
Features: Robin Hood, Snow White, Baloo, Peter Pan, Bambi,
Winnie the Pooh, Mickey Mouse, Pinocchio, Charlie the Chimp,
Pongo (101 Dalmatians), Dumbo, Donald Duck
1980's   £8 $13
1990s   £6 $10
1990 (World)
Features: Goofy, Mickey Mouse, Scamp, Donald Duck, Gyro
Gearloose, Madam Mim
DISNEY MAGAZINE (London Editions/World)
1980's-1990's
1980's   £8 $13
1984 (64pg) (London Editions) (fc)
Comic Strips: Donald Duck in Motorcycle Madness (7), Mickey
Mouse in The Vanishing Car Trick (9), Big Bad Wolf in Foul Play (6),
Beagle Boys in The Decline and Fall of the Perfect Crime (7), Brer
Rabbit in Flower Power (5), Goofy in Bargain of the Month (5),
Uncle Scrooge in All For A Dime (10)
1990's   £6 $10
DISNEY TIME (Fleetway/World)
1970's-1990s
1970's   £10 $16
1978 (Fleetway) (80pg) (fc/bw)
Features: Huey Louie and Dewey, Scamp, Jungle Book, Dumbo,
Dopey, Robin Hood, Winnie the Pooh, Piglet, Captain Hook, Donald
Duck, Thomas O'Malley, Lady and the Tramp
1980's   £8 $13
1980 (Fleetway) (80pg) (fc)
Features: Dumbo, Jungle Book, Bambi, Little Hiawatha, Cinderella,
Dumbo, Peter Pan, Winnie the Pooh, Huey Louie and Dewey
1990's   £6 $10
1990 (World) (64pg)
Comic Strips: Goofy Gets Through, Mickey Mouse Out of Place,
Scamp Santa's Helper!, Mickey Mouse Forgetful!, Donald Duck
Xmas Delay!, Downhill Pacer!, Mickey Mouse Dog Watcher, Madam
Mim Spellbound Xmas!, Li'l Wolf Bird Brain!, Mickey Mouse The
Hole, Gyro Gearloose Tree-Mendous Trouble!
1991 (World) (64pg)
Comic Strips: Donald Duck in A Magic Christmas, Christmas Post!
Li'L Wolf in Christmas Cash, Duck Tales in Buddy Can You Spare A
Dime?, Madam Mim in Snow Problem, Mickey Mouse in Fly Me to
the Moon
DR. KILDARE (World)
1964-1966   £15 $24
©1963 (96pg) (fc)
Comic Strips: The Haunted Patient, The Doctor and the Gambler, A

Doctor Snuggles 1982

Dr Who 1966

Dr Who 1985

Stubborn Man
Dell Comics Reprints
Photo Cover
Based on the Medical TV drama starring Richard Chamberlain
DOCTOR SNUGGLES (Polystyle)
1982 (64pg) (fc)   £5 $8
Created by Jeffrey O'Kelly
Comic Strips: The Burning Forest (15), The Undersea Party (15)
Spoon Jumping (3), The Water Planet (12), The Nervous River (13)
Based on the childrens animated TV series
DOCTOR WHO (World/Marvel)
1966-1986
©1965 - (96pg) - 1st annual   £35 $56
Writer: David Whittaker
Text Stories: The Lair of Zarbi Supremo, The Sons of the Crab, The
Lost Ones, The Monsters from Earth, Peril in Mechanistria, The Fish
Men of Kandalinga
Features 'official' Dr Who monsters The Voord, Zarbi, Sensorites
and Menoptra
William Hartnell illustrated cover
©1966 - (96pg) -Scarce   £60 $96
Features comic strip
William Hartnell illustrated cover
©1967 - (96pg) -Scarce   £35 $56
Text Stories include : Planet of Bones
Features companions Polly and Ben
Patrick Troughton illustrated cover
©1968 (96pg) - (Scarce)   £50 $80
Comic Strips include: Freedom By Fire
Text Stories include: Valley of the Dragons, Atoms Infinite, The
Microten Men - Features companions Jamie and Victoria
Patrick Troughton, Frazer Hines and the Cybermen illustrated cover
©1969-1970   £30 $48
©1969 (96pg)
Comic Strips (2x6tc): The Vampire Plants, Robot King
Text Stories: The Dragons of Kekoro (fc), The Singing Crystals, The
Mystery of the Marie Celeste, Grip Of Ice (fc), Man Friday (fc),
Slaves of Shran, Run the Gauntlet (fc), A Thousand and One Doors
(fc)
Features companion Zoe (replacing Victoria)
Patrick Troughton photo cover
©1970 (96pg)
Variant spines - white & pink
Text Stories include: Caverns of Horror
Features companion Liz Shaw and Brigadier Lethbridge-Stewart
Jon Pertwee illustrated cover
1973-1975   £15 $24
1973 (80pg)
1st coverdated
Features companion Jo Grant, Captain Mike Yates and the Master
Jon Pertwee photo cover
1974 (80 pg)
Comic Strips include: Menace of the Molags
Art: Steve Livesey
Jon Pertwee cover
1975 (80pg)
Comic Strips: Dead on Arrival (6fc), Art: Edgar Hodges
After the Revolution (6tc)
Text Stories: The House That Jack Built (7), Revenge of the

Phantoms (5), The Time Thief (7), Fugitives from Chance (8), The
Battle Within (5), Before the Legend (5), Scorched Earth (6)
Story: Keith Miller
1st published story from a Dr Who fan
Features companions Jo Grant and Sarah Jane Smith with Brgadier
Lethbridge-Stewart
Jon Pertwee photo cover
1976-1979   £10 $16
1976 (64pg)
Comic Strips: The Psychic Jungle (6 tc) Neuronic Nightmare (6 fc)
Comic Strips and text stories art: Paul Crompton
Features art: Paul Green and Paul Crompton
Features companions Sarah Jane Smith and Harry Sullivan
Tom Baker photo cover
1977 (80pg)
Cover art: Paul Crompton
Comic Strips: The Body Snatcher (6fc), Menace of Metalupiter (6tc)
Art: Paul Crompton
Text Stories: War on Aquatica (5), Cyclone Terror (4), The Time
Snatch (5), The Eye Spiders of Pergross (4), Detour to Diamedes
(4), Double Trouble (4), Secret of the Bald Planet (7)
Text stories and features art: Paul Crompton, Glenn Rix, David Fryer
and Dave Hart
Features companions Sarah Jane Smith and Harry Sullivan
Tom Baker illustrated cover
Large format
1978 (64pg)
Cover art: Paul Crompton
Comic Strips: The Rival Robots (6 tc), The Traitor (6 fc)
Comic Strips and text stories art: Paul Crompton
Features art: Paul Green
Features companion Sarah Jane Smith
Tom Baker illustrated cover
1979 (64pg)
Cover art: Paul Crompton
Comic Strips: The Power (6fc), Emsone's Castle (6fc/tc)
Comic Strips and text stories art: Paul Crompton
Features companion Leela
Tom Baker illustrated cover
1980-1986   £8 $13
1980 (64pg)
1st 'official' Dr Who cover logo
Comic Strips: Terror on Xaboi (6tc), The Weapon (6fc)
Features companions Romana and K-9, Art: Paul Crompton
Tom Baker photo cover
1981 (64pg)
Variant covers - cover date/ no cover date
Cover date (scarce)
Comic Strip: Every Dog Has his Day (6fc)
Features companions Romana II and K-9, Art: Glenn Rix
Tom Baker photo cover
1982 (64pg)
©1981 No cover date
Tom Baker/Peter Davison cross-over
Features companions Adric and K-9, Art: Glenn Rix
Tom Baker/Peter Davison photo cover
1983 (64pg)
©1982 No cover date
Comic Strip: On The Planet Isopterous (6 fc)
Comic strip and text stories art: Glenn Rix

Double Deckers 1972

Dragonheart 1997

Duck Tales 1993

Features companions Adric, Teegan and Nyssa
Peter Davidson, Teegan and Nyssa photo cover
1984 (64pg)
©1983 No cover date
Features five incarnations of the Doctor, Art: Mel Powell
Peter Davidson and Teegan, Photo cover
1985 (64pg)
Cover date featured on spine
21st Year Anniversary Issue
Features companion Peri, Art: Mel Powell
Colin Baker photo cover
1986 (64pg) - Final annual
Art: Melvyn Powell
Colin Baker photo cover
Based on the BBC TV sci fi series

DOCTOR WHO & DALEKS OMNIBUS (St Michael)
1976   £12 $19
DOCTOR WHO AND THE INVASION FROM SPACE (World)
1965 (48pg) (Very scarce)   £60 $96
Features William Hartnell
DOCTOR WHO - AMAZING WORLD OF (World)
1976
1976 - with poster and cards   £20 $19
1976 - without poster and cards   £10 $16
Promotion for Ty-Phoo Tea
Originally only available by mail order from World the annual came
with a poster and set of Dr Who cards. Later sold in W H Smith
outlets - Reprints two strips and text stories from 1976 annual plus
reprint of TV 21 Dalek comic strip. Also includes two new text
stories.
DOCTOR WHO - ADVENTURES IN TIME AND SPACE (World)
1981   £10 $16
Cover art: Paul Crompton
Compilation of past Dr Who annuals including David Whittaker story
from the first annual
DOCTOR WHO SPECIAL (Galley/W.H.Smith)
1985 (192pg)   £8 $13
Art: Paul Crompton, Glenn Rix, Melvyn Powell
Comic Strips: Mission for Duh (6tc), Dead on Arrival (6fc), The
Power (6fc), Emsone's Castle (6tc), On the Planet Isopterus (6fc),
Text Stories: Death to Mufl, The Vampires of Crellium, Flashback,
War on Aquatica, On the Slippery Trail, A New Life, The Planet of
Dust, Danger Down Below, The Penalty, The God Machine, The
Armageddon Chrysalis, The Haven, Night Flight to Nowhere, The
Oxaqua Incident, Winter on a Mesique, The Creation of Camelot,
Class 4 Renegade, The Volcanis Deal, The Nemertines, Day of the
Dragon, The Real Hereward, The Deadly Weed, Vorton's Revenge,
The Time Savers, The Mystery of the Rings
Annual Reprints
Colin Baker photo cover
DOCTOR WHO YEARBOOK (Marvel)
1991-1996   £8 $13
Photo Covers
DONALD DUCK (IPC/Fleetway)
1970s   £8 $13
1977 (96pg) (fc)
Features: Donald Duck, Scamp, Gladstone Gander, Huey, Dewey &
Louie, Little Wolf, Goofy, Daisy Duck

DONALD & MICKEY (Fleetway)
1973-1976 (80pg) (fc/tc/bw)   £8 $13
Comic Strips: Mickey Mouse, Donald Duck, Huey Dewey and Louie,
Scrooge McDuck, Goofy, Pluto, Chip 'N' Dale, Scamp, Big Bad Wolf,
Aristokittens
DOUBLE DECKERS (World)
1972 (80pg) (fc)   £10 $16
Photo Cover
Based on the Childrens BBC TV series
DOUGAL (BBC/Odhams)
1971-1973   £10 $16
Based on 'Magic Roundabout' character
DRACULA'S SPINECHILLERS (World)
1983   £10 $16
©1982
Cover art: Glenn Rix
Comic Strips (fc/bw): Castle Dracula (20) (3 pt), Twins of Evil (17)
Based on Hammer films
DRAGONHEART (Grandreams)
1997   £5 $8
©1996 (62pg)
Photo features
Based on the movie starring Dennis Quaid
DRAGONSLAYER
1981   £5 $8
DREAMER FOR GIRLS (DC Thomson)
1984   £5 $8
DREAMSTONE (World)
1992   £5 $8
Based on the animated TV series
DUCK TALES (Fleetway)
1993 (64pg) (fc)   £5 $8
Editor: Mike Phipps
Comic Strips: Coin Crazy (24), The Littlest Gizmo Duck (8), Its
Lucky to be Smart (16), Launch Pad McQuack in Low Flying on the
Cheap (1), Tarzan Swings Again (1)
Disney Comics Reprints
Based on the animated TV series
DUNCAN DARES
1988
©1987   £6 $10
Based on the BBC TV series starring Peter Duncan
DUNGEONS AND DRAGONS (World)
1986-1987   £8 $13
1986 (64pg)
Endpaper and contents page: Paul Green
Full-colour text stories and games
Based on the animated TV series
DUKES OF HAZZARD (Grandreams/Purnell)
1980-1986   £10 $16
There are 3 different annuals ©1979 (Grandreams)
©1979 (1980)
Priced at £1.95
Strips and text stories Art: Paul Green
Comic Strips: The Circus comes to Town (bw), Hogg Tied (fc),
Hurricane Harry (bw)
Luke and Bo standing in front of General Lee in a country setting
photo cover

Dukes of Hazzard 1985

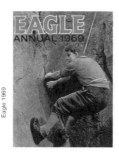

Eagle 1969

Eagle 1984

EA

©1979 (1981)
Priced at £2.25
Comic Strips (bw): A Run for the Money, Mad Moonshine Mix up,
Country Blues
Luke and Bo standing in front of the Hazzard County Court House
photo cover
©1979 (1982) also reads ©1982 Weekly Reader Books
Priced at £2.50
Comic Strips: Saddled with Trouble, Road Hogg
Features: Catherine Bach, Tom Wopat and John Schneider inter-
views by Roger Elwood.
Luke, Bo, Daisy, Uncle Jesse and General Lee photo cover
©1983 (64pg) (Purnell)
Writer: Glynis Langley
©1984 (64pg) (Purnell)
©1985 (64pg) (Purnell)
Colour/bw photo features and stories
Based on the TV series

DYNOMUTT& MUMBLY (World)
1979 (64pg) (fc)   £8 $13
Comic Strips (featuring Blue Falcon): Little Miss Goody Two Shoes
(10), Repulsive Finster (6), The Astounding Mr. Mastermind (10),
Identity Crisis (5), Mother Goose's Nursery Crimes (11), Beach
Blanket Baboon (3)
Based on the Hanna Barbera characters

EAGLE (Hulton/Longacre/Odhams/Fleetway)
1951-1975, 1983-1990's
1 (1952) - Scarce   £60 $96
2-4   £40 $60
Number 4 (Hulton) (180pg)
Editor: Marcus Morris
Comic Strips: Storm Nelson, Old Ted's Tale, Luck of the Legion
Dan Dare Pilot of the Future (8fc), Operation Triceratops by Harold
Johns & Gret Tomlinson, P.C. 49 in The Case of the New Champ
(6lw) by Alan Stranks, Jeff Arnold in A Hard And Fast Case (4fc),
Writer: Charles Chilton, Art: Harry Bishop
Picture Strip (6bw): The Street-Arabs' Friend (Dr Barnardo), Writer:
Chad Varah, Art: Norman Williams
5-9   £25   £40
Number 9 (Hulton) (176pg)
Editor: Marcus Morris
Endpaper: Thelwell
Comic Strips: Dan Dare in The Vanishing Scientists (8fc), Jeff Arnold
in Gun For Hire (4lw), Writer: Charles Chilton
Art: Desmond Walduck
Harris Tweed, Extra Special Agent in The Haunting of Humbug Hall
(4bw), Storm Nelson and the Black Hand Gang (4lw)
Writer: Edward Trice, Art: Richard Jennings
Waldorf and Cecil in The Forgers (6bw), by Hickey, Cecil Rhodes
Patriot and Pioneer (4lw), Writer: Godfrey Rayne
Art: Peter Jackson
Dividing Trail (4lw), Writer: H. Mills, Art by C. L. Doughty
Jack o' Lantern meets The Devil of Bransbury (4fc)
Writer: George Beardmore, Art: Robert Ayton
The Silver Scorpion 'A Luck of the Legion story' (4lw)
Writer: Geoffrey Bond, Art: Martin Aitchison
Fridtjof Nansen Explorer and Lover of Men (4lw)
Writer: Alan Crain, Art: Thewenetti
Cavendish Brown M.S. in The Case of the Dum-Dum Bullet (4bw)

Writer: Bill Wellings, Art: Pat Williams
Text Story 'The Chinese Pirates' features Art: Michael Noble
1960's   £20 $32
Number Ten - 1961 (Longacre) (176pg)
Dated dustjacket cover - Editor Clifford Makins
Endpaper by Thelwell
Comic Strips featuring: Luck of the Legion, Dan Dare, Storm Nelson,
Jack O' Lantern, Jeff Arnold, Waldorf & Cecil, Harris Tweed
Picture Strips (4x2lw): Robert Clive of India, Writer: Peter Forster,
Art: Hardee
Log Cabin to White House (Abraham Lincoln) , Writer: Godfrey
Rayne, Art: Peter Jackson
1969 (Odhams) (128pg)
1970-1975   £15 $24
1970 (116pg)
Comic Strips: The Iron Man (4tc), The Hoodoo (4bw), Mickey Merlin
(4bw), The Guinea-Pig (4fc), The Iron Man (4bw)Dan Dare and the
World of Thought (4fc), Blackbow The Cheyenne (5bw),
Slumberjack (2bw), Sky Buccaneers (6tc)
Text Stories: Ransom for a Colt, Edward Whymper, Shadow of the
Guilotine, The Great Race for Dawson (Art: D. Gilroy), Undersea
Patrol, Satellite One-Zero
Features: Collecting picture (cigarette) cards, Charlie Chaplin, Alfred
the Great
1972 (128pg)
Comic Strips: Dan Dare and the Mekon Menace (8fc), The Runaway
Engine (7tc), The Siege of Castelmorrone (8tc), The Bombardment
of Paris (7tc), The Unfinished Duel (8tc)
Text Stories: Descent to Danger, The Bumper Bundles, The Train
that Drowned a Plane!, The Mystery of Grelsea Island, The Last
Victory
Features: Horatio Nelson
1973 (128pg)
Comic Strips: Dan Dare and the Planet of Peril (9fc), The Great
Train Chase (11tc), Attacked by Ants (5tc), Chief Joseph's Long
March (10tc)
Text Stories: The Charioteers, Racing with a Wreck, The Battle of
Johnson's Drift, Portugee's Ride
Features: Pele, The Story of Arsenal, The Attack of Pearl Harbour
1983-1990's   £8 $13
1983 (Fleetway)
Comic Strips (fc): Dan Dare in Menace of the Mekon, Return of the
Mekon, The Collector - Tall Story
Photo Strips (bw): The Collector - The Silver Lining, The Liquid
Thunderbolt & Smokey!, The Adventures of Fred, Sgt Streetwise
Selected Text Stories: Green Fingers by Arthur C. Clarke
The Invisible Assassin - A Dan Dare story
1984 (96pg) (fc/bw)
Comic Strips: Dan Dare Pilot of the future, Dan Dare (Pilot of the
Future), Yellow Fever, The Adventures of P.C. 49 (From the famous
radio series by Alan Stranks)
Photo Strips: The Makul curse, Joe Soap, Sgt Streetwise
1985 (96pg) (fc/bw)
Dan Dare Pilot of the Future, Could you be a Joe Soap?, One Eyed
Jack, Sgt Streetwise, Doomlord, Samurai's Vengeance, The Hand,
One Eyed Jack
1987 (96pg) (fc/bw)
Comic Strips: Dan Dare Pilot of the Future, The Thirteenth floor,
One eyed, Jamie, Doomlord, The Spidermen, Night of the Battlers,
SOS

Eastenders 1987

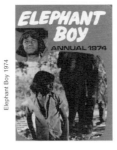

Elephant Boy 1974

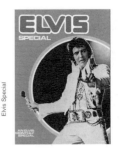

Elvis Special

1989 (96pg) (fc/bw)
Comic Strips: Dan Dare, Joe Soap and Dave came too (photo strip), M.A.C.H. 1, Computer Warrior, Doomlord, Invasion, Death Wish Duo, Detective Zed, I'm Dreaming of a White Christmas (Author A. Stone - Artist R. Smith),Tightrope
1990 (96pg) (fc/bw)
Comic Strips: Dan Dare, Doomlord, The Sarge, Charley's War, Kid Cops, Depth Bombs Away!, Johnny Red, Deathsquad, Computer Warrior, Revenge of the Eagle, Storm Force
1991 (96pg) (fc/bw)
Dan Dare Pilot of the Future, Toys of Doom, Storm Force, Revenge of the Eagle, Photo Finish, The Mekon, Doomlord, Computer Warrior, Sleekswift the Cheetah, Loner
Photo Strip: Sgt Streetwise
1992 (96pg)
The New Eagle Yearbook
Comic Strips: Dan Dare (6fc & 2tc) - Art: Jon Haward Dark Angels, Autograph Albert (2), Up In Arms, Computer Warrior, My Pet Alien!, Death Wish (2), Charley's War, Soup Squad, Doomlord
Pin Ups: Betty Boo, Paula Abdul, Wendy James, Craig McLachlan, Sonia, Gloria Estefan, Human League, Madonna, Michaela Strachan
Based on the UK comic

EAGLE FOOTBALL
1963	£10	$16

EAGLE SPORTS (Hulton)
1951-1973
1 (with dw)	£25	$56
1 (without dw)	£15	$24
2	£15	$24
3-8	£12	$19
1960's	£10	$16
1970's	£8	$13

EASTENDERS (BBC TV) (Grandreams)
1987-1989	£8	$13
©1986 Special (64pg)
Editor John Barraclough, Writer: Tony Lynch
Art: Jeremy Barlow and John Petts
Full colour photo features
Based on the BBC TV Soap

EAST 17 (Grandreams)
1996-1997	£3	$5
©1995 (48pg)
Editor: Melanie J Clayden, Writer: Mike Hrano
©1996 (64pg) - 'East 7eventeen'
Writer: Mike Hrano
Based on the UK pop boy band

EDD THE DUCK (Grandreams)
1990-1991	£5	$8
There are two annuals both ©1989
©1989 (64pg) Cover price £4.25
Includes spoof comic strips (fc): Duck Whittington, News Edd-Lines, Top Of The Pops, Edd The Duck Visits Ramsay Street (Neighbours), The Six O'Quack News, Little Edd Riding Hood, Start Wreck (Star Trek), Duck Turpin
Editors: Christina and Tim Mackay-Robinson
Art:Amusement Arcade, Writer: Allen Cummings
©1989 (64pg) Cover Price £4.50
Includes spoof comic strips (fc): Octoducky, Duck Dares Free Fall,

Duck Dares Rock Climbing, The Olympic Games
Based on the BBC TV puppet character

ED STEWART'S STEWPOT (World)
1972	£6	$10
Based on the Radio One DJ

ELEPHANT BOY (World)
1974 (80pg)	£8	$13
Comic Strips: The Tryant (20fc), The Fishing Cat (20fc), Horn of Plenty (20fc)
Photo Cover
Based on the TV Series

ELVIS Special (World)
1970s-1980s
1970's	£8	$13
1980's	£6	$10
'An Elvis Monthly Special' - Editor Todd Slaughter
'Written and compiled by those fans who knew and loved Elvis Aaron Presley' - Colour/b/w photo features

EMERGENCY! (World)
1979	£25	$40
Includes Charlton Comics reprints and photo features
Based on the TV series starring Randoph Mantooth

EMERGENCY-WARD 10 Girls' Annual (Purnell)
1963-1964
1963	£20	$32
©1962 (128pg) (bw)
Art: Eric Dadswell, Angus McBride
Picture Strips (6x4): Stolen Ambulance, A Strange Patient, The Jewel Thieves, Diagnosis-Correct, The Safe-Cracker
Text Stories plus photo features on: Charles Tingwell, Jill Browne, Desmond Carrington, Peter Howell, Robert McLeod
Photo cover features Jill Browne (Staff nurse Carole Young)
1964	£15	$24
©1963 (128pg) (bw)
Art: Eric Dadswell, Ken Houghton
Picture Strips: Linda's Lesson (5), Never Jump To Conclusions (4), A Race For Life (4), There's Many A Slip (5)
Text Stories plus photo features on: Jill Browne, Desmond Carrington, John Line, John Alderton, Carol Davies, Paula Byrne, Kerry Marsh, From Script to Screen
Includes a script of a scene from a televised episode
Photo cover features Jill Browne and Desmond Carrington (Dr. Chris Anderson) (fc)
Based on the Medical TV drama series

ENGLAND CRICKET TEAM (Grandreams)
1981-1982	£5	$8
©1980 (64pg) (bw/fc)
Editor: John Barraclough and Alan Lee, Writer: Alan Lee
Features: Down Under by Ian Botham, Derek Randall, Bernard Thomas, Graham Dilley, Geoff Boycott, Geoff Miller, Mike Brearley, Wayne Larkins, Derek Underwood, Phil Edmonds, John Lever, Peter Willey, Graham Gooch, Mike Hendrick, Bob Willis
©1981 (64pg) (bw/fc)
Editor: John Barraclough, Writer: Alan Lee
Features: Geoff Boycott, Brian Rose, Ian Botham, Chris Old, Australian Tour Special, David Gower, Bob Willis, David Bairstow, John Emburey, Graham Gooch, Peter Willey, Roland Butcher, Paul Downton, Graham Dilley, Graham Stevenson

ENID BLYTON'S BEDTIME (World)

Ewoks 1989

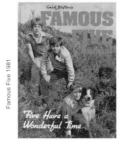

Famous Five 1981

Fab 208 1979

1970-1980's
1970-1979   £8 $13
©1969 (96pg)
Cover/Art: Jo Berriman
Text Stories: A Tale of the Blue-eyed Cat, The Birthday Spell, Silly-One and Artful, The Lost Princess, Tale of a Tail, The Surprising Saucepan, The Monkey and the Pop-gun, The Ride to Happiness.
1976 (62pg)
Cover/Art: Jo Berriman
Text Stories: Whiskers for the Cat, The Seven Crosspatches, Lazy Little Pimmy, Brer Rabbit's Christmas Supper, Brer Bear's Bad Memory, In the King's Shoes.
1977 (80pg) Large Format
Art: Jo Berriman, David Fryer, Paul Green and David Hart
1978 (64pg)
Art: Jo Berriman, Melvyn Powell, David Fryer, John Millington, Anthony Lomas and Paul Green
1979 (64pg)
Art: Jo Berriman, Susan Aspey, David Brian, John Millington
1980's   £6 $10
©1982 (64pg)
Cover/Art: Jo Berriman
Text stories: Meddle Goes Shipping, I'd Never Have Guessed It Brer Rabbit, The Impatient Wizard, Good Idea Amelia Jane, The Marvellous White, The Lost Thimble Plant, Brer Rabbit is So Cunning, The Day The Princess Came

ENID BLYTON'S BIG STORY Annual (Purnell)
1972-1975   £8 $13
©1971 (128pg)
Text Stories: The Clever Servant, You'd Better Look Out!, The Bear on Wheels, The Most Surprising Pen, Mr Tantrum and the Fog, Josie Click and Bun Give a Party, The Magnificent Treacle Pudding, Nobody Liked Him, All the Way to Santa Claus, The Grabbit Chair, A Day at Aunt Lucy's, He Really Was a Nuisance, Mr Smile Plays a Trick
©1974 (96pg)
Text Stories: Sammy the Scribbler, The Tale of Yah-Boo, She Hadn't Any Friends, Simple Simon Goes to Camp, The Magic Rubber, The Cuckoo in the Clock, Silly Little Goofy, The Girl who had Hiccups, The Pig with Green Spots, Two Noisy Children, Doll in the Cushion

ENID BLYTON'S FAMOUS FIVE (Purnell)
1970's-1980's   £8 $13
©1977 (96pg) (bw)
Go on a Hike Together
©1978 (96pg) (bw)
Go Adventuring Again
©1979 (96pg) (bw)
Go to Smuggler's Top
©1980 (96pg) (bw)
Five Go To Mystery Moor
©1981 (96pg) (bw)
Five Have a Wonderful Time
©1983 (80pg) (bw)
Five Have a Mystery to Solve
All Purnell titles are 96 pg and contain complete story split into text chapters and fc/b/w comic strips

ENID BLYTON'S FAMOUS FIVE (Grandreams)
1990's   £5 $8
N/D (1996 estimate) (64pg) (fc) - Cover Price - £5.50

Text Stories: Happy Christmas Five!, Five have a Puzzling Time
Editor Tony Lynch
Designed by Sue Bartram and Melanie Clayden Art: Simon Girling Associates - Photo cover
Based on the ITV series

ENID BLYTON'S SECRET SEVEN (Purnell)
1980's   £8 $13
©1979 (96pg) (bw)
Well Done, Secret Seven
©1980 (80pg) (bw)
Puzzle for the Secret Seven
Complete story split into text chapters and comic strips

EQUALIZER (World)
1987 (Scarce)   £15 $24
Comic Strip art: Glenn Rix
Photo Cover
Based on the TV crime series starring Edward Woodward

ERIC CANTONA (Grandreams)
1995   £4 $7
Photo features
Based on the French soccer star

EVERY BOY'S Annual (Juvenile Productions)
N/D
1930's-1950's
1950's   £20 $32
Stories by W.E. Johns and others

EVERY BOYS' BOOK OF SPORT
1950's   £15 $24
1952 (1st)

EVERY GIRL'S (Pilgrim Press/Juvenile Productions)
1950's   £25 $40
©1951 Vol.1
©1955 (N/D) Vol.4
Stories of School, Adventure and Sport
Includes 4 colour plates by Thomas Heath Robinson

EWOKS (Marvel)
1989 (64pg) (fc)   £8 $13
Comic Strips: The Underwater Kingdom (19), Rites of Power (15),
Writer: Dave Manak, Art: Warren Kremer
Star Comics reprints
Text Stories: Chief Chirpa Kidnapped, Return of the Great One, The Ice Princess
Based on the Star Wars characters

EXPRESS Annual (Beaverbrook)
1958-1960   £20 $32
Becomes TV Express 1961
No.1- Biggles and the Crash that Wasn't - 5 page story
Editor: Reginald Taylor, E.W. Johns

FAB 208 (IPC/Fleetway) - Originally called FABULOUS
1960's-1981
1960's   £20 $32
1969 (80pg)
Features: Monkees, The Herd, Beatle Age, The Bee Gees, Pop Artists, George Best, Davy Jones, Riding the Range (TV Westerns), The Guru (film), Amen Corner
Pin Ups: The Monkees, The Beatles, The Herd, The Bee Gees, Hywell Bennett, Donovan, The Tremeloes, Amen Corner, George Best, Davy Jones, Dave, Dee, Dozy, Beaky, Mick and Tich, Michael

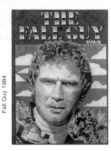

Fall Guy 1984

Fantastic Four 1980

Flintstones © 1968

York
Small Photos: Sandie Shaw, Lulu, Cilla Black, Jane Asher, Judy Greeson
1970's £15 $24
1972 (80pg) (fc/tc)
Features: Georgie Best, Jackson Five, Cliff, Steve McQueen, Cilla, Ryan O'Neal, Robert Redford, Robert Plant, Andy Williams, Kenny Everett, Jack Wild, Tony Blackburn, Kid Jensen, Peter Firth, David Cassidy, Noel Edmonds, Mick Jagger, The Osmonds
1973 (80 pg)
Features: The David Cassidy File, George Best, FAB Remembers Pete Duel, Crazy for Marc! (Bolan), Cill Black & Cliff Richard Pin Ups (fc) include- The New Seekers, Slade, New World, Rod Stewart, George Best, The Partridge Family, The Osmonds, The Jackson Five, Ben Murphy, Jack Wild, Paul Newman, Steve McQueen, Roger Moore and Tony Curtis, Wayne Maunder, James Stacy, Robert Redford
1975 (80pg)
Features: The Osmonds Plan for Living, David Cassidy on Hawaii, Devastating David Essex, Donny Osmond on Scenic Utah
1976 (80pg)
Features: Donny Osmond, Bay City Rollers, Wings, The Rubettes, Elvis Presley, 10cc, Steve Harley, Elton John, Shaun Cassidy, Pilot, Kenny, Glitter Band, Mud, Rod Stewart, Sweet, Michael Crawford, Splinter, David Essex, Jackson Five, David Bowie, The Goodies, Jackson Five, Sparks, Roxy Music, Bad Company, David Cassidy, Richard O'Sullivan, Leo Sayer, Wizzard, Alvin Stardust, David Essex
1979 (72pg)
Features: The Osmonds, The Professionals, Abba, Showaddywaddy, Bay City Rollers, Fonzie, Shaun Cassidy, John Travolta
1980 £10 $16
Features: John Travolta, Elvis, Leif, Andy Gibb, Bee Gees, Superman, Child, Marie, Martin & Lewis (Professionals), Shaun Cassidy & Parker Stevenson, The Osmonds, Kate Bush, Olvia, Peter Powell, Boomtown Rats, Debbie Harry
1981 'Yearbook' £8 $13
Based on the girls magazine

FA BOOK for Boys (Heinemann)
1950's £15 $24
©1958 (196 pg tc) No11

FA ENGLAND (World)
1990's £3 $5

FA PREMIERSHIP (Grandreams)
1990's £3 $5

FALL GUY (Grandreams)
1982-1985 £8 $13
1982 (64pg) (red cover)
Comic Strips (bw): The Hunters & The Hunted, Electric Bass
1983 (64pg) (yellow cover)
Comic Strips (bw): Jumping Town, Horse Sense
1984 (64pg) (blue cover)
Comic Strip (bw): Back Door Bust, Stuggle in the Studio
Based on the TV series starring Lee Majors

FAME (World)
1983 -85 £8 $13
1983 (64pg)
Art: Melvyn Powell
Photo features and text stories

Photo cover
1984 (64pg)
Art: Melvyn Powell
Photo Cover
1985 (64pg)
Two variants of the 1983 annual exist. One version has 'Annual 1983' missing from the covers, spine and interior.
Based on the TV Show

FANTASTIC (Odhams)
1968-1970 £10 $16
Based on the UK comic

FANTASTIC FOUR Comic Annual (World)
1970-1971
©1969 (96pg) £15 $24
Comic Strips (fc): All strips Writer: Stan Lee, Art: Jack Kirby
The Master Plan Of Doctor Doom! (23), Inks: George Bell
The Return Of The Mole Man! (22), Inks: George Bell
Enter--The Elemental! (20), Inks: Joe Sinnott
The Infant Terrible! (23), Inks: George Bell
©1970 £12 $19
Based on the Marvel comic characters

FANTASTIC FOUR Marvel Presents (Grandreams)
1980-1982
1980 £10 $16
©1979 (64pg)
Comic Strips: Here There be Witches, Enter: Salems Seven
Based on material © 1976 by Marvel Comics Group
1981-1982 £8 $13
©1980
Comic Strips: Madrox the Multiple Man! (tc/fc)
Writers: Len Wein, Chris Claremont
Art: Buscema, Stone & Sinnott
We Have to Fight the X-Men! (fc/tc) FF #28 Reprint
Writer: Stan Lee, Pencils: Jack Kirby, Inks: Chic Stone
Based on the Marvel comic characters

FANTASTIC FOUR Television Picture Storybook (PBS)
1969 (Scarce) £15 $24
Based on the Marvel comic characters

FANTASTIC MAX (Fleetway)
1990 (64pg) £5 $8
Picture Strip: A Night to Remember (6fc), Love-a-Duck (8fc)
Based on the Hanna Barbera character

FERN HOLLOW
1983 £5 $8

FILM FUN Book
1938-1961
1950-1955 £40 $60
1956-1959 £30 $48
1960-1961 £25 $40
Based on the UK comic

FILM SHOW
1950's-1960's
950's (with dj) £30 $48
1950's (without dj) £20 $32
1960's (with dj) £20 $32
1960's (without dj) £10 $16
1962
Elizabeth Taylor photo cover

Flintstones 1969

Flower Fairies Not Dated

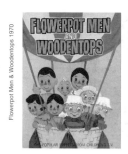

Flowerpot Men & Woodentops 1970

1963
'With Stars of the Screen in Colour'
Features: Sean Connery, Sophia Loren, Cliff Richard
Sophia Loren photo cover
FILM and TELEVISION PARADE
N/D (1950's)   £25 $40
Includes: Elizabeth Taylor, Rex Allen, Peter Pan, Genghis Khan,
Sword and the Rose
Richard Todd photo cover (fc)
FIREBALL XL5 (Collins)
1964-1967
©1963 (96pg) (Scarce)   £40 $60
©1964   £30 $48
©1965-©1966   £25 $40
Based on the Gerry Anderson puppet series
FIREBALL XL5 'A Big Television Book' (World)
1965
©1964   £25 $40
FIREMAN SAM (Redan/Grandreams)
1980's - present
1980-1985   £6 $8
1986-1994   £5 $8
1992 (64pg) (fc)
1993 (64pg) (fc)
1995-present   £3 $5
1995 (48pg) (fc)
Picture Strips (7x2): Birthday Twins, The Newspaper Round, The
Missing Keys, The Little Car, Computer Chaos, Part Tricks, Sweets
Based on the ITV animated series
FIVE 100% Totally Unofficial Special (Grandreams)
2000
©1999   £3 $5
Based on the UK Boy Band
5 STAR Special (Grandreams)
1987 (64pg) (fc)   £4 $7
Editor: Jayne Lanigan, Writer: Robin Mackintosh
Based on the UK pop group
FLASH GORDON (World/Brown Watson)
1967-1968, 1977-1979, 1981
1967-1968   £12 $19
1977-1981   £10 $16
©1977 (64pg) (Brown Watson)
Editor: Sal Gentile, Art: Pat Boyette
Cover Art/Endpaper: J. Britton
Comic Strips: Mission into the Mystic Realm (21tc/fc), Time Waits
For All Men (7fc), The Intruder (7fc), The Creeping Menace (14tc)
Charlton Comics reprints
Includes one page feature on Flash Gordon creator/artist Alex
Raymond and b/w photo features on the movie serial
Based on the newspaper comic strip character
FLINTSTONES (World/Atlas/Marvel)
1960's-1990's
1960's   £15 $14
©1968 (Atlas) (64pg) (Scarce)   £20 $32
Comic Strips (fc): The Great Dodo Hunt (6), Cave Kids in the Big
Catch (6), In Quest of a Quarry (10), Cave Kids in Beaslty
Behaviour (4), Too many Clues (8), Cave Kids in the Rare Reward
(4), Will Success Spoil Rock Flintstone? (10)

©1969 (80pg) (tc/fc) (Atlas)   £20 $32
Comic Strips: Holiday Hassle (8tc), Cave Kids in The Vanishing Tree
(4fc), Gone with the Bird (8fc), Cave Kids in The Little Big Shot (4fc),
Strained Relations (5tc), A Bad Day in Brimstone (10tc), The
Sculptor (5tc), Private Eye Yi Yi (5tc), The Flea-O-Saurus Safari
(4fc), Dino on the run (4tc), 4 newspaper strips (1tc)
1970's   £10 $16
1980's 'Flintstone Family Cartoon' (World)   £8 $13
1987 (64pg) (World)
Comic Strips (fc): One Gun too Many, Mother was a Mechanic, At
the Boy Scout Jamboree, The Orbit Bit, The Butler Didn't Do It - No
Butter, Just for the Record
1990's   £5 $8
1991 (64pg) (Marvel)
Art: Paul Gamble
Comic Strips: Flintstone - Mega Movie Star, Feeling Ill Getting
Better, Weight-Up - U.S. reprints
Based on the Hanna-Barbera cartoon animated series
FLINTSTONES Television Story Book (Newtown)
1962   £10 $16
©1961 (96pg)
FLINTSTONES AND FRIENDS (Marvel)
1980's   £8 $13
©1988 (64pg)
Comic Strips (fc): The Flintstones in A Stroke Of Genius (14), Yogi
Bear in Yogi (9), Yogi at the Circus (7), Top Cat in Sky Divers (4), A
Short Romance! (3)
Text stories: Top Cat, Wacky Races, Scooby Doo
© 1989 (64pg)
Comic Strips (fc): The Flintstones in Christmas Party (32),
Hibernating With Yogi (Chapter 2), Christmas with Huck and Quick
Draw (Chapter 3), A Very Merry Top Cat (Chapter 4), The Happiest
Day Of All (Chapter 5)
Writer: Mark Evanier, Pencils: Kay Wright, Inks: Scott Shaw
Text stories: Scooby Doo, Wacky Races and Yogi Bear
This annual was published in both hardback and softback versions
FLINTSTONES (Grandreams)
1994   £4 $7
©1993 (48pg)
Writer: Tony Lynch, Editor Melanie Clayden
Condensed story adapted from the original film script
Photo annual includes short profiles of the main stars (fc)
Based on the Movie starring John Goodman
FLOWER FAIRIES (Grandreams)
1980's   £5 $8
N/D (Estimate 1986) (64pg)
Editor: Rosemary Lanning
Photo Cover
Based on the Flower Fairies books published by Blackie & Sons
FLOWERPOT MEN and WOODENTOPS (World)
1970's   £15 $24
©1969 (64pg)
Text stories featuring Bill and Ben and the Woodentops
Based on the BBC children's puppet series
The FLUMPS (BBC)
1978   £8 $13
FLYING DOCTOR (Dean)
1964   £15 $24
©1963 (120pg)

Fraggle Rock 1984

Funky Phantom 1976

Garfield 1993

Writer: Arthur Groom
Based on the Australian TV and radio series
FOLLYFOOT (World)

1974-1976	£5	$8

1975 (80pg) (fc/tc)
Endpaper: Glenn Rix
Art: Glenn Rix, Walter Howarth
Comic Strips: Red Tempest, The Stranger, Slugger's Secret, Gipsy Rock, Queen for a Day, Hideout at Follyfoot, Phantom at Follyfoot
Photo Cover
1976 (64pg) (fc/tc)
Endpaper: Glenn Rix
Art: Glenn Rix, Walter Howarth, David Hart and Paul Green
Comic Strips: One Good Turn (8fc), The Secret Shooting (6tc), Dora Lends a Hand (6tc), Accident (6fc), A Star is Born (6fc), A Rival for Dora (8tc)
Photo cover
Based on the Yorkshire TV children's series
FOOTBALL FAN (Harry Darton)

1972 (116pg) (fc/bw)	£5	$8

Features: George Best, Billy Bremner, Mike Channon, Steve Heighway, Geoff Hurst, Francis Lee, Roy McFarland, Alan Mullery, Peter Osgood
FOOTBALL STAR PARADE Football Annual by GOAL (IPC)

1970/1971	£7	$11

FORGET ME NOT FARM (World)

1993 (64pg) (fc)	£5	$8

Writer: Mike Amatt, Art: Edgar Hodges & Ken Morton
Based on the Childrens BBC TV series
FOUR FEATHER FALLS (Collins)
1961-1962

©1960 (Scarce)	£40	$60

'Television's Four Feather Falls'

©1961	£35	$56

'Tex Tucker's Four Feather Falls'
Based on the Gerry Anderson Western puppet series
4th DIMENSION (BBC)

1974-1975	£6	$10

1974 (78pg)
Comic Strip: Captain Radio (3x2bw)
Comic strip art: Phillip Jacobs
©1974 - No.2 (78pg) (fc/tc/bw)
Comic Strip: Captain Radio (3x2bw)
Photo cover featuring John Dunn
Based on the BBC Radio 4 programme with John Dunn
FRAGGLE ROCK (Grandreams)

1984-1986	£8	$13

©1983
Writer: Jocelyn Stevenson
Art: Manhar Chanan, Pam Storey, Jo Lawrence, Sue Venning
Includes photo strips and text stories
Based on the Jim Henson characters
FRANK BRUNO Special (Grandreams)

1988 (64pg)	£4	$7

Based on the UK boxer
FRANKIE GOES TO HOLLYWOOD (Opal Quill/Grandreams)

1985-1986	£5	$8

1985 (48pg) (Opal Quill)

©1985 (64pg) (Grandreams)
Based on the UK pop group
FRANKIE STEIN WHOOPEE (Fleetway)

1976-1977	£10	$16

Based on the UK comics character
FRIENDS 100% Unofficial Special (Grandreams)

2000	£7	$11

©1999 (48 pg)
Writer: Michael Heatley, Teresa Maughn
Based on the US TV Series
FRONTIER CIRCUS (Purnell)

1963	£12	$19

©1962 (96pg)
Writer: Arthur Groom, Art: John Burns
Comic Strips (8bw): Tony's Secret Mission, A Chapter of Accidents, The Man with the Whistle
Based on the TV Western Series
FUNNIES Album (Swan)
1943-1957

1950's	£35	$56

FUNKY PHANTOM (Brown Watson)

1975-1976	£12	$19

©1974
Featuring Dastardly and Muttley In their Flying Machines
Comic Strips: Funky Phantom in Ghost of the Hour, Toying With Danger (tc), Harlem Globetrotters in Westward Whoa! (fc), Wacky Races in The Scavenger Scramble (fc)
©1975
Comic Strips: Funky Phantom in Ghostly Gold (12tc), Funky Phantom in Ghost of Montezuma (25fc), Motormouse and Autocat in What's the Motor with You? (6fc), Motormouse and Autocat in Wheelin' and Dealin' (6fc), Dastardly and Muttley in their Flying Machines in Command Performance (6fc), Funky Phantom in The Chicken Avenger (13tc)
Text Stories: Stable Spook
Based on the Hanna Barbera cartoon characters
GALAXY RANGERS Adventures of (Marvel)

1989 (64pg)	£7	$11

Endpaper: Kev Hopgood and John Burns
Comic Strips: For a Few Startones More, Script: Ian Rimmer, Pencils: Kev Hopgood, Inks: Dave Harwood
A Fistful of Credits, Writer: Dan Abnett, Pencils: Jeff Anderson, Inks: Dave Elliott
Winds of Terror, Writer: John Freeman, Pencils: Phil Gascoine, Inks: Simon Coleby
Text stories: The Enemy Within, Writer: John Freeman, Art: Andy Lanning/Liam Sharp
Convoy, Story: John Freeman, Art: Kirk Etienne/Dave Elliott
Tall Tales from Duffy's Place, Story: Dan Abnett, Art: Andy Wildman
Based on the animated TV series
GARFIELD (Ravette/Grandreams)

1991-1995	£5	$8

1991 (64pg)
Writer: Jim Kraft
©1993 (64pg)
1995 (48pg) (smaller format) (Grandreams)
United Feature Syndicate Inc. strips by Jim Davis
Writer: Gordon Volke
Based on the newspaper comic strip

Gemini Man 1978

Ghostbusters Filmation 1987

Girl 1982

GI

GARY GLITTER (World)
1975-1977
1975 (80pg)   £8 $13
Comic Strips: The Gary Glitter story - Mike My Inspiration, The Gary
Glitter story - I Always Knew I'd Make It
1976-1977   £7 $11
1976 (72pg)
Comic Strips: The Time I Nearly Gave Up (4bw)
Includes lots of photo features
1977 (80pg)
Entitled 'The Glitter Annual'
Features Gary Glitter and the Band
Based on the Pop Star
GARY LINEKER'S STRIKER (World)
1992   £4 $7
SEE: Striker
GAZZA Children's Annual (Grandreams)
1991 (64pg)   £4 $7
Writer: John Moulding
Based on the UK soccer star
GEMINI MAN (Brown Watson)
1978
©1977 (64pg)   £12 $19
Art: Ian Gibson
Comic Strips (bw): Gemini Man - Prologue (2), Chinese Takeaway
(4), Snatch (6)
Includes Ben Murphy fc photo feature with Pete Duel (wrongly
credited as Roger Davis) 'Alias Smith and Jones' photo
Photo Cover
Based on the sci fi TV series starring Ben Murphy
GENE AUTRY Adventures
1950's   £15 $24
GENE AUTRY Comic Annual (World)
1950's-1960's
1950-1955   £25 $40
1956-1959   £20 $32
1960's   £15 $24
GENE AUTRY Stories (Adprint)
1950's
No.1 - 1954   £20 $32
No. 2 onwards   £15 $24
Based on the Western movie star
GEOFF BOYCOTT Cricket (Fleetway)
1980 (96pg) (fc/tc/bw)   £5 $8
Based on the UK cricket star
GEORGE BEST Soccer Annual (Pelham Books)
1968-1970's
1968 - No. 1 (120pg) (with dj)   £20 $32
1969 - No.2 (120pg) (with dj)   £15 $24
1970's (with dj)   £10 $16
Based on the UK soccer star
GET ALONG GANG (Marvel/Grandreams)
1984-1987   £5 $8
1984
1986 (64pg)
Editor: Jenny O'Connor
Based on the animated TV series
GHOSTBUSTERS Filmation's (World))

1987 (64pg) (fc)   £8 $13
Comic Strip: Enter the Dragon Slayer (6)
Based on the animated TV series
G.I. JOE 'The Action Force' (Marvel)
1990-1991   £8 $13
See: ACTION FORCE
GIRL (Hulton/Longacre/Fleetway)
1953-1965 (Hulton/Longacre)
1980's (Fleetway)
1953 (with dj)   £30 $48
1954-1959 (with dj)   £25 $40
1957 (176pg) Number Five
Picture Strips: Belle of the Ballet Mother Goose in Paris (8fc) Writer:
George Beardmore, Art: Stanley Houton
At work with Janet Fashion Artist (2bw), Art: Marjorie Slade
Robbie of Red Hall in The Prophecy (4bw) Writer: George
Beardmore, Art: Roy Newby
Three Sisters of Haworth (4bw) Writer: Pamela Green & Kenneth
Gravett, Art: Eric Dadswell
Lettice Leefe (1bw)
The Rajah's Secret (4bw) Writer: Betty Roland, Art: Charles Paine
Lady without Fear (4bw), Writer: Chad Varah, Art: Gerald Haylock
Wendy and Jinx (4fc) Writer: Valerie Hastings, Art: Ray Bailey
Safety in Numbers (4bw), Writer: Joan Stannard, Art: Eric Wade
Dog Show (2bw), Writer: John May, Art: J T La Fontaine
1960-1965 (with dj)   £15 $24
1962 (176pg) Number Ten
Editor Clifford Makins
Picture Strips: Sally of the Seven Seas (4bw), Writer: Alan Jason,
Art: Dudley Pout
The Story of Ruth (2bw), Writer: Alan Jason, Art: Robert Ayton
Belle of the Ballet in La Belle Arenska (8fc), Writer: George
Beardmore, Art: Stanley Houghton
Lillian Starr Angel of Peshawar (4lw), Writer: Godfrey Rayne, Art:
Alan Crisp
Lettice Leaf The Greenest Girl In School (1bw), Art: Ryan
Angela and the Runaway Heiress (4lw), Writer Betty Roland, Art:
Dudley Pout
Bride of Adventure (4lw), Writer: Godfrey Rayne, Art: Roland Davies
Susan of St. Bride's in The Old Medal (4fc), Writer: Ruth Adam, Art:
Ray Bailey & Philip Townsend
Satchmo - The True Story of Louis Armstrong - The Grand Old Man
of Jazz (4lw), Writer: George Beardmore, Art: Alan Crisp
The Story of Kathleen Ferrier (4lw), Writer: Chad Varah, Art: Robert
Ayton
Includes bw photo feature on Laurence Harvey and Clemence
Bettany (with Peter Sellers) Dustjacket (fc)
1980's   £8 $13
1982 (96pg)
Comic Strips (bw): The Dance Dream, Dark Star Wish
Photo Strips: Cuckoo in the Nest, My Friend Tinks
Pin Ups: Cliff Richard, Dollar
1983 (96pg)
Comic Strip: What's wrong with Rhona
Photo Strips: Double Take, Cinderella's Dream
Pin Ups: Abba , Sting
1984 (96pg)
Comic Strip: Journey Into Fear (28bw)
Photo Strips: The Break Up, A Home for Lonely?

Features: Barry Manilow, Madness, Duran Duran, Cliff Richard, Olivia Newton John, Buster Bloodvessel
Pin Ups: Adam Ant , Toyah, Madness
1987 (96pg)
Comic Strip: Lorna of the Lake (24bw)
Photo Strips (b/w): Just My Luck, The Day Geaorge Michael Spoke To Me..., Back To The Past
Pin Ups (fc): Madonna, Scritti Politti, Thompson Twins, Pete Burns, David Easter, Marillion, Go West, Pet Shop Boys, A-Ha, Stephen Duffy, Madness, Feargal Sharkey, Simple Minds, Level 42, Echo & The Bunnymen, Nik Kershaw, King, Nick Heyward, Midge Ure, Kaja
1988 (96pg)
Photo Strips: Santas Last Stand, Twilight Forest, Ghostbusters, Watching the Detectives
Pin Ups (fc): Nick Kamen, Janet Jackson, A-Ha, Daryl Hall, Red Box, 5 Star, UB40, Heaven 17, China Crisis, Simply Red, Limahl, Bon Jovi, Bucks Fizz, Owen Paul, Style Council, INXS, Mr Mister, Queen and Eurythmics, Jermaine Stewart
Features on Spandau Ballet and A-Ha
Based on the UK Comic

GIRLS' CRYSTAL
1940-1976

1950's	£25	$40

1958 (164pg)
Comic Strips (bw/fc): The Secret of the Silver Locket, Merril and the Mystery Skis, Only Star Could save their Farm, The May Queen's Strange Quest, Rival Ballet Dancers of St Mary's, Their Exciting Holiday in the Rockies, Susie's Letter Box Ruse, Friends of the Vanished Princess, Lolita of the Banana Plantation, Isabel's Turkish Adventure

1960's	£15	$24

1969 (160pg)
Comic Strips (bw/tc): Cloris & Claire, Alone Against the Fourth Form, Miss Show Off, Perilous Masquerade, Linda of Lantern House, Jackie's Circus Friends, Secret in the Sand, Kim's Surprise Scoop, Just Jo, Mamselle X

1970's	£8	$13

Based on the comic

GIRL'S FAVOURITE (City)

1971 (96pg) (fc)	£7	$11

Comic Strips: Acacia Ave, Hobo the Hound, Diana of the Highway, The Flying Sisters,Our Village, The Happy Wanderers, Lucky Charm, Alone in London, The Sisters Bold,Hobo the Hound, Lucky Charm, Lost in the West, Our Village

GIRL FILM & TELEVISION (Hulton/Odhams)
1957-1966

1957 (No.1) (132pg) (with dj)	£25	$40
(without dj)	£15	$24
1958-1959 (132pg)	£20	$32
(without dj)	£10	$16
1960-1966 (with dj)	£15	$24
(without dj)	£8	$13

GIRL FROM U.N.C.L.E. (World)
1968-1970

1968	£20	$32
©1968 (96pg)	£15	$24

Comic Strip (fc): The Kid Commandos' Caper (26 two-part)
Gold Key reprint - Includes text stories and features

1970	£12	$19

Photo Cover
Based on the TV spy series starring Stephanie Powers

GIRL GUIDES (Collins/Purnell)
1920's-1994

1950's	£15	$24
1960's	£10	$16
1970's	£7	$11

1974 (96pg)
Comic Strips: A Guide has Courage (5bw) by Robert Moss
Art: Sheila Connelly
©1978 (80pg)
Editor Robert Moss
Picture Strip: Haggis Hunt in Scotland (2bw) by Joyce Burns, Art: Sheila Graber

1980's	£5	$8
1990-1994	£4	$7

GIRL TALK (World)

1978 (64pg) (fc/tc/bw)	£6	$10

Endpaper: Paul Crompton
Comic Strips: Living Doll, Love is Like This, My Dream Valentine,
Features: Leo Sayer, Robert Palmer, Electric Light Orchestra

GIRL TALK (BBC)

2000-present	£4	$7

Based on the UK girls comic

GIRLS' WORLD (Odhams/Longacre)
1960s-1970s

1960's	£10	$16
1970's	£8	$13

1971 (96pg) (Odhams)
Comic Strips: Guardians of the Pool (4tc), Busker Princess (4bw), A Friend for Blackie (4bw), Queen of Hearts (5fc), Safari Holiday (4bw), Its in the Stars (3tc), Two for Treasure (4tc)
Features: Mary Hopkin, Lynn & Vanessa Redgrave
1972 (96pg)
Comic Strips: Dare you Debbie! (4tc), Writer: Chris James, Art: Badia, Dear Walter (4lw), Grans Little Friend (4fc), Anyone Can Cook (3lw), The Wild One (4lw), Looking After Wendy (4tc)
Text Stories: Smile Please Mrs Prittle, Writer: Laurie Kuhrt, Art: Gareth Floyd, Redsands Gymkhana, All Packed Up - Writer: D. Cork, Art: Ferguson Dewar
The Tudor Rose - Writer: Denise Wackrill, Art: Gareth Floyd
Miss Belle - Writer: Peter Jones

GLADIATORS (Grandreams/World)

1992-1997	£4	$7

1994
Editor: Brenda Aspley
Writer: Melanie J Clayden
©1995 (Grandreams)
1995-1997 (World)
Based on the TV series

GLO FRIENDS (World)

1987-1988	£5	$8

Based on the toy range

GOAL (IPC)

1970's	£7	$11

GODZILLA (Grandreams)
1999

©1998 (64pg) (fc)	£5	$8

Goofy 1976

Gran 1985

Grange Hill 1981

Writer: Nichola Tyrrell - Designed by Jason Bazini
Based on the screenplay by Dean Devlin & Roland Emmerich
GOODIES (World)
1974 (78pg)   £7 $11
Starring Bill Oddie, Graeme Garden and Tim Brooke Taylor
Photo cover
Based on the BBC comedy series
GOOFY (Fleetway)
1970's   £8 $13
©1975 (80pg)
Comic Strips (fc/tc) featuring: Goofy, Pluto, Moby Duck, Donald
Duck, Scamp, Bambi and Thumper, Chip 'n' Dale, Grandma Duck,
Gyro Gearloose and Uncle Scrooge
GORDON T GOPHER Philip Schofield's (World)
1989-1991   £5 $8
Based on the Childrens BBC TV hand puppet
GRAN Annual (Polystyle)
1985   £4 $7
©1984 (64pg)
Based on the Childrens BBC TV series
GRANDSTAND SPORTS BBC TV (World)
1979 (fc/tc) (64 pg)   £8 $13
21st Anniversary Edition
Features: Frank Bough, Steve Ovett, Gareth Edwards, Keith Fielding
and Bob Wilson
Based on the BBC TV sports show
GRANGE HILL (Grandreams/Fleetway)
1981-1989
©1980   £8 $13
Comic Strips (bw): What a Shower,
Art: John Cooper
1982-1989   £6 $10
©1980 (64pg) (Grandreams)
Comic Strips: What a Shower! (8bw), Match Play (8fc), Homework
Hitch (8bw) - Art: John Cooper
Features Peter 'Tucker' Jenkins (Todd Carty)
1982-1987 (Fleetway 80 pg)
1982 - 2nd annual
Features Tucker Jenkins
1983
Includes Todd Carty full-colour photo feature and Zammo pin-up and
text story
Photo Strip (bw): The Chips Are Down
Features Annette Firman and Fay Lucas
1984
Photo Strip (bw): New Year Night Out - featuring Duane and Pogo,
Shop
Cornered! -featuring Annette and Fay
Includes an interview with Susan Tully (Suzanne Ross)
1985
Photo Strips (bw): Goodbuy Boys - featuring Julie and Fay,
Off The Hook - featuring Zammo
Write On Roly! - featuring Roland Browning
Includes Q&A's with Lee Macdonald (Zammo McGuire) and Nadia
Chambers (Annette) plus interview with Paula-Ann Bland (Claire
Scott)
1986
Photo Strips (bw featuring Grange Hill cast):
Fancy That!, Off The Rails, Photo-Finish

Also features illustrated fc text stories, pin-ups and features
1987 (Fleetway) (80pg)
Packed with photo features and photo strips
Pin Ups: Lee Macdonald (Zammo), George Wilson (Ziggy), Melissa
Wilks (Jackie), John Holmes (Gonch), Jonathan Lambeth (Danny),
John Alford (Robbie), Bradley Sheppard (Hollo), Ricky Simmonds
(Ant), Alison Bettles (Fay), Tina Mahon (Ronnie), Simone Hyams
(Calley), Ruth Carraway (Helen),
1988 (World) (64pg)
Endpaper pin-ups of Ricky Simmons (Ant), Amma Asante (Cheryl),
Layout: Paul Green
Finished art: Paul Crompton and Glenn Rix
Alison Bettles (Fay) and Simon Vaughn (Fred)
Comic Strips (2x6 fc): Trip to the Seaside, The Rolypoly Bowl
Photo cover
Based on the childrens BBC TV series
GRAN 'N' POPS (Dean)
N/D (50's)   £15 $24
Writer: Arthur Groom - Art: Lawson Wood
First story - Gran 'N' Pops Great Idea
GREAT GRAPE APE (Stafford Pemberton)
1980 (64pg)   £8 $13
Cover art: Paul Green
Comic Strips (fc) feature Great Grape Ape and Beegle Beagle
Based on the Hanna Barbera animated TV series
GREEN HORNET (World)
1967-1968   £25 $56
Based on the TV series starring Bruce Lee as Kato
GREYFRIARS HOLIDAY Annual for Boys and Girls
1980's
1980's (with dj)   £8 $13
(without dj)   £4 $7
Howard Baker Reprints
GUMMI BEARS
1987-1988
1987 (80pg)   £5 $8
Comic Strips: Gummi Games! (8fc), The Signpost (2bw), High Flying
Fun (10bw), Cubbi's Kite (2fc), Clever Catch (2bw), A Spell of
Success (10fc)
Based on the animated TV series
GUNSMOKE (Purnell/World)
1964-1967, 1974-1975
1964-1967   £12 $19
©1966 (96pg)
Stories by John Challis, Art: Denis McLoughlin
Comic Strips (bw): Thunder in the Hills (12), Kansas Killers (10)
Reprints the newspaper strip by Harry Bishop
1974-1975   £8 $13
1975 (World)
Comic Strips and text stories
Photo cover
Based on the TV western series starring James Arness
HAPPY DAYS (Stafford Pemberton)
1979-1982   £8 $13
1979 (64pg) (fc)
Comic Strip: Fonzie's New Bike (6 fc)
Includes interviews and pin ups of the stars
Photo cover
1980 (64pg) (fc)

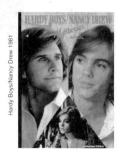

Comic Strips: The Candy Coloured Jeep, Hole in One, Match Point 1981 (64 pg) (fc)
Comic Strips: The Strange Beggar (6), Question of Muscles (11)
Happy Days #6 reprints
Feature: Idols of the Fifties
Art: Paul Green
Includes photo features from the TV series
Photo cover
Based on the TV series starring Henry Winkler

HARDY BOYS/NANCY DREW MYSTERIES (Grandreams)
1980-1981   £10 $16
© 1979 (64pg)
Comic Strips: Gold Smugglers (6 bw), The Marina Mystery (6 fc),
Shark (6fc), Pterodactyl (6 bw), The Phantom Flyer (6 bw)
Includes features and pin-ups (fc) on the stars of the show
Photo cover
© 1980 (64pg)
Comic Strips: Trouble on Oiled Water(6bw), The Case of the Muddy
Pants (6fc), Mystery of the Missing Millionaire (6fc), The Ghost of
Gravesdyke Grange (6bw)
Includes features and pin-ups (fc) on the stars of the show
Based on the TV series starring Shaun Cassidy, Parker Stevenson
and Pamela Sue Martin

HARLEM GLOBETROTTERS (Brown Watson)
1973-1974   £12 $19
Featuring Dastardly and Muttley and The Perils of Penelope Pitstop
Based on the Hanna Barbera characters

HAROLD HARE'S OWN (Fleetway)
1960's (84pg)   £12 $19
Comic Strips (fc/tc) feature: Harold Hare, Dick and Hoppy, Wendy
and her Wonderful Toby Jug, Buster, Willie Wizz, Dagwood Duck,
Flopsy Flufftail, Moony, Billy the Bouncing Ball, Toad, Ratty and
Mole, Katie Country Mouse, Peter Puffin, Pinocchio
1961 - 'A Sunshine Annual' - Also features Bengo the Boxer Pup by
Tim in two illustrated text stories
Art: Hugh McNeil, Peter Woolcock, Phiilip Mendoza, Bill Lacey,
Neave Parker
Landscape format (smaller format from 1962 on)
Based on the UK comic

HART TO HART (Stafford Pemberton)
1983 (64pg)   £8 $13
Comic Strip (fc): The Freeway Affair (6)
Photo cover
Based on the TV series starring Robert Wagner and Stefanie
Powers

HAWKEYE and the LAST OF THE MOHICANS (Adprint)
1950s
1958 (No.1)   £20 $32
Writer: Michael Holt, Art: George Shaw
1959   £15 $24
Writer: David Roberts., Art: Ron Embleton
Based on the TV series starring Lonchaney Jr

HAZELL (Stafford Pemberton)
1979-1980   £6 $10
1979 (64pg) (fc)
Comic Strips: Take the Money & Run, The Cost of Winning, The
Brotherhood
1980 (64pg) (fc)
Comic Strips: Hazell visits the Hairdresser (7), Striker (7)

Based on the private investigator TV series starring Nicholas Ball
HEARTBEAT
1983   £6 $10
Features: Kim Wilde, Abba, Soft Cell, Gary Numan and more

HECTOR'S HOUSE (BBC)
1970-1972   £12 $19
Based on the childrens BBC TV puppet series

HEIDI (Grandreams)
1982-1983   £5 $8
©1981 (64pg) (fc)
Comic Strips: Heidi, The Untermeyer Tunnel, Fire on the Alm
©1982 (64pg) (fc)
Comic Strips: Dete's Return (8tc), The Bear Necessities (8tc)
Photo features
Based on the TV Series

HE-MAN (World)
1990 (64pg) (fc)   £6 $10
Comic Strip: The Drumskalan From The Denebrian Swamp (8)
Cover art: Paul Crompton, Art: Paul Crompton and Paul Green
Re-vamped version of Masters of the Universe
See: MASTERS OF THE UNIVERSE

HENRY'S CAT (Purnell)
1980's   £5 $8
Based on the childrens BBC animated series

HENRY'S CAT Storybook (St Michael)
1984
©1983   £6 $10
Writer: Stan Hayward, Art: Bob Godfrey

HENRY COOPER'S SPORTS (Brown Watson)
1976
©1975 (80pg)   £5 $8
Features: James Hunt, Bjorn Borg, Barry Sheene, Muhammad Ali
and Joe Bugner
Based on the UK heavyweight boxer

HEY DIDDLE DIDDLE (Fleetway/IPC)
1970's (72pg)   £4 $7

HI! (D.C. Thomson)
1990's   £5 $8
Features photo strips, fashion and pin ups

HI DE HI (Stafford Pemberton)
1983 (64pg) (fc)   £6 $10
Art: Edgar Hodges
Comic Strips: Cinderella Maid, EGGs-Ample for Ted
Based on the BBC TV comedy series

HIGH CHAPARRAL (World)
1970-1973
©1969 (fc/tc)   £12 $19
Comic Strip: Apache Justice (26fc), Art: Tufts
Gold Key Reprints
Photo Cover
1970-1973   £10 $16
Based on the TV western series

HOLLY HOBBIE (World)
1979 (64pg) (fc/tc)   £8 $13
Based on the US greetings card character

HOLLYWOOD ALBUM (Sampson Low Marston)
1946-1950's
1950-1955 (with dj)   £25 $40

Holmes and Yoyo 1978

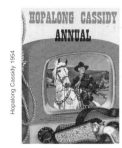

Hopalong Cassidy 1954

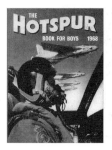

Hotspur 1968

1950-1955 (without dj)	£15	$19
1956 on (with dj)	£20	$32
1956 on (with dj)	£10	$16

Editor: Ivy Crane Wilson - Hollywood correspondent for the London "Star"

'Ninth' (nd) (164pg) (fc/bw)
Title Page (fc): Grace Kelly in To Catch A Thief
Features by: Gene Autry, Vincent Price, Jane Powell, Jeff Chandler, Olivia DeHavilland, Paul Stewart, Dana Andrews, Suzan Ball, Ava Gardner, Jack Lemmon, Spencer Tracy, Gloria Talbot, Jack Palance, May Wynn, Dewey Martin, Dan O'Herlihy, Ann Miller, Shelley Winters, Jeff Richards, Ronald Reagan, Jane Russell, Howard Keel, Virginia Mayo, Michael Kidd, Kim Novak, Steve Forrest, Richard Widmark, Dan Dailey, Henry King, Piper Laurie, Edmund Purdom, Dick Powell, Glynis Johns, Jay Morley Jr, Robert Francis, Danny Kaye
Pin Ups (fc): Mamie Van Doren, Dana Andrews, Suzan Ball, Jack Palance, Terry Moore, Gloria Talbot, Donna Percy, Penny Edwards, Ursula Theiss, May Wynn, Jeff Richards, Mona Freeman, Dean Martin and Jerry Lewis, Virginia Mayo, Kim Novak, Steve Forrest, Piper Laurie, Edmund Purdom
'Twelth' ©1958 (130pg) (fc/bw)
Title Page (fc): Hal Marchand wife Candy
Features by: Pat Boone, Richard Basehart, Jeanne Crain, Lloyd Nolan, Claire Bloom, Joan Collins, Phyllis Kirk, James Arness, Shirley Jones, Leslie Neilsen, Sophia Loren, Joanne Woodward, Kay Kendall, Dan Duryea, Valerie French, Charlton Heston, Tony Randall, Dianne Foster, Maureen O'Hara, Ronald Howard, Zsa Zsa Gabor, Mickey Rooney, Yul Brynner, Clark Gable, Anthony Quinn
Pin Ups (fc): Kim Novak, Dorothy Malone, John Saxon, Lee Remick, Pat Boone, Sophia Loren, Jean Wallace, Rory Calhoun, Jeanne Crain, Claire Bloom, Paul Newman, Rossano Brazzi, Pier Angeli, Mitzi Gaynor, Sandra Dee, Dolores Hart, Joan Collins, James Arness, Jeff Chandler, Carroll Baker, Shirley Jones, Joanne Woodward, Kay Kendall, Valerie French, George Nader, Cornell Borchers, Anna Kashfi, Tony Randall, Maureen O'Hara, Dustjacket (fc): Shirley Jones and Pat Boone in April Love (front), John Raitt and Doris Day in The Pajama Game (back)

HOLMES AND YOYO
1978	£8	$13

Based on the TV series

HOME and AWAY (World/Grandreams)
1988-1991	£5	$8

©1987 Annual (Grandreams)
Estimate 1988 - Cover Price £4.25
Stephen, Carly & Bobby on cover - 1st
Writer/Editor: Melanie J Clayden
Design/Layout: Nigel Money
©1987 Annual (Grandreams)
Estimate 1989 - Cover Price: £4.25 - Orange Cover
Writer/Editor: Kesta Desmond
Layout/Design: Louise Ivimy
©1987 Annual (Grandreams)
Estimate 1990 - Cover Price: £4.50 - Craig McLachlan on cover
Writer: David Nicholls, Kesta Desmond
Layout/Design: Louise Ivimy
©1987 Annual (Grandreams)
Estimate 1991 - Cover Price: £4.50 - White cover
Writer: John Kercher

Layout/Design: Joanna Winslow
©1990 Special (World) (64pg) - £4.25 - Tom, Carly & Frank/Roo on Cover
Writer/Editor: Clive Hopwood
Based on the Australian soap

HONG KONG PHOOEY
1975	£12	$19

Based on the Hanna Barbera animated TV series

HOPALONG CASSIDY ADVENTURES (Adprint/Purnell)
1950's	£20	$32

©1958 - No. 6 (Purnell)
Writer: Charles Hitchcock, Art: Hans Helweg
Based on the Western movie character

HOPALONG CASSIDY (Adprint/Miller)
1954-1961		
1954	£25	$40
1955-1961	£20	$32

1954 (Adprint) (70pg) (fc)
Writer: Elizabeth Beecher
Picture Strip: Rustlers At Bar 20-Art: Pete Alvarado
Text Stories: Hopalong Cassidy and the Bar 20 Cowboys, The Feathered Friend, The Big Rodeo, The Lost Gold Mine, Art: Sahula Dycke, Hopalong Cassidy and the Two Young Cowboys (11), Art: John Higgs
Based on the characters created by Clarence E. Mulford and the film/tv series starring William Boyd
©1960 - No.2 (L. Miller) (98pg) (bw)
'Hopalong Cassidy Western Comic Annual'
Card covers
Comic Strips: The Five Carver Brothers (35), Lady From Boston (30), Commanche Chief (29), Art: Dan Spiegle
Photo/art cover (fc)
Newspaper strip reprints
Based on the Western movie character

HORSE WORLD (World)
1973 (104pg)	£6	$10

Comic Strip: Unexpected Event (6)
Art: Leonard Ward, Editor: James Gleeson

HOTSPUR BOOK for Boys (D.C. Thomson)
1966-1981 (2nd series)		
1966	£20	$32
1967-1970	£15	$24
1970-1975	£10	$16
1975-1981	£8	$13

1977 (128pg) (tc)
Comic Strips: Red Star Robinson, Ossie the Outlaw, Nick Jolly, Dick Turpin's Ride To York, Dim Dan the Boobyguard, The Team of the Dragon, Ernest Rutherford-The Man Who Split The Atom, The Bobby of Black Rock, Robin Hood, The Iron Teacher, Cowardy Custer, Charlie's Aunt, The Scarlet Hawk, The Black Sapper, King of the Whip, Lonely Larry, Three Against The Lion
1978 (128pg) (tc)
Comic Strips: King Cobra, Ossie The Outlaw, Viva Ruff and Reddy, Wilson's Totem Tests, Dim Dan, Danny Boyd, Skyscraper Kidd, The Scarlet Hawk, The Big Palooka, The Peabody Problem, Kenji the Samurai, Red Star Robinson, Cast Hook and Strike, Cowardy Custer, Ossie the Outlaw, Bernard's Day Off
1979 (128pg) (tc)
Comic Strips: The Man Called Wilson, King Cobra, Dozy Danny,

How the West Was Won 1979

Hurricane 1971

Impossibles 1969

Willie the Winner, Red Pepper, The King's Shilling, Grasshopper Green, Danny Boyd - Golfing Star, The Big Palooka, The Scarlet Hawk, Spring-Heeled Jackson, Flying Fury, Bernard the Boot, Medic Muldoon, Ossie the Outlaw, Courage Is Not Just A Word
Based on the UK comic

HOW (Associated Newspapers/ITP)
1960's-1970's (Look In ITP)

N/D (Estimate 1967) (Priced 10'6)	£10	$16

Daily Mail Book (First Annual) (96pg) (tc)
Photo Cover

1973 (World)	£8	$13
©1974 (96pg)	£8	$13

Endpaper: Featuring UK pop group Sweet
Features: Sweet (6)
Based on the Childrens ITV series

HOW THE WEST WAS WON (Brown Watson)
1979

©1978 (64pg) (fc)	£8	$13

Comic Strips: Sacred Ground, Rough Justice
Based on the TV Western series starring James Arness and Bruce Boxleitner

HUCKLEBERRY HOUND (World/Peveril/Atlas)
1950's -1960's

1959 (World)	£15	$24
1963 (Peveril) - Scarce	£15	$24

'A Big TV Bumper Book'

1960's	£10	$13
©1968 (Atlas) - Scarce	£12	$19

©1959 (96 pg)
With Yogi Bear, Mr Jinks and Pixie & Dixie
Comic Strips (fc): Huckleberry Hound - Snowman Safari, The New Idea, The Dirty Birdie, Badge 13 Three Quarters, Big Game Hunter, The Big Tow, Yogi Bear - The Awful "It", The Hat Hassle, Something Fishy, Pixie, Dixie and Mr Jinks - Lone Star Hero, The Abominable Showman, The Icy Mice
Based on the Hanna Barbera cartoon character

HUCKLEBERRY HOUND WINTER FUN (World)
Big Television Book

1960	£12	$19

Based on the Hanna Barbera cartoon character

HUCKLEBERRY HOUND Television Story Book (Newtown)

1963	£15	$24

©1962 (96pg)
Based on the Hanna Barbera cartoon character

HUCKLEBERRY HOUND & YOGI BEAR (World)

1981	£8	$13

©1980
Based on the Hanna Barbera cartoon characters

HULK/INCREDIBLE HULK (World/Marvel/Grandreams)

1977-1985	£8	$13

Also known as 'The Incredible Hulk Annual'
1978 (64pg) (fc)
INCREDIBLE HULK (World)
1979 (64pg) (fc)
Comic Strips: A Refuge Divided, Cover Artists: Gary Brodsky & Joe Sinnott, Writer: Gary Friedrich, Pencils: Marie Severin, Inks: Syd Shores , Defender of the Realm, Writer: David Kraft, Art: Keith Giffen and Chic Stone
Marvel Comic strip reprints

INCREDIBLE HULK (Grandreams)
©1979 (64pg)
Comic Strips (UK): Secret Army (12bw), Terror of the Swamps (4fc), Art: John Higgins
The Coming Of The Hulk (6bw), by Stan Lee and Jack Kirby
Includes photo feature profiles of Bill Bixby and Lou Ferrigno
Photo cover
Based on the TV Series
HULK (Marvel/Grandreams)
©1980
Comic Strips: Might of the Mechadroid (3 parts), Enter the Exterminator (part 2), Showdown in the Slums (part 3), The Ringmaster (10fc), Plot: Stan Lee, Art: Jack Kirby
End of the Hunt (6bw), Art: David Lloyd
4 page feature on The Hulk's comic history plus photo files on Bill Bixby and Lou Ferrigno
Photo cover
Based on the TV Series
HULK (Marvel/Grandreams)
1981 (64pg) (fc) - Cover Price £2.25
Comic Strips:
Mogol: Writer: Roy Thomas, Art: Herb Trimpe
Again the Glob: Writer: Roy Thomas, Art: Herb Trimpe
Shadow on the Land: Writer: Len Wein, Art: Herb Trimpe
Marvel Comic strip reprints
HULK (Marvel/Grandreams)
Not Dated (64pg) (fc)- Cover Price £2.50
Comic Strip: And Six Shall Crush the Hulk
Writer: Chris Claremont, Art: Sal Buscema and Jack Abel
©1984 (64pg fc) - Cover Price £2.95
Comic Strip (fc): What If Rick Jones Had Become The Hulk? Writer: Don Glut, Pencils: Sal Buscema, Inks: Bill Black
Ring Around The Rhino! Writer: Gary Friedrich, Art: Marie Severin, Inks: Frank Giacoia
Marvel Comic strip reprints
HUNTER (World)

1987	£8	$13

Photo Cover
Based on the TV police series starring Fred Dryer and Stephanie Kramer
HURRICANE (IPC/Fleetway)
1960's-1970's

1960's	£12	$19
1970's	£8	$13

©1970 (160pg) (fc/tc/bw)
Comic Strips: The Juggernaut from Planet Z, HMS Outcast, They Came from the Sea, Olac the Gladiator, Danny Jones, He Rides Alone, Typhoon Tracy, Sword for Hire, Skid Solo, The Slogger from Down Under,Typhoon Tracy, Tiger of the Deep, Helmet Head, Danny Jones, The Inquisitors
Based on the UK comic
IAN BOTHAM'S SPORTS (Purnell)

1984	£5	$8

©1983
Based on the UK cricket star
IDEAL Book for Girls (Dean)

1950's	£10	$16

The IMPOSSIBLES (Atlas)
1969

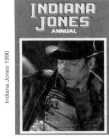

Indiana Jones 1990

Its a Knockout 1977

Jackie 1978

©1968 (64pg)   £20 $32
Comic Strips (fc): The Impossibles vs. The Mirror Man (6), The
Jetsons: Auto-Pappy (8), Frankenstein Jr. in The Image Invasion
(12), Frankenstein Jr. # 1 reprint
Space Ghost in Zorak's Revenge (10), Space Ghost #1 reprint
Frankenstein Jr. meets The Flea Man (4), The Jetsons in How To
Mine A Moon! (7)
Text Stories (tc 2x4): The Impossibles Cure a Doctor, Frankenstein
Jr. in A Spook In His Wheel
Based on the Hanna Barbera animated series

INCREDIBLE COTTAGE (Grandreams)
1982   £6 $10
Based on an idea by Willie Rushton

INDIANA JONES (Marvel)
1991
©1990 (64pg)   £6 $10
Endpaper: Luigi Stefanelli/Gina Hart
Features: Patrick Mulkern/Louise Cassell
Comic Strips (fc): Gateway to Infinity (22), The Harbingers (22)
Writer: David Michelinie, Pencils: Ron Frenz, Inks: Danny Bulanadi
U.S. Marvel reprint
Includes photo features (fc) from the movie Indiana Jones and the
Lost Crusade

INDIANA JONES AND THE TEMPLE OF DOOM
(Marvel/Grandreams)
1985
©1984   £6 $10
Cover Art: Butch Guice
Comic strip adaptation of the movie
Based on the Movie starring Harrison Ford

INTERNATIONAL FOOTBALL ILLUSTRATED (World)
1962-1970   £8 $13

INSPECTOR GADGET (Marvel)
1986-1989   £8 $13
1986 (64pg)
Comic strip: Doctor Claw Drops Out
1987 (64pg)
Comic strip (fc): Don't Bank On It (45)
1989 (64pg)
Gadget and the Loch Ness (fc)
Based on the animated TV series

I SPY (News Chronicle)
1950's
No.1 - 1954/1955 (card covers) (118pg)   £20 $32
Picture Strip: Silent Flight (2tc), Writer/Art: W M Hammond
Feature: Television limelight - photo features on Kidnapped,
Huckleberry Finn, Silver Skin, Rumplestiltskin, The Snowman,
My Brother Sterling and My Sister Pat by Sterling and Pat Moss
1956 - No. 2 (132pg)   £25 $40
Picture Strips: Cocos Island Treasure (5tc), Writer/Art: W. M
Hammond, Peter and Penny solve a Dockland Mystery (3fctcbw),
Writer/Art: Zena Flax
Text Story: Fishy Business (7fctcbw) by W. E. Johns - Biggles
Adventure
1957 onwards   £15 $24
Based on the News Chronicle feature

I SPY (Polystyle)
1970's-1980's
1970s   £6 $10

1980s (64pg) (fc/tc)   £5 $8
Children's hobby annual
IT'S A KNOCKOUT ANNUAL (World)
1977 (80pg)   £8 $13
Comic Strip: Knocked-Out (6tc)
Based on the BBC TV gameshow
IT AIN'T HALF HOT MUM (World)
1977   £10 $16
Based on the BBC TV comedy series starring Windsor Davies
ITV ANNUAL for Boys and Girls (TV Publications)
1964 (104pg) (fc/bw)   £15 $24
Editor: Huw Thomas
Comic Strip: No Hiding Place (8bw)
Photo Stories: 77 Sunset Strip - The Cabaha Caper (8bw), Hawaiian
Eye - Danger in the Deep (8bw), Writer: Alan Fennell
Features: Fireball XL5 (4bw), Bert Weedon (4bw), Survival (8fc/bw),
Writer: Aubrey Buxton, Thank Your Lucky Stars (6fc/bw), Police 5
(4bw)
Full page autographed colour photos of Cliff Richard, Helen Shapiro
and Joe Brown
ITV SATURDAY SOCCER SPECIAL (Grandreams)
1981
©1980 (64pg)   £5 $8
Features soccer personalities
Illustrated Cover
IVOR THE ENGINE (Stafford Pemberton)
1978 (64pg)
Picture Strips: Delivery Charges, A Safe House
Text Stories: Ivor's Friends, Pigeon Post, Gold Mining, The Letter
Based on the Childrens TV Series written by Oliver Postgate and
Peter Firmin
JACK & JILL (Fleetway/IPC)
1950's-1980's
1950's   £20 $32
1960's   £10 $16
1970's   £7 $11
1980's   £5 $10
Picture strips include: Jack and Jill, Gregory Grasshopper, The
Enchanted House, Harold Hare, Old Mother Hubbard, Teddy Bear,
Nurse Susan and Dr David, Nutty Noodle, Flip Tail the Otter, Katy
Country Mouse, Wink and Blink, Freddy Frog, Tiger Tim and the
Bruin Boys, Snuggles the Koala Bear, Gregory and the Dormise,
The Wombles
Based on the UK comic for young children
JACKIE (D.C. Thomson)
1966-1993
1966   £20 $32
1967-1969   £15 $24
1970's   £10 $16
1975 (96pg)
Comic Strips: Miranda's Man (6bw), Fang (2bw), Our Guilty Secret
(5bw), What Have I Let Myself in For (7bw)
Features: Gary Glitter, David Cassidy, Slade, Top of the Pops, Elton
John, The Osmonds
1978 (96pg) (fc/bw)
Comic Strips: The Adventures of Leonard J. Watkins, A Time to
Love Forever, Madge & Beryl, Remember Me My Love
Features: Dead End Kids, The Quest TV show, Fonz, Flintlock
1980's   £8 $13

Jackie 1992

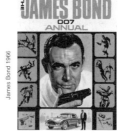

James Bond 1966

James Bond Octopussy 1984

1981 (96pg)
Small features on: David Essex, Noel Edmonds, Police, Rod Stewart, Nolan Sisters, Francis Rossi of Status Quo, Eddie Kidd, Peter Powell, Kid Jensen, Geoff Downes of the Buggles, Keith Chegwin, Shakin Stevens, Thereze Bazaar of Dollar, Kermit the frog, Marie Osmond, Superman, Lewis Collins, Bob Geldof, Sting, B.A Robertson, Lemmy of Motorhead, Bodie & Doyle of the Professionals, Miss Piggy, Dave Vanian of the Damned, Humphrey Bogart, Erik Estrada, Dr Hook
1983 (96pg)
Small features: Rick Parfitt, Simon Le Bon, Sting, Stewart Copeland, Martin Kemp, Adam Ant
1984 (96pg)
Small features: Adam Ant, Sting, David Jaymes of Modern Romance, Jennie McKeown of the Belle Stars, David Bowie, Joe Jackson, Kate Garner of Haysi Fantaysee, Nick Beggs of Kajagoogoo, Michael Jackson, Alan McClusky of O.M.D, Musical Youth, Mark Almond of Soft Cell, Edwyn Collins of Orange Juice, Phil Oakey of the Human League, Mari Wilson, Michael Mullins of Modern Romance, Kevin Rowland of Dexy's Midnight Runners, Nick Heyward, Chris Foreman of Madness, Jim Kerr of Simple Minds,
1985 (96pg)
Features: Boy George, Paul Weller
1986 (96pg)
Photo Strips: The Alternative Fairy Story, Forbidden Kisses, And Anyone Who Knows Me
Comic Strip: Madge & Beryl
Star Files: Star Files on Sade, Nick Heyward, Steve Norman of Spandau Ballet, Captain Sensible and Curt Smith of Tears for Fears
Features: Thompson Twins (Alannah Currie), Kim Wilde, Paul Young, Adam Ant, Big Country, Nick Heyward
1988 (96pg)
Fact Files: Michael J Fox, Simon O'Brien, Aha, Tom Cruise, Joey Tempest, Ben (Curiosity Killed the Cat),
Pin Ups: Nick Berry, Michael J Fox, Aha
1989 (96pg)
Pin Ups: Wet Wet Wet, Madonna, Bros, Pet Shop Boys
1990's   £5 $8
1991 (96pg)
Features: Kylie Minogue, Corey Feldman, Christian Slater, Patrick Dempsey, Johnny Depp, Corey Haim
Pin Ups: Jason Donovan, New Kids on the Block, Matt Dillon, Marti Pellow
Small features: Tony Curtis, Tyrone Power, Clark Gable, Frank Sinatra, Montgomery Clift, Steve McQueen, Peter O'Toole, Marlon Brando, Errol Flynn, James Dean, Paul Newman
1992 (96pg)
Photo Strips: Three's Company (fc), Silly Games (bw), Another Christmas (fc)
Pin Iups (fc): Phillip Schofield, New Kids On The Block
1993 (96pg)
Star Files: Keanu Reeves, Winona Ryder, Christian Slater, Robert Downey Jnr
Pin Ups: Jason Priestley, Christian Slater
Based on the UK girls comic
JACKPOT (Fleetway)
1970's-1980's
1970's   £10 $16
1980's   £8 $13
1985

Comic Strips - no credits
Laster Eraser, The Incredible Sulk, Full O'Beans, Jack Pott, Nipper, Top of the class, Will Power, The Park, Jakes Seven, Kaboom, Nipper, The Katts, Mike's Bike, Kid King, Cry Baby, The Fixer, The Winners, Jail Birds, Scooper, It's a Nice Life, Will Power, Little Miss Muffit, Laser Eraser, Milly Onaire and Penny Less, Top of the Class, Danger Mouse, Little and Large, Lenny
Based on the UK comic
JAG (Fleetway)
1969-1973
1969 (Scarce)   £15 $24
1970-1973   £10 $16
Based on the UK comic
JAMIE and the MAGIC TORCH
1979   £10 $16
Based on the childrens ITV series
JAMES BOND 007 (World)
1966-1968   £30 $48
©1965 (128pg)
Cover Art: R. W. Smethurst
Comic Strips (bw): The Imposter, The Day Manchester Slept, Panic Search, The Scar-Faced Assassin, The Face At The Window, They Called Him The Chameleon
Includes full page photos (fc) from 'Dr. No', 'From Russia With Love', 'Goldfinger' and 'Thunderball'
JAMES BOND 007 MOONRAKER Special (World)
1980
©1979   £10 $16
Art: Melvyn Powell
Mixture of photos (fc) and artwork features (fc/tc)
JAMES BOND OCTOPUSSY 007 (Marvel/Grandreams)
1984
©1983   £10 $16
Writer: Steve Moore, Art: Paul Neary
Feature text: Richard Hollis
Roger Moore feature (12)
Comic Strip film adaptation
Photo Cover
JASON DONOVAN (Grandreams/World)
1989-1991 (64pg)   £4 $7
©1990 (Grandreams)
1990-1991 (World)
Based on the Australian actor/singer
JELLY BABIES Bassett's (World)
1992 (64pg)   £4 $7
Editor: John Malam
Writer: Julie Jones, Art: David Moss and John Walmsley
JEM (World)
1987-1988   £8 $13
1987
Comic Strips (fc): In the Beginning, Desperately Seeking Synergy
1988
Comic Strips (fc): In the Beginning, Higher and Higher, Two Kind of Courage
Based on the children animated TV rockstar
JETSONS (World)
1960's   £15 $24
©1964 (96pg)

Jinty 1983

Joe 901 969

Judge Dredd 1981

Comic Strips: Rosey's Reward, The No Place to Play Day, The Lunch was all Dough, No Vacancy, The Play is the Thing, Maid of Metal, The Folksinger Swinger, Two Fiddlers are Cheaper than Three, Winning Back Father, Canine Camper Caper, Double Dating, Having a Horsie Holiday, The Last Word, Nosey - By Nice, Birds without Feathers Don't Stick Together
Goldkey reprints
Based on the Hanna Barbera animated space family series

JIGSAW (World)
1984 (64pg)   £4 $7
Janet Ellis photo cover
Based on the childrens BBC TV series

JIMBO & THE JET SET (Grandreams)
1980's
©1987   £6 $10
Contributions from: Simon Maddocks, Peter Maddocks, Clive Dawson, Lorraine Smith
Comic Strips (fc): Jimbo Gets his Skates on (6), The Great Air Show (7), Little Red Devil (7)
Based on the children's BBC TV animated series

JIM'LL FIX IT (Purnell)
1981-1982   £7 $11
©1980 (64pg)
Features: Abba, Fawlty Towers, All Creatures Great and Small
Photo Cover
©1981 (64pg)   £5 $8
Based on the BBC TV series

JIMMY HILL Soccer Book
1969   £7 $11
Based on the UK soccer presenter

JIMPY Daily Mirror (Mirror)
1950's   £15 $24

JINTY (Fleetway)
1970's-1980's
1970's   £6 $10
1980's   £5 $8
1983 (128pg (tc/bw)
Comic Strips: Little sisters (3), The carnival of flowers (5), The mystery of martine (30), A picture of the past (2), The thirteenth hour (3), Call of the sea (3), No place like home (3), The strawbery handerchief (4), Snowbound (4)
Based on the UK girls comic

JOE (Purnell)
1968 (56pg)   £6 $10
Writer and Art: Alison Prince, Joan Hickson
Based on the Childrens BBC watch with mother T.V series

JOE 90 (City)
1969-1970
1969   £20 $32
1970   £15 $24
©1968 (96 pg)
Comic Strips (fc): Lust For Gold, Deadly Toy, Rat Trap, Phantom Light, Ambush, Doctor Fawkes, Checkmate, Operation Torch
Includes schematics of Culver Bay Cottage and Mac's Lab and stills (fc) from the series
Photo cover
Based on the Gerry Anderson TV series

JOE 90: TOP SECRET COMIC (City)

1970   £15 $24
©1969 (96pg) (fc/tc)
Comic Strips (fc): Joe 90 (2x6) in Black Gold, Snatch to Slavery, Land of the Giants (1x5, 1x7), Star Trek (6), The Champions in Error of Judgement (6), Campbell Man of Speed (6), Ninepence + Tenpence = Sport (6)
Text stories (fc) include: The Champions in Deadline Discovery, Joe 90 in Double Strike
Photo endpapers include Stuart Damon (The Champions), Joe 90, Star Trek (Kirk, Spock & Uhura)
Photo cover features Joe 90, The Champions

JOE 90 Story Book (City)
1969
©1968   £12 $19
Forbidden Island
Based on the Gerry Anderson TV series

JOHN TRAVOLTA (Stafford Pemberton)
1980-1981   £8 $13
1981 (48 pg)
Editor: Alan Walsh, Art (fc): Paul Green
Features: Deborah Causton
Includes photo features and scenes from 'Grease' (fc/bw)

JONNY QUEST (World)
1966-1967
©1965 (96pg) (fc)   £25 $40
Comic Strip: The Mystery of the Lizard Men (32), Jonny Quest #1 reprint
Text stories: Capers On Capri, The Plot on Power Island, Black Gold, The Town of Lost Men, The Riddle of Shark Bay
©1966   £20 $32
©1966 (96pg) (fc)
Text stories: The Secret of Pirate's Cove, Bandit Bounds In, The Giant 'Eye' On Space (Jodrell Bank tour), The Isle of Cats, Crater Capers, The Ruby Ray
Based on the Hanna Barbera animated adventure series

JOHN WAYNE Adventure (World)
1954-1960   £20 $32
1954-1956   £20 $32
©1955 (96pg) (tc)
Comic Strips: John Wayne - Festival in La Tamale (12)
Reprints U.S. comic by Toby Press
Red Hawk - Lands Beyond the Sunset (6), Art: Bob Powell
Straight Arrow - Danger Trail (7), Return From Death (7)
Reprints U.S. comic by Magazine Enterprises
Travel and Transportation on the Old Trails (1pg)
Text Stories: Steve Sawyer-Indian Fighter by Zed Montana, The Last Stage to Tucson by Frank L. Austin, The Spook of Hoe-Down Hollow by Clinton Stewart, Black Bart has the Last Laugh by Zed Montana, Apprentice Texas Ranger by Cal Hawkins, Silver Legs to the Rescue by Zachary Farland
1957   £25 $40
1958-1959   £20 $32
1960   £25 $40
Based on the movie star

JOLLY GNOMES
1950's   £15 $24

JUDGE DREDD (Fleetway)
1981-1995
1981 (96pg)   £15 $24

Judy 1965

Judy 1970

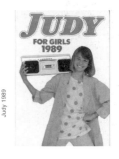

Judy 1989

Comic Strips: Pinboing Wizard (6fc), Writer: John Howard, Art: Mike McMahon
Max Normal The Pinstripe Freak! (11bw), Writer: A. A. Grant, Art: Casanovas
Compulsory Purchase (7fc) Writer: John Howard, Art: Mike McMahon
The Fear that Made Milwaukee Famous! (16fc), Writer: John Howard, Art: Mike McMahon
Walter the Wobot (8bw), Writer: G. P. Rice, Art: B. McCarthy
Shok! Walter's Robo-Tale (6bw), Writer: Rogan/O'Neill, Art: O'Neill
Includes a feature on the history of Judge Dredd and the first Judge Dredd comic strip story
1982   £12 $19
1983-1989   £10 $16
1985
Comic Strips: The Big Bang Theory, Writer: Alan Grant, Art: Ezquerra
Judge Anderson, Writer: Grant/Grover, Art: Emberton
Judge Dredd, Writer: John Wagner, Art: Gibson/McMahon
Tarantula, Writer: T B Grover, Art: Ezquerra
Dredd's Dozen, Writer: John Wagner and Alan Grant, Art: Ron Smith
In the Eat of the Night, Writer: T B Grover, Art: Ezquerra
1990-1995   £8 $13
Based on the 2000AD comic character
JUDY For Girls (D.C. Thomson)
1960's-1990's
1960's   £10 $16
©1966 (128pg) (fc/tc)
Comic Strips: Bobtail the Beach Rescue, Collen and the Last Witch, Fay Farrell Ship's Nurse, Bobby Dazzler, Petra the Party Maker, Katy's Casebook, The Hobbies of Holly, Sandra and the Vengeance Ballet, Margot Fonteyn, Skinflint School, Figures of Fun,Topsy and the Holiday Camp Spy, Weird World
Picture Strip: 'Harry Secombe'
1969 (128pg)
Comic Strips: Fay Farrell (4fc), The Hobbies of Holly (6fc), Topsy on her Toes (6fc), Our Class (2tc), Me and My Family (4tc), Wee Slavey (2tc), Fiona of the Fells (3tc), Lorna's Leprechaun (4tc), Junior Nanny (2tc), Mandy at the Mobile Zoo (2tc), The Girl Who Could Do Anything (6fc), The Dreams of Alwyn (4tc), Annie's Ark (2tc), Sandra and the Captive Ballet (8tc), Bobby Dazzler (6tc), Skinflint School (5fc), Bobtail The Beach Rescue (5fc)
Picture Strip: Spike Milligan
1970's   £8 $13
1975 (128pg)
Picture Strip: Beatles Growing Up
1976 (128pg)
Picture Strip: Carly Simon
1979 (128pg)
Comic Strips: The Summer House (7fc), Art: Coffond
Contest for Katie (3fc), Val of the Valley (4fc), The Hobbies of Holly (4), Rod Hull & Emus (3), Big Spender (5fc), Bobby Dazzler (4fc), Junior Nanny (4tc), Boyfriends (2tc), Skinflint School (4tc), Schoolgirl Veg (5tc), Saucy Sal (6tc), Roger de Courcey (2fc), Big Sister (3fc), Wee Slavey (5fc), Orphan Island (2fc)
Illustrated Pin Up: David Soul, Mike Yarwood
Pin Ups: The Carpenters
Features: The Goodies, The Muppet Show, London Palladium
1980's-1990's   £5 $8
1980 (128pg fc/tc)

Comic Strips: Hobbies of Holly (3), Gentle Jenny (6), Wee Slavey (3), Meet Johnny Nash (2), Schoolgirl Vet (3), The Fish Twins (5), First Time Faith (3), Danger Men at Work (2),Cora Cupid (3), Val of The Valley (4), Junior Nanny (4), Dark Danger (6), Bobby Dazzler (3), Meet Wings (3), The Ghost of The Grange (5), Orphan Island (5), The Homecoming (4)
Pin Ups: Elton John, Cliff Richard
1981 (128pg)
Comic Strips: Cora Cupid, Wee Slavey, First-Time Faith, Big 'N' Bertha, Schoolgirl Vet, Boyfriends, Junior Nanny, Danger, Min at Work!, Kenny Everett, Terror For Tina, The Immortal Dancer
Illustrated Pin Ups: John Travolta, David Soul
Pin Ups: David Essex
1982 (128pg)
Comic Strips: Lost Saturday, Junior Nanny, Danger, Min at Work!, Wee Slavey, Big 'N' Bertha, Born To Dance, Cora Cupid, Schoolgirl Vet, Bobby Dazzler, First-Time Faith, Boyfriends, The Haunted Churchyard, Party Girl
Photo Strip: The Racket
1983 (128pg) (fc/tc)
Comic Strips: Mother Goose (5), Tulips (5), Wee Slavey (3), Junior Nanny (3), Bobby Dazzler (2), Girl with The Golden Smile (3), Stranger in The Snow (5), Val of The Valley (5), Cora Cupid (3), Trial Run (5), Schoolgirl Vet (3), Big 'N' Bertha (2), Superbabe (5), Well Kept Secret (2), Anita's Butler (3), The Toymakers Daughter (6), Hearts to Mend (3), Secret Skater (5), Danger Min at Work (2), Betty's Bloodhound Butler (3), The Bond (4), Hunted (6).
Illustrated Pin Ups: Noel Edmonds, Peter Davison
1986 (128pg)
Comic Strips: The Mirror (4), Junior Nanny (3), Liz's Lucky Day (3), Mother Goose (2), Wee Slavey (2), In Loving Memory (4), School Girl Vet (3), A Friend of Mine (3), Cora Cupid (3), Big 'N' Bertha (2), The Joker (5), Girl With The Golden Smile (3), A Shy Sort of Girl (5), Stay at Home (5), Secret of The Cromlech (5), Community Nurse (3), Katie's Cat (5), Bobby Dazzler (2), Waiting for Tomorrow (5
1988 (128pg)
Comic Strips: Appointment with Fear, (5), Wee Slavey (3), Granny Handy's Candy (3), The House on the Hill (3), Junior Nanny (3), The Ghost Hunters (5), Superstitious Sal (5), Harvey Go Home (2), Bobby Dazzler (3), A Sprig of White Heather (3), Cinderella Jones (3), Cora Cupid (3), Community Nurse (3), Homefinder Hilary (3), Mother Goose (3), Magic Moments (5), The Gift (4), Schoolgirl Vet (3), Waiting (4), Exhibit 134 (5), Two Shy People (4)
1990 (128pg)
Comic Strips: Bobby Dazzler, Judy & Co., Cinderella Jones, Pepper the Pony, Wee Slavey, Junior Nanny, A Package for Paula, The Ghost of Armley Fell, Laura's Lesson, Jinny's Journey, Saturday Date, Lost on the Moor, Dog
Photo Strip (fc): Night of the Cat
Based on the UK girls comic
JUNE (Fleetway)
1960's   £10 $16
1962 (128pg)
Comic Strips: Kathy at Marvin Grange School (6bw), Cloris & Claire (2bw), Dianas Diary (8fc), Baby Mandy (6bw), The Wonder Dog (6bw), Jenny (2tc), Sally at the Island Hospital (5bw), Susan Gets Her Story (4tc)
Stories: The Five Find-Outers and Dog in Tackle the Mystery Sneak Theif by Enid Blyton - Art: D.C.E.
Who'll Take Care of Sharon? - Writer: Alice Terry

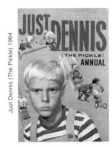

Just Dennis (The Pickle) 1964

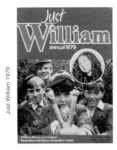

Just William 1979

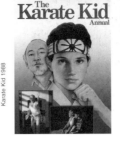

Karate Kid 1988

Tina and the Dancing Team - Writer: E. Norbury
Flower-Girl Ann - Writer: P. G. Bird
Home for a Gypsy - Writer: Sarah Flower
Stellas Jungle Pet - Writer: Sarah Flower
1963 (128pg)
Comic Strips: Kathy at Marvin Grange School (6bw), Cloris and
Claire (2bw), Jenny (2fc),
Text Stories: My Friend Pavlo - Writer: Gerald Durrell
Cottage For Sale - Writer: Frances Cowen
Pepita and the TV Star - Writer: Jane Higgins
Hunt the Smuggler - Writer: Michael Bennett
Happy Birthday Mr President - No Credits
Dixie of Dockland - Writer: J. W. Jennison
1969 (128pg)
Comic Strips: Lucky's Living Doll (6fc), Vanessa from Venus (6tc),
Jenny (1tc), Girl Gulliver in Space (7bw), Bessie Bunter (2tc), The
Ghost of Wild Jack (8tc), The Frightened Nurse (3tc), Melody From
the Past (6tc), Fancy to the Rescue (6bw), Bessie Bunter (4bw),
Kathy at Marvin Grange (6tc), Jenny (1fc), Zanna of the Jungle (8fc)
Text Stories: Bobs of Bowmans Green - Writer: Jane Derwent
Cherrys Biggest Prize - No Credits
The Campers in Creepy Castle - Writer: Jean Theydon
The Donkey and the Knight - No Credits
Peggy and Patch - No Credits
Oh Lucky Sue - Writer: Denise Barry
1970's   £7   £11
Based on the UK girls comic

JURASSIC PARK (Grandreams)
N/D Estimate 1992   £5 $8
Writer: Tony Lynch, Editor Melanie J Clayden, Design by Louise
Ivimy and Susan Bartram
Adapted from the original Jurassic Park script
Includes photos (fc) from the film
Based on the Steven Spielberg movie

JUST DENNIS (The Pickle) (World)
1964
©1963 (96pg)   £15 $24
Comic Strips (fc): Colour Crazy (10), Plane Foolish (11), Dennis in
Orbit (5), Shortys Tall Stories (3x4), Dennis Acts Up (11), Scrambled
Shopping (9), Chinese Happy New Year (8), Scary Stuff (3), Pitter
Patter Painter (9)
Fawcett Comics reprints
Photo Cover
Based on the US TV comedy series

JUST DENNIS Bumper TV Book (Peveril)
1963   £15 $24
Photo cover
Based on the US TV comedy series

JUST WILLIAM (World)
1978-1979   £5 $8
1978 (64pg)
Comic Strips: William's Worrying Day, The Prince of Sheba
Art: Edgar Hodges
Photo Cover
1979 (64pg)
Comic Strips: Williams at the Circus, William's Trying Day, William
and the Wandering Spirit
Art: Edgar Hodges
Photo Strip: Fancy Bargain

Photo Cover
Based on the Childrens ITV series starring Bonnie Langford
KARATE KID (Grandreams)
1988-1989
©1987 (64pg)   £7 $11
Comic Strip: Turning the Tables (8 bw)
Includes photos (fc) and profile of the stars
Based on the movie starring Ralph Macchio and Pat Morita
KEN DODD'S DIDDYMEN (World)
1974   £10 $16
Based on the UK comedian
KENNETH WOLSTENHOLME'S BOOK OF WORLD
SOCCER (World)
1960's (128pg bw)   £8 $13
©1965
Bobby Charlton photo cover (fc)
Based on the UK soccer commentator
KENNY (World)
1977 (80pg)   £6 $10
Pinups and Profiles of the Band
Based on the UK pop group
KENNY DALGLISH SOCCER Annual (Brown Watson)
1980
©1979 (64pg)   £5 $8
Features: Ray Clemence, Danny McGrain, Paul Breitner, Bobby
Murdoch, Franz Beckenbauer, Daniel Passarella, Rivelino, Denis
Law, Johan Cruyff, Pele, George Best
Based on the UK soccer star
KENNY EVERETT VIDEO SHOW (Stafford Pemberton)
1980-1981   £8 $13
Based on the TV show
KEVIN KEEGAN'S BOOK OF BRITISH FOOTBALL (World)
1981   £5 $8
Based on the UK soccer star
KEVIN KEEGAN'S SOCCER ANNUAL (World)
1977-1978 (64pg)   £6 $10
Based on the UK soccer star
KEYPERS (Fleetway)
1988-1990   £5 $8
1990 (64pg fc)
Picture Strips: The Music Maker, The Land of Games, Letterland,
Rainbow Treasure
Art: John Donnelly
Based on the toy range
KIDDYFUN (Swan)
1950   £20 $32
KIT CARSON (Amalgamated Press)
1954-1959
1954 (1st) (116pg)   £25 $40
Cover and frontpiece Art: D.C. Eyles
Comic Strips: Kit Carson Drives 'Em West (14fc), Art : D. C. Eyles
Buffalo Bill in Rescued From The Redskins (2bw), Kit Carson and
the Army Deserters (16fc), Buffalo Bill's Close Call (2bw), Kit Carson
and the Rodeo Raiders (10fc), Kit Carson and the Iron Horse (6fc)
Contains three full-colour plates by D. C. Eyles
1955-1959   £20 $32
1956
Comic Strips: Kit Carson and the Wonder-Guns (12fc), Here comes

K-9 1983

Kojak 1978

Kung Fu 1976

Billy the Kid (5bw), Kit Carson and the Kiowa Fury (16fc), Billy the Kid and the Mystery of Injun Joe (6 bw), Buffalo Bill and the Golden Lance of the Pawnees (2bw), Kit Carson Battles Through (16fc), Buck Jones and the Red Bandit (21bw)
1958 (114pg)
Comic Strips: Desert Battle-Wagons (fc), Wins Through (fc), Outlaw (bw), Kit Carson and the Wild Stallion (fc), Davy Crockett and the Prairie Gypsies (bw)
Based on characters appearing in Sun and Comet UK comics

KLONDIKE (United Artists)
1961 £12 $19
Writer: George Adamson. Art: Eric Dadswell and Pat Williams
Based on the Television Series

K-9 (World)
1983 (64pg) £15 $24
Cover Art/Endpaper: Glenn Rix
Text stories and features
Photo/Illustrated Cover
Based on the BBC TV Dr Who spin-off

KNIGHT RIDER (Grandreams)
1983 -1987
©1982 (64pg)
Cover Price - £2.75 (1983 annual) £8 $13
Cover - Knight Rider logo in red with blue shadow
Comic Strips (lw): Knight Rider (2), Break out (6), Devil Valley (8)
©1982 (64pg)
Cover Price - £2.95 (1984 annual) £8 $13
Cover - Knight Rider logo in yellow with red shadow
Comic Strips: Beware of Imitations, Crime Buster Kitt
©1982 (64pg)
Cover Price - £3.25 (1985 annual) £8 $13
Cover - Knight Rider logo in yellow with black shadow
Comic Strips:
©1982 (64pg)
Cover Price - £3.50 (1986 annual) (Scarce) £10 $16
Cover - Knight Rider logo in yellow with brown shadow (black background)
Comic Strips: Kitt - Napped, Rallying Cry
©1982 (64pg)
Cover Price - £3.75 (1987 annual) (Scarce) £10 $16
Cover - Knight Rider logo in red with yellow shadow (black background)
Comic Strips: Kitt - "Knight Rider" (2bw), Deadly Game (8fc), Hunted (8bw)
Based on the TV series starring David Hasselhoff

KNOCKOUT FUN Book (Amalgamated Press)
1941-1962
1950-1959 £15 $24
1960-1962 £12 $19

KNOCKOUT (Fleetway)
1970's-1980's
1970's £7 $11
1970's £6 $10
1981 (128pg)
Comic Strips: Sammy Shrink, Sonny Storm, Beat your Neighbour, Little Devil, The Toffs and Toughs, Super Seven,Go for Golden, The Haunted Wood, Son of Sir, Pete's Pockets, Joker, Gary's Glider, Moose, Speed family in Space, Boney, My Bruvver, Fuss Pot
Based on the UK comic

KOJAK (Stafford Pemberton)
1977-1979 £8 $13
1977 (64pg)
Comic Strips: Double Talk (5fc), A Christmas Caper (4fc), Hot Pictures (4fc)
Art: Melvyn Powell
Feature: Telly Savalas (6pg)
Photo Cover
1978
Illustrated Cover
1979 (64pg)
Comic Strips: Where's Crocker (6fc), The Wedding Party (7fc), Amateur Night (6fc)
Photo Cover
Based on the TV Series starring Telly Savalas

KRANKIES (Grandreams)
1983 £6 $10
Comic Strips: Tea for Two Only (bw), Joking with Jimmy, (bw) Drumming up trouble (bw), Classroom Comics (fc), Jimmy the Menace (fc), Just Jimmy (fc), Putting on a brave face (fc), Jump to It (bw), The Audition (bw) Putting on the Agony (bw), It's Hard Work Relaxing (bw)
Based on the UK comedy duo

KRAZY (Fleetway)
1970's-1980's (96pg)
1970's £7 $11
1980's £5 $8
1985
Comic Strips include: Buytonic Boy, Kelly's Telly, Pongalongapongo, The Krazy Gang, Hit Kid, The World's Worst..., Gong'of Kong, Handy Andy, Birdman and Chicken
Based on the UK comic

KUNG FU (Brown Watson)
1975-1977 £10 $16
©1974
Comic Strips: The Bounty Hunter, The Rustlers, Dream Shadow
Comic Strip art: Demond Walduck, Text story art: Melvyn Powell
Writer: Steve Moore
©1975
Comic Strips: Quest of Peril, The Savage Four, Indian War
Based on the TV series starring David Carradine

KYLIE MINOGUE (Grandreams/World)
1989-1991 £7 $11
1989 (Grandreams) features Jason Donovan
©1990 Special(Grandreams)
©1990
Photo features (fc)
1990-1991 (World) (64pg)
Writer: Chrissie Camp
Photo features (fc)
Based on the Australian soap star/pop singer

LADY LOVELY LOCKS and the PIXIETAILS (Marvel)
1989 (64pg) (fc) £8 $13
Comic Strips: The Rescue! (7), The Enchanted Island! (12), A Prince's Tale! (6)
Based on the toy range

LADY PENELOPE/PENELOPE (City/Century21/IPC)
1967-1972
©1966 (96pg) £25 $40

Laff-A-Lympics 1980

Lamb Chop and Charlie Horse 1980

Laurel and Hardy 1970

Comic Strips: Undercover Secretary (fc), Perils of Parker (3fc),
Marina in Rescue in Titanica (4fc), The Everglades Affair (8fc),
Space Family Robinson - Tam meets the Trydans (5fc), The Man
from Uncle (4fc), Stay Healthy and Die (7fc)
Features: The Walker Brothers, Adrienne Posta
1968-1969 £20 $32
©1968 (96pg)
Comic Strips (fc): Lady Penelope in Symphony of Death (7), Duel in
the Jungle (6), Perils of Parker (2x2), The Monkees in Once Upon A
Time (6), What Did That Dog Say? (2x2), The Spectrum (4),
Sobotage Session (8) - Art: Frank Langford
Captain Scarlet in Apres Ski (5) - Art: Frank Langford
Bewitched (3) - Art: Bill Titcombe
Includes The Angels photo text story 'Deadly Decoy' (4), Penny's
4/Shot Beatles Diary 1963-68 (4) and Behind the Scenes with The
Tremeloes (4)
Pin Ups (fc): The Beach Boys, The Bee Gees and Dave Deee,
Beaky, Mick and Tich
1970 £15 $24
©1969 (96pg)
Comic Strips (fc): Penelope meets The Guru (6), What Did That Dog
Say? (2x2), Perils of Parker (2x2), Class Six Sterndorf in Signal
S.O.S. (5), Lady Penelope in Icebourg (6), Penelope in Double
Trouble (8), Night Caller (5) - Art: Frank Langford
A Ghost On Saturday (5) - Art: Frank Langford
Up, Up and Away (5) - Art: Frank Langford
Pin Ups (fc): Dave Dee, Long John Baldry, Engelbert Humperdinck,
Anita Harris, Manfred Mann, Tom Jones
1971-1972 £10 $16
Entitled 'Penelope Annual' from 1969
Based on the UK girls comic

LAFF-A-LYMPICS Cartoon Annual (World/Fleetway)
'Hanna Babera'
1980-1981 £10 $16
©1980
Comic Strips: The Miraculous Moon Meet (bw), Writer: Mark
Evanier, Art: Owen Fitzgerald, Inks: Scott Shaw
The Discount of Monte Cristo (bw), Writer: Mark Evanier, Art:
Roman Arambula, Inks: Scott Shaw
No Game Today...The Yogi Yahooeys, The Scooby Doobies, The
Really Rottens (bw), Writer: Mark Evanier-Art: Scott Shaw, Dan
Spiegle, Jack Manning
Now You See Them... (fc/bw), Writer: Mark Evanier, Art: Paul Norris,
Roman Arambula & Scott Shaw
Two variants of the 1980 annual exist. One version has '1980'
missing from the cover

LAMB CHOP (World)
1972 £8 $13
Shari Lewis photo cover
Based on the BBC TV series

LAMB CHOP and CHARLIE HORSE Shari Lewis (World)
1980 £8 $13
Writter: Frances Lindsay
Based on the BBC TV series

LANCER (World)
1970 (96pg) (fc) £12 $19
Dell reprint and UK text stories
Based on the TV Western series starring James Stacy and Wayne
Maunder

LAND OF THE GIANTS (World)
1970-1971
1970 £15 $24
©1969 (96pg) (fc/tc)
Comic Strip (fc): The Mini-Criminals (26 two-part)
Gold Key reprint and UK text stories
Photo cover
1971 £12 $19
©1970 (96pg) (fc/tc)
Comic Strips: Operation Mini-Surgeon (26 two-part)
Based on the Irwin Allen TV Series

LAND OF THE GIANTS Television Story Book (PBS)
1969 £12 $19
Based on the Irwin Allen TV Series

LARAMIE (World/Purnell/Dean & Son)
1960-1965
1961 £20 $32
1962-1965 £15 $24
©1961
Writer: Alex Gifford-Art: Patrick Williams
©1962 (Purnell) (96pg) (bw)
Writer: Gordon Grimsley-Art: Alex Henderson
Comic Strips (8x3bw): Snowbound, The Quiet Town, Mike the
Nursemaid-Robert Fuller/John Smith Photo cover
©1963 (Purnell)
Writer: Gordon Grimsley, Art: John Burns
©1964 (Dean)
Art: John Burns
Based on the TV Western series starring Robert Fuller

LAREDO (World)
1966 (96pg) (fc) (Scarce) £15 $24
Dell strip reprints and UK text stories
Photo cover
Based on the TV western series starring William Smith and Neville
Brand

LAUREL & HARDY LARRY HARMON'S (Brown Watson)
1970-1975
©1969 (96pg) £15 $24
Comic Strips: The Cold Gold Caper, Salt Water Daffies
1971 on £10 $16
©1972 - No.1
Comic Strips (fc): Rocketship Rumpus, The Puppy, The Aerial, The
Treasure House, Washing The Car, Private Detectives, Self
Defence,
©1973
Comic Strips (fc): In Days of Olde, The Home-Made Car, Treasure
Trail, The Piggy-Bank, The New House, Hair Lotion
©1974
Comic Strips (fc): Absent Minded Sam, The Horoscope, Mystery Story,
Art Appreciation, The Chef, Olly's Plane, Stan the Painter
©1977 (64pg)
Comic Strips: Where's That Fire! (11tc), Picnic (7fc), The Cross
Country Race (8fc), Shopping Expedition (6fc)

LARRY THE LAMB (Grandreams)
1982
©1981 £7 $11
Picture Strips: Dennis - The Circus Star (3fc), The Lost Key (1tc),
Larry's Surprise Birthday Party (2tc), The Magic Spell (2tc), Who
Stole the Cream? (2tc), A Life on the Ocean Waves (2tc), The

Arkville Dragon (1tc), Toytown's Untidy (1tc), Penny for the Guy (2tc), The Skating Contest (2tc), Day at the Seaside (1fc)The New Coach Horn (1fc), Good Luck - Bad Luck (1fc), Larry the Fireman (2fc)
Photo Stories: Larry's Luck (4), A Christmas Scare in Toy Town (4)
Text Stories: The Pirate's Holiday Cruise, The Toytown Carnival, Based on the Childrens TV show

LASSIE Television Storybook (Swan)
1960	£15	$24

LEGEND OF CUSTER (Atlas)
1968 (Scarce)	£15	$24

Based on the TV Western series starring Wayne Maunder

LENNY THE LION's (Daily Mirror)
1960-1964
1960	£15	$24

©1959
1961-1964	£10	$16

Based on the popular UK hand puppet

LETTERLAND (Collins)
2000-present	£4	$7

LEONARDO DiCAPRIO 100% Unofficial Special (Grandreams)
1999-2000
©1998-99	£5	$8

LES FERDINAND (Grandreams)
1997
©1996 (64pg)	£4	$7

Writer: Les Ferdinand and Tony Lynch
Based on the Newcastle United soccer star

LION (AP/Fleetway)
1954-1983 (128pg bw)
1954	£40	$60
1955	£30	$48
1956-1958	£20	$32
1959-1964	£10	$16
1965-1969	£8	$13
1970-1983	£6	$10

Comic Strips include: Phantom Force 5, Paddy Payne, Trelawny of the Guards, Adam Eterno, The Spooks of St Luke's and Robot Archie
Based on the UK comic

LION BOOK OF SPEED (Fleetway)
1963	£10	$16

LION BOOK OF WAR ADVENTURES (Fleetway Five Star)
1962 (140pg)	£12	$19

Comic Strips, text stories and features (bw). Full colour endpapers and two features

LITTLE GREEN MAN (Grandreams)
1985	£5	$8

LITTLE MISS & MISSES (World)
1990's	£5	$8

Based on Roger Hargreaves characters

LITTLE MONSTERS (Grandreams)
2000	£4	$7

From a concept by Tony Garth

LITTLE STAR (D.C. Thomson)
'Specially for little girls and little boys'
1978-1985	£5	$8

1978
1985 (64pg)
Picture Strips include (fc): Tiny and Tim, Goody Gumdrops, Fizzle, the Fiery Dragon, Wuff, Fenella the Forgetful Fairy
Based on the UK comic

LIVERPOOL Soccer Special (Grandreams)
1980's-1990's	£5	$8

LOGAN'S RUN (Brown Watson)
1979
©1978 (64pg)	£8	$13

Comic Strips: Logan's World (3tc), Sunrise...Moonset (8fc), City of the Nighthawks (8tc), Art: David Lloyd
Includes text stories and photo profiles on Gregory Harrison, Heather Menzies and Donald Moffat
Photo cover
Based on the TV sci-fi series

LONE RANGER (Adprint/world /Brown Watson)
1953-1970's
©1952 (World)	£25	$40

Comic Strips (fc): Double Ambush, Garland's Grudge, Young Hawk, Terror Trail, Annie Oakley (Little Sure Shot), The Wagon Train, Young Hawk and his Friends - Dell reprints
Text stories: Four Good Legs, The Hide of the Bull
N/D (World) (96pg) Priced at 7/6
Cover Art: Lone Ranger on Silver being held up at gunpoint by an outlaw wearing a red shirt
Comic Strips (fc): Rustler's Hide-Out (12), Stand-Ins For Murder (15), Unwelcome Visitors (15), The Outlaw's Fiancee (12), The Law Lady (8), Young Hawk in Grand Canyon Adventure (10), Young Hawk (7) - Dell reprints
1953-1955	£20	$32
1956-1959	£15	$24
1960's	£10	$16

N/D (World) (96pg) Priced at 7/6
Cover Art: Lone Ranger knee-deep in a river punching an outlaw wearing a red shirt
Comic Strips include (fc): Rocky Ridge Mystery, Apache Peril, Across the Canyon, Young Hawk
Includes Lone Ranger #72 reprints
1964 (World)
Text stories: Douglas Enefer, Joe Morrisey, Mae Broadley, J.W. Elliot
Art: Walter Howarth
1970's	£8	$13

©1975 (Brown Watson)
Endpaper features photos from the classic TV series (fc)
Comic Strips (fc): The Story of the Lone Ranger, The Story of Tonto, The Fanned Six-Gun, Ranger Jim's Ordeal, Garland's Grudge,The Law Lady - Reprints Lone Ranger #1
©1976 (Brown Watson)
Text stories art: John Bolton
Comic Strips: The Sacred Cave (tc), The Renegade Leader (fc), Tell-Tale Trail (fc), The Dangerous Escort (fc), The Vanished Gold Dust (fc), The Haunted Cave (fc), The Terrorized Town (fc), Reward For Sam (tc)
Lone Ranger #6 and #8 reprints

LONE RANGER ADVENTURE STORIES (Adprint)
1958-1961
No1 - ©1957	£20	$32

Movie adaptation by Arthur Groom

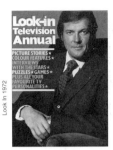
Look In 1972

Look In 1974

Look In 1978

LO

No 2 -©1958   £15 $24
©1958 (96pg) (fc/bw)
Adapted by Richard Lewis from the Television Series
Text stories: The Law and Miss Aggie, Decision for Chris McKeever,
The Angel and the Outlaw, A Harp for Hannah, Dead-Eye, Journey
to San Carlos - Art: Don Lawrence
Photo cover (fc)
©1959-©1960   £12 $19
©1959
Text stories: Richard Lewis - Art: Don Lawrence
©1960
Text stories: David Roberts - Art: Eric Dadswell
LONE RANGER Television Picture Story Book (PBS)
1963, 1967
1963   £12 $19
1967   £10 $16
LONE STAR (Atlas)
1940's-1950's   £15 $24
1958
Featuring Ace Cowboy Steve Larrabee, Space Ace, Captain Dirk
Cutlass and Trooper Bill Archer
1959 - No. 10
LONE STAR WESTERN
1960-1970   £12 $19
LOOK AND LEARN Book For Boys (Amalgamated/Fleetway)
1962-1980's
1962 (Scarce) - with dustjacket   £15 $24
1962 - without dustjacket   £10 $16
1963-1965   £12 $16
1966-1969   £10 $16
1970-1975   £8 $13
1976-1980's   £5 $8
1980 (128pg) (fc/tc/bw)
Educational features (art/photo)
Features : Cheats Had a Hard Time in Olympia, The Roaming
Romanies, The Fighters Who Knew No Fear (the Boxers), The
Wrights Proved Them Wrong (Wright Brothers), Strange Secret of
the Stone Circle (Stonehenge), When Sinbad Sailed The Seas,
Jaws of Death, The Pretender Kings, Devil Dance, The Boy From
the Backwoods (Abraham Lincoln), The 'Angel' Who Went to Prison
(Elizabeth Fry), The Sahara, Campbell- The Record Breaker, The
Sad Empress (Josephine), Test Match Triumph (Jim Laker), Race of
a Thousand Corners (Monaco GP), The Lionheart's Prison,
Everyone Loves Dubrovnik, Birds of Legend
LOOK AND LEARN Book of Speed & Power (Fleetway)
1979 (80pg)   £8 $13
LOOK-IN FASHION MODEL (ITP)
1971   £8 $13
LOOK IN TELEVISION ANNUAL (ITP)
1972-1991
©1971 (96pg)   £15 $24
Cover features: Roger Moore
Front Endpaper: Please Sir cast
Rear Endpaper: Behind the Scenes of a TV Studio
Comic Strips: Please Sir (2fc), Brights Boffins (2x2bw), Please Sir
(3bw), Crowther in Trouble (2bw), Timeslip (6bw), Please Sir (2bw)
Feature: Timeslip, Magpie, World of Sport, Roger Moore (The
Persuader), Leslie Crowther, Catweazle,
Pin Ups: Richard Davies, Eric Flynn, David Nixon, Reg Varney, Sid

James, Ayshea, Deryck Guyler, John Alderton
Roger Moore photo cover
1973-1980   £10 $16
©1972 (94pg)
Cover features: Catweazle, Leslie Crowther, On the Buses
Cover Art: Arthur Ranson
Front Endpaper: Follyfoot
Rear Endpaper: Junior Showtime Studios
Comic Strips: Please Sir (2x2fc), Writer: John Esmonde & Bob
Larbey, Catweazle (6bw), Crowther in Trouble (2x2bw), The Fenn
Street Gang (2x2bw) Writer: John Esmonde & Bob Larbey,
On the Buses (2fc/2bw) Writer: Ronald Wolfe & Ronald Chesney,
Follyfoot (6bw), On the Buses (4bw), Writer: Ronald Wolfe & Ronald
Chesney, Art: Harry North,
Text Story: The Treasure of Oak Island (2bw), Art: Angus McBride,
No Through Road (3), UFO (2)
Features: Jack Hargreaves, Doctor in the House, Walt Disney, Colin
Blunstone, Bring em back alive (big game hunting)
Small Features: Gary Warren, Jack Wild, Mark Lester, Tom Jones,
Burt Bacharach, Dionne Warwicke, The Carpenters,
Pin Ups: Steve Hodson, Gillian Blake, Ed "Stewpot" Stewart, Peter
Cleall, Carol Hawkins, Rolf Harris, Wendy Padbury, Adrian Wright
©1973 (96pg)
Cover Art: Arthur Ranson
Front Endpaper: Black Arrow
Rear Endpaper: Arthur of the Britons
Comic Strips: Les Dawson Superflop (3x2fc/bw), Pathfinders (6bw),
Ken Goodwin (2bw), David Cassidy (6bw), Ken Goodwin (2bw)
Photo Text Stories: On the Buses - Blakey Falls in Love, Writer:
Ronald Wolfe & Ronald Chesney
Fenn Street Gang, Writer: John Edmonde and Bob Larvey
Features: Gone Fishing with Jack Hargreaves, Behind the News at
Ten
Small Features: Follyfoot, The Osmonds, The Sweets, David
Cassidy, On the Buses, Bless this House, Black Beauty, Skippy
Pin Ups - Tony Anholt, Robert Vaughn, David Cassidy, Gillian Blake,
Steve Hodson, Gunter Netzer, Kevin Keegan
©1974 (96pg)
Cover features: Sid James, David Essex, Ed Stewart, Robin Nedwell
Cover Art: Arnaldo Putzu
Front Endpaper: Black Beauty
Rear Endpaper: Boy Dominic
Comic Strips: Michael Bentines Potty Time (2fc), Kung Fu (4bw),
Doctor at Sea (2x4bw/2bw), Bless this House (2bw), Black Beauty
(5bw), The Tomorrow People (6bw)
Photo Text Story: Bless this House (4pg) featuring Sid James
Features: Behind the scenes with Stewpot, The Making of Man
About the House, Leeds United (War of the Roses), Collecting
Stamps, The Year of Kung Fu (David Carradine), Survivial Special,
Young Cook of the year 1974 (Dawn Hanley)
Small Features: Alvin Stardust, David Essex, Gary Glitter, Olga
Korbut, Ilie Nastase, Anne Moore, John Conteh, Geoffrey Boycott,
Filbert Bayi
Pin Ups: Alvin Stardust, Slade, Gary Glitter, David Essex, David
Cassidy, Allan Clarke, Mick Channon, The Osmonds, Ben Murphy,
Robin Newell, Mick Robertson, The Sweet, Suzi Quatro
©1975 (80pg)
Cover features Bay City Rollers
Cover painting by Arnaldo Putzu
Front Endpaper: The Tomorrow People

Look In 1981

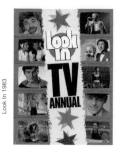
Look In 1983

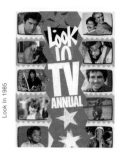
Look In 1985

Rear Endpaper: LWT's Control Room
Comic Strips: Benny Hill (2bw), Bless this House (2bw), Doctor on the Go (2bw), The Tomorrow People (5bw)
Text Story: Rogue's Rock: The Agents of Doom (4)
Features: Stamps on Stamps by Michael Clarke, Clangers, Arnaldo Putzu (artist)
Small Features: Space 1999, UFO, Bay City Rollers,
Illustrated Pin Ups: Mick Robertson, Planet of the Apes
Pin Ups - Planet of the Apes, Tomorrow People, Pilot, David Essex, Mervyn Day, Alan Hudson, Steve Harley, Alvin Stardust
©1976 (80pg)
Cover Features: Six Million Dollar Man,
Cover Illustration: Arnaldo Putzu
Front Endpaper: Flintlock
Rear Endpaper: Mike Reid
Comic Strips: Man about the House (2bw), The Benny Hill (2bw), The Tomorrow People (4bw), Doctor on the Go (2bw)
Text Story: Space 1999 (4)
Features : Gerry Anderson (4), Flintlock (Mike Holoway), Lee Majors (2), History of Television (4), Magpie Team at Warwick Castle, Stamp collecting (sporting stamps)
Small Features: Bay City Rollers, Showaddywaddy, Queen, Slade, Dan Dare, Mickey Mouse, Look In, Comics
Pin Ups: Slik, Queen, Michael Holoway, Lee Majors, Kevin Keegan, Gordon Hill, Robin Nedwell, Geoffrey Davies
©1977 (80pg)
Cover Illustration by Arnaldo Putzu
Cover Features: Abba, Six Million Dollar Man, Bionic Woman, Kermit
Front Endpaper: The Tomorrow People
Rear Endpaper: Jesus of Nazareth
Comic Strips: Benny Hill (2bw), Doctor on the Go (2bw), Space 1999 (6bw)
Text Story: The Tomorrow People - Race Against Time (6bw)
Features - Bionic Woman Lindsay Wagner and Bionic Man Lee Majors (4), Muppets (4), Flockton Flyer, Flintlock (2), Gerry Anderson (2), Abba (2),
Small Features: Syd Little and Eddie Large, Stamp collecting (jubilees and anniversaries), Just William, James Bond (4)
Pin Ups - Lee Majors, Lindsay Wagner, Miss Piggy, Kermit, Flintlock, Trevor Francis, Ray "Butch" Wilkins, Abba
©1978 (80pg)
Cover Features: Abba, Fonz, Star Wars, Mickey Mouse, Lee Majors, Lindsay Wagner
Cover art: Arnaldo Putzu
Front Endpaper: Six Million Dollar Man
Rear Endpaper: The Muppet Show
Comic Strips: Benny Hill (2bw), The Tomorrow People (6bw)
Features - The Mindblowers (Daleks & UFO's) - 4 page feature, The Year of the UFO - 2 page feature, Swing along with Abba - 2 page feature, Ian Ogilvy (The Saint), Corgi Toy Factory, Skateboarding, The Tomorrow People, How (Fred Dinenage), The Songbirds (Debbie Harry, Bonnie Tyler, Elkie Brooks, etc.), Charlies Angels, The Famous Five, Happy Birthday Mickey Mouse, Lee Majors & Linsday Wagner
Pin Ups - Mark Hamill, Logan's Run, Abba, Henry Winkler, Ian Ogilvy, Shaun Cassidy, Kenny Dalglish, Steve Coppell, Donna Summer, Baccara, Charlie's Angels, Lee & Linsday
©1979 (80pg)
Cover features: John Travolta, Fonzie, Charlies Angels, Benny Hill, Elvis

Cover Art: Arnaldo Putzu
Front Endpaper: Famous Five
Rear Endpaper: Dick Turpin
Comic Strips: Benny Hill (2bw),
Space 1999 (10bw) - Writer: Angus Allan, Art: John Burns
Features - Sci Fi Shows, John Travolta, Joanna Lumley, Boney M, Famous Five, Benny Hill, Blondie, Richard O'Sullivan, Elvis, Charlies Angels, Fonzie
Pin Ups: Oswaldo Ardiles, Kevin Keegan
1981-1991   £8 $13
©1980 (80pg)
Cover Features: Bob Geldoff, Mork & Mindy, Sapphire & Steel, Superman, Sting, Worzel Gummidge
Cover Art: Arnaldo Putzu
Front Endpaper: Worzel Gummidge (Jon Pertwee)
Rear Endpaper: Benny Hill Show
Comic Strips: Abba - The Early Years (13bw)
Writer: Angus Allan, Art: Arthur Ranson
Features - Kenny Everett, Debbie Harry, The Muppets, Worzel Gummidge, The Smurfs, Charlies Angels, Laurel & Hardy, Eric & Ernie, Mork & Mindy, Tom Baker, Charlies Angels
Pin Ups: Jimmy Pursey, Bob Geldof, Sting, BJ and the Bear, Mork & Mindy
©1981 (80pg)
Cover features: Worzel Gummidge, Cliff Richard, Metal Mickey
Cover Art: Analdo Putzu
Front Endpaper: Bjorn Borg and Brian Moore
Rear Endpaper: Worzel Gummidge
Comic Strips - Black Beauty (7bw), Smurfs (2bw)
Text Story: Sapphire and Steel - The Albatross
Features - Special Effects, Cliff Richard, Metal Mickey, Smurfs
Pin Ups - The Police, Cliff Richard, Adam and the Ants, Buck Rogers in the 25th Century, Worzel Gummidge, ABBA
©1982 (80pg)
Cover Features: Lee Majors, Parker, Toyah, Bobby Ball, Adam Ant, Dangermouse, Sebastian Coe, Spiderman
Front Endpaper: Suggs of Madness
Rear Endpaper: Razzmatazz
Features - Pop Videos, Puppet Parade (Kermit, Emu etc.), Charades, Britains Cartoonists, Stuntman (Fall Guy and Spiderman), Pleased to Meet you - Cannon & Ball, Adam Ant, Toyah, Sebastian Coe, Nicholas Hammond (aka Spiderman), Lee Majors
Comic Strips - Cannon & Ball (2bw), Meet the Smurfs (10bw), Danger Mouse (2bw)
©1983 (80pg)
Cover Features: Matthew Kelly, Bucks Fizz, Christopher Reeve, Leoy, Freeway, Simon Le Bon, Keith Harris & Orville, Russ Abbot, Madness, June Croft
Front Endpaper: Boy George
Rear Endpaper: Cannon and Ball
Features: Shakin Stevens, Matthew Kelly, Christopher Reeve, June Croft, Simon Le Bon, Russ Abbot
Small Features Bucks Fizz, Madness, Human League, Lord Charles, Orville, Nookie, Emu, ET, Star Wars, Battlestar Galactica, Close Encounters, Star Trek, Space 1999, Freeways, Hart to Hart
Comic Strips - Cannon & Ball (2bw), Further Adventure of Oliver Twist (12bw) - Writer: Angus Allan, Art: Arthur Ranson, It's Madness (2bw)
©1984 (80pg)
Cover Features: Shakin Stevens, Knight Rider, Robin of Sherwood,

Look In 1988

Look In 1991

Look In TV Comedy 1975

LO

Tracey Ullman, Gary Coleman, Cannon and Ball, Mr T, Mick Robertson, Torville & Dean, Harrison Ford
Front Endpaper: Robin of Sherwood
Rear Endpaper: Thompson Twins
Featues: Harrison Ford, Boy George, Mick Robertson, Torville & Dean, Gary Coleman, Tracey Ullman
Small Features: James Bond, Logans Run, The Avengers, Mickey Mouse, Danger Mouse, Roland Rat, Robin of Shewood (starring Michael Praed), Knight Rider, Magnum, CHiPs, Doctor Who, Star Trek
Comic Strips: Cannon & Ball (2x2bw), Worzel Gummidge (11bw), Writer: Angus Allan, Art: Michael Noble, Cannon & Ball
1986 (First Dated Cover) (80pg)
Cover Features: Mr T, Nik Kershaw, Super Gran, Roland Rat, Zara Long, George Michael, Sue Robbie, Jan-Michael Vincent, Andy Ruffell, Dempsey & Makepeace.
Front Endpaper: Knight Rider
Rear Endpaper: Filming Super Gran
Features: George Michael, Jan-Michael Vincent, Roland Rat, Andy Ruffell, Mr T, Nik Kershaw, Soap Operas,
Small Features: Wham, Hart to Hart, Dempsey & Makepeace quiz
Comic Strips - Cannon & Ball (2x2bw), Dick Turpin featuring Richard O'Sullivan (15bw) Writer: Angus Allan, Art: Martin Asbury
1987 (80pg)
Cover features: Jason Connery, Aha, Hayley Price, Return of the Antelope, Tommy Boyd, Madonna, Five Star, Martin Bell, Boris Becker, Michael J Fox, Shakin Stevens
Front Endpaper: Return of the Antelope
Rear Endpaper: Airwolf
Features: Jason Connery, Madonna, Aha, Tommy Boyd, Boris Becker, Michael J Fox , Shakin Stevens
Comic Strips - Bobby Ball (2bw), The Fall Guy featuring Lee Majors (15bw) Writer: Angus Allan, Art: Jim Baikie, Shakin Stevens (2bw)
1988 (80pg)
Cover features: Inspector Gadget, Alf, Bobby Davro, Anneka Rice, Cannon & Ball, Joanne Conway, Roger Black, Five Star, Jimmy Cricket
Front Endpaper: Do It (Sheelagh Gilbey)
Rear Endpaper: Robin of Sherwood (Michael Praed)
Features: The Jets, Joanne Conway, Jimmy Cricket, Bobby Dravo, Mel & Kim, Roger Black, Alf (4), 5 Star Family (6), Treasure Hunt , Dangermouse and his friends from Cosgrove Hall (Chorlton & the Wheelies, Cockleshell bay, Count Duckula etc),
Small Features: Emlyn Hughes, Jimmy Greaves, Impressionists, The years of '88 (4) - Art: Tom Gilling and Writer: Harriet Llewellyn
Comic Strips: The A Team (8bw), Writer: Angus P Allan - Art: Arthur Ranson, Cannon & Ball (2x2bw), Robin of Sherwood - 8 page b/w comic strip
Writer: Angus P Allan, Art: Arthur Ranson
1989 (80pg)
Cover features: Alf, Andrea Arnold, Gary Lineker, Madonna, Rick Astley, Five Star, Stephen Hendry, Cilla Black, Timmy Mallett
Front Endpaper: Cannon & Ball
Rear Endpaper: Get Mucky (Charlotte Hindle)
Features: Timmy Mallett, Bros, Stephen Hendry, Debbie Gibson, Cilla Black, ALF
Small Features: Comic Strip Heroes, Stable Stars, 5 Star - The Facts, The Hit Factories (Pop), Roller Skating, The Real Ghosts, Dance Crazy
Comic Strips - Knight Rider featuring David Hasselhoff (10bw),

Black Beauty (10bw)
1990 (80pg)
Cover features: Count Duckula, Kylie Minogue, Sean Kerly, Jason Donovan, Mork & Mindy, Yazz, Carol Vorderman, Michael Jackson, Pippin
Front Endpaper: WAC Studio
Rear Endpaper: Blockbusters
Features: Kylie Minogue, Sean Kerly, Yazz, Jason Donovan, Carol Voderman, Michael Jackson, Doggy Stars, Chartbusters from down under, Movie Sequel Madness, The Voices Behind the Cartoons, American Classics (The Munsters, Adams Family, Batman, I Dream of Jeannie, etc.), The years of 90's
Comic Strips - Buck Rogers in the 25th Century - Sweet Dreams? (9bw) Writer: Angus Allan, Art: Arthur Ranson, Famous Five - Smugglers and Secret Passages (9bw), Writer: Angus Allan, Art: Mike Noble
1991 (80pg)
Cover features: David Hasselhoff, New Kids on the Block, Home & Away, Scooby Doo, Jason Donovan, Dan Akroyd, Kylie Minogue, Garfield, Rolf Harris
Features: David Hasselhoff, Michaela Strachan, Garfield, Jennifer Capriati, Michael J Fox, Sonia, New Kids on the Block, Press Gang, Childrens Ward, Streetwise, Phoenix Hall, Home & Away, Sports, Rolf Harris
Comic Strips - Robin of Sherwood (8fc), Writer: Angus Allan, Art: Mike Noble and Arthur Ranson

LOOK-IN TV COMEDY (ITPLtd)
1975-1976   £8 $13
©1974 (94pg)
Cover features: Benny Hill, Tommy Cooper, Sid James, Les Dawson, Mike & Bernie Winters
Features by: David Lanning
Front Endpapers: Rod Hull and Emu
Rear Endpapers: Stanley Baxter
Comic Strips: Bless This House (4bw) - Art: John Cooper
On The Buses (4bw) - Writer: Ronald Wolfe & Ronald Chesney
Features: Benny Hill, Jimmy Tarbuck, The Comedians, Michael Crawford, Morecambe & Wise, Les Dawson, Richard O'Sullivan, Tommy Cooper, Freddie Starr, Dick Emery, The Two Ronnies, Animated cartoon characters (Disney & Hanna-Barbera), Bless This House (Sid James), Father Dear Father, Mike and Bernie Winters Photo Cover
©1975 (80pg)
Front Endpaper: Freddie Starr, Les Dawson, Tommy Cooper, Benny Hill
Rear Endpaper: Benny Hill, Laurel and Hardy, Freddie Starr, Les Dawson
Cover Art: Arnaldo Putzu
Comic Strips: Benny Hill (2bw), Doctor on the Go (2bw), Bless This House (4bw)
Features: Carry On team, Stephen Lewis, Benny Hill, Les Dawson, The Goodies, Mike Reid, Norman Wisdom
Pin Ups: Stephen Lewis

LOOK IN POP ANNUAL (ITV Books Ltd)
1983   £8 $13
©1982 (80pg)
Editor: Neil Tennant, Designer: Richard Krzyzak, Cover Design: Hamish
Features: Electro Pop (OMD, Depeche Mode, Kraftwerk, Soft Cell),

Louise 1999

Madonna 1994

Magic Roundabout 1986

Pop Goes Britain (a pop music map of the British Isles), The Old Timers (Abba, Cliff Richard, David Bowie etc.), The Story of Eurovision, How a record becomes a hit (Altered Images), Adam Ant (Words and Pictures), Home is... the place the stars call home, Look in Pop Panel (Gary Numan and Charyl Baker answer readers questions)
Comic Strips: Elvis - The Story - His Rise to Fame (8bw) Artist: Arthur Ranson
Pin Ups: The Human League, Kim Wilde, Haircut 100, Bucks Fizz, Altered Images, Adam Ant

LOONEY TUNES (World)

1990's	£5	$8

1992 (64pg)
Features: Bugs Bunny, Sylvester, Tweety, Porky Pig, Elmer Fudd, Daffy Duck, Yosemite Sam, Road Runner, Wile E. Coyote, Foghorn Leghorn, Pepe Le Pew, Tasmanian Devil
1993 (64pg)
Comic Strips (fc): Lifestyles of the Looney Tunes (4) Writers: Joe Orlando & Joey Cavalieri - Art: John Costanza
Babysitter Blues with Sylvester and Tweety (10) Text: G. Brusasca & J. McAleer, Design: G. Scott
Porky Pig in The Gift (4), Bugs Bunny with Yosemite Sam in Pirates On Patrol (12) Text: Alex Filed & John Broadhead, Design: R. Sidos
Bat-Duck (8) Writer: Nick Nomad - Art: Rich Hoover
Rocket Rabbit (4) Writer: Jim Fanning - Art: Stephen DeStefano & John Costanza
Bugs Bunny in The Trunk (4)
Also includes Foghorn Leghorn's Answers To Everything and Daffy's Doodles feature pages
1998 (112pg)
Comic Strips (fc): Daffy Duck in Romeo & Drooliet, Writer: Dana Kurtin, Penciller: Walter Carzon, Inks: Scott McRae
Lot O' Misery, Writer: Dave King, Pencils: Nelson Luty, Inks: Horacio Ottolini
Sense and Insensitivity, Writers: Dana Kurtin and Dan Slott, Pencils: Pablo Zamboni
Multi Bunny Blues, Writer: Bobbi JG Weiss, Pencils: Horacio Saavdra, Inks: Ruben Torreiro
Holed Up, Writer: David Weiss, Pencils: Horacio Saavdra, Inks: Ruben Torreiro
It Takes a Saint to Make a Complaint, Writer: David Cody Weiss, Pencils: Horacio Saavedra, Inks: Ruben Torreiro
Catch As Catch Can't, Writer: Jack E nyart, Pencils: Horacio Saavedra, Inks: Ruben Torreiro
Writer: Dana Kurtin and Dan Slott, Pencils: Nelson Luty, Inks: Horacio Ottolini
Psylvester, Writer: Dana Kurtin and Dan Slott, Pencils: Nelson Luty, Inks: Horacio Ottolini

LOST IN SPACE (Grandreams)

1999
©1998 (64pg) (fc)   £5 $8
Writer: Tony Lynch
Based on the screenplay by Akiva Goldsmith
Designed by Dave Saunders
Features: Photos photos from the film
Adaptation of the movie script

LOST WORLD: JURASSIC PARK (Grandreams)

1998
©1997 (64pg) (fc)   £5 $8

writer Tony Lynch and adapted from the original movie script
Features photos from the movie (fc)

LOUISE

1999
©1998   £5 $8
Based on the UK pop singer

LUCIE ATWELL'S Annual (Dean)

1940's-1970's		
1950's	£30	$48
1960's	£20	$32
1970's	£15	$24

MADONNA Special (Grandreams)

1987-1994	£8	$13

©1986 (64pg) (fc)
Writer: John Kercher
Features: Madonna - The Story, On Fashion, Fact file, Jewellery, Keeping Fit, Starchild, On Film, Likes and Dislikes
©1988 (64pg) (fc)
Editor: Jayne Lanigan
Features: The Actress, Sean Penn, Fitness, On Tour in England, Wembley Concert, Chris Finch,
©1992 (48pg) (fc)
Features: Blonde Ambition, Screen Scene, Record Achievements, The Hit List, Madonna on Fitness, Express Yourself, Outrageous Costumes, Madonna On Tour
©1993 (48pg) (fc)
Writer: Michael Heatley
Features: Hollywood Career, Greatest Hits, Truth or Dare, Men in her Life, Material Girl
Based on the pop star/actress

The MAGIC BALL (World)

1974 (68pg) (fc)   £6 $10
Comic Strips (2x5): The Story of the Undersea Pirate, The Wicked Spotted Ball
Art: Brian Cosgrove, Mark Hall, Bridget Appleby, Graham Moores, Sylvia Kenyon, Keith Scoble, Katherine Wride, Roy Evans
Based on the Cosgrove Hall animated TV series

The MAGICIAN (Brown Watson)

1976
©1975 (64pg) (fc/bw)   £10 $16
Comic Strips (16x2fc): The Illusion of the Kidnapped Boy, Black Magic, Art: John Bolton
Text stories also feature John Bolton art
Based on the TV series starring Bill Bixby

MAGIC ROUNDABOUT (Odhams/Fleetway/World)

1968-1990's		
1968 (Odhams) (76pg) (fc)	£15	$25

1st annual - Writer: Jane Carruth, Art: N. Fersen
Picture Strips (fc): Dougal's Magic Specs, Dougal's Secret Hoard, A Ride on the Tricy-bus, Dougal-The Brave Matador, the Fancy Dress Parade, Snowman Dougal, Dougal and the Cuckoo Clock, King of the Pies, Dougal's Space Rocket, Zebedee's Christmas Presents, Mr. MacHenry's Magic Flowers, Surprise! Surprise!

1969-1975	£12	$19
1976-1979	£10	$16
1980's	£8	$13

1986 (Fleetway)
Comic Strips: Butterfly Trouble, The Sugar Tree, The Cheeky Rubber, Dougal's Seaside, Merrytime, Dougal Through the Looking

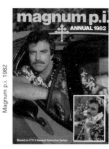

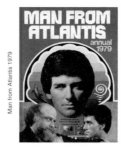

Glass, Dougal's Song, The Sugar Box, Wizard Dougal, The Ice Cream Igloo, Surprise Trip
1990's   £5 $8
1993 (World) (64pg)
Adapted by Pat Kelleher, Art: Primary Design
1994 (World)
Adapted by Pat Kelleher, Editor: Brenda Apsley, Art: Primary Design
Based on the Childrens TV puppet series
MAGNUM P.I. (Stafford Pemberton)
1982-1984   £8 $13
1982
Comic Strips: Daddy's Little Girl, The Burning Stops, Harry Blong's Harvest, Death of a Drunken Woman
Photo cover
Based on the TV Detective series starring Tom Selleck
MAGPIE (Atlas/World)
1967-1979
1967-1969   £10 $16
1970-1979   £8 $13
©1969 (Atlas)
Features: Pick of the Pop Parade (The Marmalade, Cilla Black, Hermans Hermits, Lulu, The Casuals, The Love Affair, The Tremeloes
©1970 (World) - '2nd Annual'
1974
Editorial: Alison Wade, Design: Robert Claxton
Susan Stranks, Mick Robertson and Doug photo cover
1976
Editorial: Alison Wade, Design: Sari Finch
Comic Strip (fc): The Forging of a Nation (6)
Mick Robertson, Doug and Jenny Hanley photo cover
©1979
12th Yearbook
Edited by Vivien Bowler
Based on the Childrens ITV magazine series
MANCHESTER UNITED Annual (Grandreams/Macdonald Queen Anne Press/Man Utd Books)
1991 - present   £4 $7
1998
Cover design Don MacPherson - Book design by David Farris
Comic Strips (4x2fc): Fred and his Wonderboots, Fred and his New TV
1999 (64pg)
Book design and Art: David Farris
Comic Strips (2x4fc): Fred and the Wool to Win, Fred and the UFO Cup Final
MANCHESTER UNITED Soccer Special (Grandreams)
1993   £5 $8
Designer: Louise Ivimy, Writer: Laurence Anthony
MAN FROM ATLANTIS (World)
1979   £8 $13
Half photo/artwork cover
Based on the TV show starring Patrick Duffy
MAN FROM U.N.C.L.E. (World)
1966-1969
1966-1967   £20 $32
©1966
Comic Strip (fc): The Rip Van Solo Affair, The Invisible Man Affair, The Explosive Affair

Text Stories: The Last Flight Affair, The Fortune Cookie Affair
1968-1969   £15 $24
©1967 (96pg)
Comic Strip (fc): The Dream and Her Stunt Girl Counterspies, The Spirit of St Louis Affair (Parts I & II)
MAN FROM U.N.C.L.E. Television Storybook (PBS)
1968-1969
©1967-68   £12 $19
©1968 (64pg) (fc)
Comic Strips: The Flying Clowns Affair (19), The Brain Drain Affair (21), Art: Mike Sekowsky
Jet Dream and her Stunt-Girl Counterspies
The Achilles Heel (4), Art: Mike Sekowsky
Splash-Down To Death (s)
Photo cover
MANDY for Girls (D.C. Thomson)
1970's-present
1970's   £8 $13
1972 (128pg) complete with dustjacket
Comic Strips: Valda (10fc), Meg of Magpie Manor (19bw), The Twopenny Times (4tc), A Home for Heather (8fc), Jill's Gentle Giant (3fc), Snapshot Susie (4fc), Away Went Wendy (9tc), My Chum Mum (5tc), Elsie's Elephant (5fc), Friend of the Lonely (4fc), The Kazoo Kids (7fc), Milly's Magic Box (6tc), The Wishing Well (6fc), Wendy the Winner (7fc)
1973 (128pg)
Comic Strips: With Love from Lindy (11fc), Caesar and Cleo (7tc), Little Miss No-Name (24bw), Carol's Cauldron (4fc), The Ghost of Sunday Manor (6fc), Carrie Chase (6fc), Elsie's Elephant (5tc), Melinda You're a Marvel (7fc), Terry and her Trike (4fc), Noah's Monkey (4tc), Tessa Pulls Her Weight (6tc), The Singing Hinneys (5fc), Mighty Minnie (8fc)
1973 (128pg)
Comic Strips: Valda (6fc), The Farmer Wants a Wife (5fc), Sisters in Sorrow (12bw), The Slave Girls (5tc), My Sister Jinx (8fc), Aunt Kate's Household Companion (6fc), Stella Starr (6tc), The Boot Laceys (4tc), Caroline and her Camera (4tc), Mighty Minnie (8fc), Queen of Koko Island (5fc), A Mystery for Melody Jones (9tc), Netta's Newshound (6fc), Melinda - You're a Marvel (6fc)
1980's   £6 $10
1981 (128pg)
Comic Strips: A Wedding for Wilma (6fc), That's Not My Gran! (35fc), The Living Lie of Linda (11tc), Lucy's Locket (4fc), Stars in her Eyes (4tc), Blind Ben's White Christmas (8tc), There was a Young Girl Who Lived in a Shoe (6tc), Gail's Guardian Angel (4tc), It'a Dare (6fc), Stella Starr (6tc), Hilary of the Happy Bus (5tc), You Little Monkey! (5fc),
1990's   £4 $7
1990 (128pg)
The Guardian Tree (39fc), I Can't Stand my Sister (4fc), I Hate Humpty (8tc), Meddling Maggie (4tc), My Little Green Prince (5fc), Something to Hide (8tc), I Want to Win (7tc), The Daffodil Dancer (8tc), Atlanta's Tale (5tc), The Return of Ted (7fc), The Secret of Cousin Tania (10tc), My Best Friend? (5fc)
2000 (128pg)
Comic Strips: Nurses on TV (10tc), The Bakers (5tc), Best Friend's Boy (6tc), Eureka Johnson (2fc), Christmas Past (8tc), Time to Talk (6tc), Penny's Place (6tc), The Haughty Horse (8tc), Suspicion! (10tc)

Manimal 1984

Martine McCutcheon 2000

Marvel 1998

2 page feature on Girl Bands (Spice Girls, Cleopatra, Bewitched, All Saints, The Corrs
Pin Ups: Bewitched, Westlife
Photo Stories
Based on the UK girls comic
MANIMAL (Grandreams)

1984	£8	$13

Comic Strip: Manimal
Based on TV fantasy series starring Simon MacCorkindale
MARMALADE ATKINS (Stafford Pemberton/World)
1984-1985

1984-©1984	£6	$10

1984 (Stafford Pemberton)
Comic Strips (fc): A Fete Worse Than..., Pop Goes Marmalade ©1984 (World)
'Television's Horrible Heroine'
Comic Strips (fc): Marmalade Lends A Hand, Marmalade - Circus Star
Based on the Childrens ITV series
MARTINE McCUTCHEON Special (Grandreams)
100% Totally Unofficial
2000

©1999	£4	$7

Photo features on the actress and singer (fc)
MARVEL (Fleetway/World)
1973-1976, 1979

1973 (128pg) (Fleetway)	£12	$19
1974-1976	£10	$16

1974 (Fleetway) (128pg)
1975 (World) (80pg)
1976 (World) (64pg)
Comic Strips (fc): A Friend in Need! (18), Writer: Len Wein, Art: Jim Mooney
Titans Three (19), Writer: Roy Thomas, Art: Sal Buscema
Confrontation (18), Writer: Roy Thomas, Art: Sal Buscema

1979 (64pg) (World)	£8	$13

Daredevil/Black Panther title reprints
Marvel Comics reprints
MARVEL ADVENTURES (Pedigree)

2000 (112pg) (fc)	£7	$11

Endpaper: George Perez
Comic Strips: Editor: Mark Bernardo
Spider-Man & Silver Surfer in First Contact
Writer: Bob Budiansky, Pencils: Alex Saviuk, Inks: J Um Babgins
The Incredible Hulk in The Monster And The Immortal
Writer: Ralph Macchio, Pencils: Andy Kuhn, Inks: Harry Candelario
Fantastic Four in The Ties That Bind
Writer: Ralph Macchio, Pencils: Andy Kuhn, Inks: Harry Candelario
X-Men in Wolf In The Fold
Writer: Ralph Macchio, Pencils: Andy Kuhn, Inks: Harry Candelario
Marvel Comics reprints
MARVEL CLASSICS (Pedigree)

1998	£7	$11

Comic Strips:
The Fantastic Four's first appearance from November 1961
Writer: Stan Lee, Art: Jack Kirby
Spiderman's first appearance from August 1962
Writer: Stan Lee, Art: Steve Ditko
The Incredible Hulk first appearance from May 1962

Writer: Stan Lee, Art: Jack Kirby
The Avengers first appearance from September 1963
Writer: Stan Lee, Art: Jack Kirby
The X Men first appearance from September 1963
Writer: Stan Lee, Pencils: Jack Kirby, Inks: Paul Reinman
Marvel Comics reprints
MARVEL COMIC Annual (World)
1969-1971

1969	£15	$24
1970-1971	£10	$16

Based on Marvel Comics characters
MARVEL STORYBOOK Annual (World)

1968	£15	$24

Text Stories feature: Ant Man, Captain America, Doctor Strange, Fantastic Four, Hulk, Iron Man, Spider-Man, Thor
Based on Marvel Comics characters
MARVELMAN (Miller)
1954-61, 1963

1954 (Scarce)	£60	$96
1955	£80	$128
1956	£30	$48
1957-1960	£20	$32
1961 -'Marvelman Adventures'	£15	$24
1963 (Scarce)	£25	$40

Based on the UK comic
MARVELMAN FAMILY (Miller)

1963 (Scarce)	£30	$48

MARVELMAN JR. (Miller)

1963 (Scarce)	£30	$48

MARY, MUNGO & MIDGE

1974	£10	$16

MASK (Grandreams)
1987-1989

	£6	$10

1987 (64pg) Cover Price £3.50
Comic Strips: When Opportunity Knox, The Romain of the Dead
Editor: Andrew Helfer, Writer: Michael Fleisher, Pencils: Michael Chen, Inks: Joe Del Beato
1988 (64pg) Cover Price £3.75
Comic Strips: The Ace Age Cometh
Editors: Mike Gold and Robert Greenberger,
Writer: Michael Fleisher, Art: Curt Swan & Kurt Schaffenberger
1989 (64pg) Cover Price £3.75
Comic Strips (8x2 fc): The Face of Tut, The Duel
All annuals contain DC reprints
Please note all 3 annuals published with ©1986 date, but the third annual also states that it is the 1989 edition.
Based on the animated TV series
MASKED RIDER 'Saban's' (Grandreams)
1997

©1996 (64pg) (fc)	£5	$8

Edited by Barrie Tomlinson
Comic Strips: Day Of The Volcano (8), The Great Ferbus Grab! (5), The Big Freeze! (6), Art: Jon Haward
Includes photo features
Based on the TV series
MASTERS OF THE UNIVERSE (World)
See: HE-MAN
1984-1989

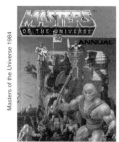

Masters of the Universe 1984

Matchbox 1980

Mates 1977

MA

1984 £10 $16
©1983 (64pg) (fc/tc)
Text Stories art: Melvyn Powell (part)
Includes photo features using the Mattel action figures
Photo cover
1985-1989 £8 $13
©1984 (64pg) (fc)
Cover Art/Endpaper: Paul Green
Comic Strip: The Necklace of Evil - Art: Paul Green
1986 (64pg) (fc)
Cover Layout: Ron Smethurst - Finished art: Paul Green
Endpaper: Paul Green
Comic Strip: The Unwelcome Guest (6) - Art: Paul Green
Text Stories Art: Paul Green and Glenn Rix
1987 (64pg) (fc)
Cover Art: Ron Smethurst - Endpaper: Paul Green
Comic Strip: The Flying Sword (6) - Art: Paul Green
Text Stories Art: Glenn Rix and Melvyn Powell
1988 (64pg) (fc)
Cover Art/Endpaper: Paul Green
Comic Strip: The Bat That Woke The Beast (6) - Art: Paul Green
Text Stories Art: Melvyn Powell and Paul Green (part)
©1988 (64pg)
Text Stories: The Traveller (7), The Shrine of the Iron Mountains (9),
The Fight for Prison Star (7), The Time Portal Opens... (8), The
Lodestone of Iron Forest (8), The Crown of Tarn (10)
1989 (64pg) (fc)
Cover Art: Ron Smethurst - Endpaper: Paul Green
Comic Strips: Snout Spout Alone (4), The Last Unicorn (6)
Art: Ron Smethurst
Text Stories Art: Paul Green, Glenn Rix and Melvyn Powell
Based on the filmation animated TV series and toy range

MASTERS OF THE UNIVERSE Storybook (World/BHS)
1986
©1985 (48pg) (fc) (Scarce) £10 $16
Cover layout: Ron Smethurst - Finished art: Paul Green
Text stories and feature art: Paul Green
Includes stills from the animated series

MATCH (Hayden Publishing)
1990's-present (112pg) (fc) £3 $5
'The Biggest & Best Football Annual'
Managing Editor: Chris Hunt, Art Director: Darryl Tooth, Designer:
Ben Bates - Staff Photographer: Phil Bagnall
Writers: Gary Sherrard, Phil Smith, Tim Unwin
Comic Strip: The X-Rated Adventures of Matchman In Footy Land
(1)

MATCH OF THE DAY (BBC)
1979-1982 £7 $11
1980 (64pg)
Features: Kevin Keegan, Alan Ball and Martin Peters, Pat Jennings,
Viv Anderson, Mick Mills, Phil Parkes, Kenny Sansom, Steve
Coppell, Dave Watson, Tony Currie, Derek Johnstone, Liam Brady,
Kenny Dalglish, Terry Yorath, Cyrille Regis, Peter Shilton
1981 (fc/bw)
Photo cover features Jimmy Hill, Kevin Keegan, Lawrie McMenemy
and John Motson
Based on the BBC TV soccer programme
MATCHBOX (Purnell)
1980-1981

©1979 (64pg)
Comic Strips (3x4 bw): The Diamond Drive, Dive into Danger, The
Hood Strikes Back
Features: Opal Monza, Grand Prix Racing, Search & Rescue
©1980
Comic Strips: Collision course, Midnight encounter, Mountain
Rescue
Photo Strips: The Green Berets, The Fire Eaters
Based on the Matchbox toy range
MATES (Fleetway)
1970's-1980's
1970's £8 $13
1977
Comic Strips: Life with Lindy, Search Me, Fever Pitch, Romance of
the week
Features: David Essex
Pin Ups: Les, Kenny, Bilbo Baggins, Mud, David Essex, Alan,
Arrows, Eric, Rod Stewart, Derek, Gary Glitter, Donny & Marie,
Woody
1978
Features: David Essex, Bay City Rollers, Donny Osmond
Pin Ups: Flintlock, G Band, Donny Osmond, Kenny, Rod Stewart,
Bay City Rollers, Buster, Queen, David Essex, Slik,
Showaddywaddy, Child
1979 (128pg)
Features: Alister Kerr of the Dead End Kids, Andy Gibb of the Bee
Gees
Pin Ups: Peter Vaughan Clarke, Paul Weller, Tavares, Brendon,
Andy Gibb, Keith Chegwin, Alessi, Real Thing, Jeff Phillips, Rosetta
Stone, Rupert Keegan, The Jacksons, Paul Nicholas, John Lloyd
1980's £5 $8
1980 (128pg) (fc/tc)
Comic Strips: The Sound of Love..., The Summer's Over, Too Bad
That I'm Too Bad, A Present for my Sister, The Manager Who
Couldn't Manage It, The Best of Friends, I Couldn't Say No
Features: John Travolta
Pin Ups: Alessi Brothers, Jacksons, Andy Gibb, Abba, David Essex,
John Travolta, Child, Leif Garrett, New Hearts
Photo cover features Lesley Ash
1981 (128pg)
Comic Strips: The Tears of a True Love, Ring out Romance, The
Double Dutch Mystery, Every little Teardrop, Midwinter Love, In the
Shadow of the Stars, The Happiness Girl
Features: Shaun Cassidy, Hardy Boys
Pin Ups: Shaun Cassidy, Ian Mitchell band, Boomtown Rats, David
Essex, Nick Van Eede, Leif Garrett, Police, Child
1982 (112pg)
Comic Strips: Pattys World, The Shop at Nightingale Square, The
Queue at the Bus Stop,
Photo Strips: Going Down, Stay away from the House
Features: David Essex, Shaun Cassidy, Olivia Newton John,
Michael Jackson, Gary Numan
Pin Ups: Police, Ray Wilkins, The Jam
Based on the UK teenage girls comic
MAVERICK (World/Grandreams)
1961-1962, 1982
1961-1962 (World) £15 $24
Text Stories: Douglas Enefer
Features Roger Moore

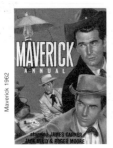

Maverick 1962

Max Headroom - Not Dated

Mickey Mouse 1963

1982   £7 $11
©1981 (Grandreams)
Comic Strips (2x8 b/w): Miss Fortune's Losing Hand, Derwent
Dexter's Dirty Deeds
Includes text stories and photo features on James Garner (fc)
Photo cover
Based on the TV Western series
MAVERICK Television Storybook (New Town)
1960-1962   £10 $16
©1961 (96pg) (bw)
Comic Strips: The Missouri Queen Renegades (19), Gunfight
Election (21), Rough 'N' Tumble (7)
Text Stories: The Big Cheat, Beau Leape to the Rescue, Showdown
at Powder Springs
Based on the TV Western series
MAX HEADROOM (Grandreams)
N/D £3.50 (Estimate 1986/1987)   £5 $8
Photo cover
Based on the computer generated TV character
MEN IN BLACK Series Official Annual (Grandreams)
1999
©1998   £5 $8
Condensed stories adapted from original Men in Black: The Series
scripts
Stories: The Psychic Link Syndrome
Based on the episode written by Steve Roberts and the Malibu
comic by Lowell Cunningham
The Farewell Syndrome: Based on the episode written by Tom
Pugsley & Greg Klein And the Malibu comic by Lowell Cunningham
Features stills (fc) from the series
Based on the animated TV series
METAL MICKEY (Stafford Pemberton/Purnell)
1983-1985   £6 $10
1983 (Stafford Pemberton)
Writer: Eve Sumner-Photographs and art: Edgar Hodges
1984 (Purnell) (64pg)
Writer: Eve Sumner, Art: Edgar Hodges
Produced by Mickey Dolenz
Based on the childrens ITV series
MICHAEL JACKSON Special (Grandreams)
1992-1994   £5 $8
©1991 (64pg) (fc)
Writer: Mick St. Michael, Design: Louise Ivimy
Photo features
©1992 (48pg) (fc)
Writer: John Kercher, Design: Louise Ivimy & Joanna Winslow
©1993 (48pg) (fc)
Writer: Michael Heatley, Design: Louise Ivimy
Photo features
Based on the pop star
MICKEY MOUSE (Dean & Son/Fleetway/Egmont World)
1931-1965, 1970's-present
1950's   £25 $40
1960-1965   £20 $32
1962
Includes Disney Characters: Mickey Mouse, Donald Duck, Goofy,
Dumbo, Scamp, Brer Rabbit, Pluto, Chip 'n' Dale
1970's   £10 $16
1980's   £8 $13

1981 (Fleetway)
Includes Disney Characters: Mickey, Goofy, Donald & Daisy, Scamp,
Beagle Boys, Winnie the Pooh, Chip 'n' Dale, Clarabelle, Scrooge
McDuck
Features: Disney's Black Hole the movie, Cartoon gallery - shows
274 well known Disney characters
1990's   £5 $8
2000 (Egmont World) (64 pg) (fc)   £5 $8
Special Millenium Edition
Editor: Shaynie Morris, Designer: Martin Shubrook
Comic Strips: Mickey Mouse in A Friend in Need, Minnie Mouse in
Fool's Luck, Goofy in Loch Mess, Donald Duck in High Steppin',
Pluto in a Mouse's Best Friend
Based on the Disney character
MICKEY MOUSE CLUB (Purnell)
1970's
©1978   £8 $13
Features: The Jungle Book, Lady and the Tramp, Winnie the Pooh,
Robin Hood, Snow White, Bambi
Based on the Disney character
MIGHTY HEROES (Opal Quill)
1984-1985   £6 $10
1984
Cover Art: T. Johnson (features Gold Key's Doctor Solar)
Comic Strips (2x30 fc): Astroman in Zero Attacks! The Fearless
Roldan in The Swamps of Terror
1985 (64pg) (fc)
Comic Strips: Fifth Dimension - Earth Attack (8), The Titans -
Commando Zeus (8), A Case for Inspector Dan - The Ribbon
Murders (30) Centaur - Into Another World (6) Fifth Dimension - The
Chelsea Butcher (8)
MIGHTY MORPHIN POWER RANGERS (Century 22 Ltd)
1995-1996   £4 $7
©1994 - 1st Edition
Editor: Dick Wallis, Design: Paul Miller
1996 (64pg) (fc)
Written and Designed by Century 22 Limited
Photo features
Based on the animated TV series
MIGHTY MOUSE (World)
1982
©1981   £8 $13
Comic Strips: Adventures of Mighty Mouse-
The Great Secret, The Bad Genie, The Good Knight, Plane Trouble,
The Magic Carpet, The Railroad Rescue, Operation Deep Freeze,
Professor Theorem's Discovery, The Air Raid
Based on the animated TV series
MIGHTY WARRIORS (Stafford Pemberton)
1979 (72pg) (fc)   £10 $16
Cover Art: Brian Lewis, Endpaper: Paul Green
Comic Strips: Doctor Solar in The Ladder To Mars (21), Dagar the
Invincible in The Sword of Dagar (25), Magnus Robot Fighter 4000
A.D. in The Micro-Giants (21), Art: Russ Manning
Gold Key comic reprints
MIGHTY WORLD OF MARVEL (Marvel/World)
1977-1979
1977   £10 $16
1978-1979   £8 $13
1978 (64pg) (World)

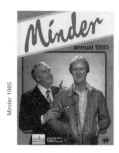

Minder 1985

Mission Impossible 1970

Mr Men No. 1 1980

Comic Strips (fc): Captain Marvel "And a Child Shall Lead You!" (18), Writer: Roy Thomas, Art: Gil Kane
Luke Cage, Power Man! "Earthshock!" (35)
Writer: Chris Claremont, Art: Lee Elias & Dave Hunt
1979 (World)
Editor: Jim Salicrup
Cover Artists: Bob Budiansky, Tony DeZungia and Pablo Marcos
Comic Strips: The Name of the Game is Death
Editor: Marv Wolfman-Writer: Chris Claremont, Plot: Marv Wolfman-Art: George Tuska and F. Chiaramonte
Death Times Two - Editor: Marv Wolfman, Guest Writer: Bill Mantlo, Layouts: Sal Buscema, Finished Art: Klaus Janson
Marvel comics reprints

MINDER (Grandreams/World)
1980, 1985-1986

1980	£7	$11

Comic Strips: Big Eyes - Little Boxes (bw), Well its only Money (fc)
Philately gets you Nowhere (bw)
Photo cover

1985-1986	£6	$10

1985 (World) (64pg) (fc)
Text stories: The Long 'Goodbye' Day, The Dogs at War, The Goons, the Bag and Miss Uttley, The French Disc- Connection
Art: Melvyn Powell
Photo Cover
1986
Photo Cover
Based on the TV series starring George Cole and Dennis Waterman

MIRABELLE (Fleetway)
1960's-1970's

1960's	£12	$19
1970's	£10	$16

Based on the UK teenage girls magazine

MIRABELLE SUNSHINE POP BOOK (IPC)

1970's	£10	$16

1975
Comic Strip: The Girl with Many Faces (featuring Donny Osmond), (4bw), What a Shy World You're Living In (featuring Gilbert O'Sullivan) (4bw), Super Slade Success Story (4bw)
Features: David Cassidy, Gilbert O'Sullivan, Donny Osmond, Brian Connolly, Gary Glitter, Lynsey de Paul, David Essex, Suzi Quatro, Noddy Holder, Marty Kristian, The Osmonds, David Bowie, Queen, Merrill Osmond, Colin Blunstone, Marc Bolan, Alvin Stardust
Pin Ups: Jimmy Osmond, Lynsey de Paul, Mud, Donny Osmond, Michael Jackson, Alvin Stardust, David Essex, Suzi Quatro, Marty Kristian, Dave Hill, Gary Glitter, Marc Bolan, Andy & David Williams, David Bowie, Rick Springfield, Queen
Based on the UK teenage girls magazine

MISSION GALACTICA (Grandreams)
1981

©1980 (64pg)	£8	$13

Comic Strips: Switch in Space, Planet of the Cyclops, Skirmish beyond Skarfrax, Final Showdown
Features: Dirk Benedict and Lloyd Bridges
Based on the TV sci fi series

MISSION IMPOSSIBLE (Atlas/World)
1968-1972
1968 (Atlas) (Scarce)

1968 (Atlas) (Scarce)	£20	$32

Season one cast

1969 (Scarce)	£15	$24

Season two cast

1972	£10	$16

Graves, Morris, Lupus painted cover
Based on the TV series

MR BLOBBY (Grandreams)
1993

©1992 (48pg) (fc)	£4	$7

Stories: Allen Cummings, Art: County Studio Ltd
Based on the BBC TV character

MR MEN Gift Book (World)
1976

©1975	£12	$19

Based on the Roger Hargreaves character

MR MEN (Thurman)
1980's

1980 - No.1	£20	$32

©1979 (64pg) (fc)
By Roger Hargreaves
Picture Strips: Mr Bump's Christmas Wish, Mr Strong and the Windy Day, Mr Dizzy the Famous Author, Mr Tickle Lends A Hand, Mr Rush, Mr Daydream's Daydream, Mr Tall and the Baloon Race, Mr Bounce, Mr Slow, Mr Clumsy's Christmas

1981	£12	$19

©1980 (64pg) (fc)
By Roger Hargreaves
Picture Strips: Mr Funny's Special Delivery, Mr Greedy's Picnic, Mr Daydream's Daydream, Mr Jelly and the Scarecrow, Mr Noisy and the Fire Brigade, Mr Nosey, Mr Mean

1982	£10	$16
1983 on	£8	$13

Based on the Roger Hargreaves character

MR MEN & LITTLE MISS (World/Egmont)
1990's - present

1996 (64pg)	£4	$7

Art: Adam Hargreaves
1997
Art: Adam and Giles Hargreaves
Original text: Roger Hargreaves
New text and design: John and Hilary Malam
1998 (64pg)
Art: Adam and Giles Hargreaves
Original text: Roger Hargreaves
New text and design: John Malam
1999 (64pg) (World)
Art: Adam and Giles Hargreaves
Original text: Roger Hargreaves
New text and design: John Malam
Based on the Roger Hargreaves character

MR MERLIN (Grandreams)

1982	£6	$10

Comic Strips: Going Ape, Here be Dragons
Photo cover
Based on the TV series

MR PASTRY's Annual (Grandreams)

N/D (Estimate 1958)	£12	$19

Comic Strips: Mr Pastry Goes Bird-Watching (3bw), Mr Pastry Does it Himself! (6tc), Mr Pastrys Idea of.... (3bw), Mr Pastry Does it Himself (3tc)

ATV Television Star Book © 1962 TP

Mummies Alive 1998

Mum's Own 1993

Based on the BBC TV character
MR T Ruby Spear's (Grandreams)
1985-1986 £7 $11
©1984 (64pg)
Comic Strips: Mr T and a Real Break (6bw), Mr T and the Island of Fear (7fc), Mr T and the Mystery Ranch (6bw)
©1985
Comic Strips: Mr T and the Good Cause Caper (7 bw) Mr T and the Blow-Away Balloon (8 bw)
Based on the animated TV series

MISTY (Fleetway)
1979-1986 £12 $19
1979 (144pg)
Comic Strips: The Swarm (7tc) The School of No Escape (36bw/tc) Blood Orange (8fc) The Pony from the Moorland Mist (36bw) End of the Pier... It Came From The Deep (8bw), Voices From the Pat (3bw), The Figure in the Fog (3bw) Wendy the Witch (1x4bw) Miss T (1bw)
1980 (144pg)
Comic Strips: Home for Tea (6tc), The Haunting of Form 2B (33bw/tc), A Little Night Music (6fc), A New Leaf for Nancy (33bw), Hand of Vengeance! (8fc), String of Seven Stories (3bw), The Chair That Chilled (3bw), Last Dance at the Disco (3bw)
1983 (112pg)
'Chilling Stories Inside...'
Comic Strips: The Last Train (7fc), Cilla the Chiller - Our Schoolgirl Spook! (1bw), Moonchild (53bw), The Curse of Castle Krumlaut (8fc)
Includes Christopher Lee photo feature (4bw)
Based on UK girl's mystery & suspense comic

MODERN GIRL (Opal Quill)
1984 (64pg) £6 $10
Features: Duran Duran, Kajagoogoo, Michael Jackson, Nick Heyward, Soft Cell, Culture Club, Wham, Human League

MONKEES (Century 21/City)
1968-1970
1968 £20 $32
1969-1970 £15 $24
©1967 (Century 21) (96pg)
Comic Strips (fc): Loot in the Boot (6), Volts Concerto in DC Minor (6), Surf City Here We Come (6), Now Read On.... (2), John Browns Body Lies a Mouldering in the Grave (6), Roll Up Roll Up See the Man Eating Lion (4), A Fishy Tale (7)
Also features datafiles on the Monkees
Based on the US pop group

MONSTER BOOK For Boys (Dean)
1950's £10 $16
MONSTER BOOK For Girls (Dean)
1950's £10 $16
MONSTER FUN (Fleetway)
1977-85 £6 $10
MONSTER IN MY POCKET
1992 £4 $7
Based on the toy range
MONSTER WRESTLERS IN MY POCKET (World)
1996 (64pg) £3 $5
Writer/Design: Mike Butcher
Art: Tim Perkins, Leo Brown, Simon Clegg and John Moore
Based on the toy range

MOON DREAMERS (World)
1988 (64pg) £5 $8
Picture Stories: The Magic Multiplying Mirror (6fc), Stumbles to the Rescue (5fc)
Based on the toy range
MOPATOP'S SHOP (Dorling Kindersley)
2000 £4 $7
Based on the childrens TV series
MORECAMBE & WISE Special (Weidenfeld & Nicolson)
1978
©1977 £15 $24
Design: John Rushton and Jacqueline Sinclair
Art Director: John Rushton
Art: Jacqueline Sinclair, Rachel Beckingham, Helen Cowcher, Steve Kingston, Neil Collins, Chris Woolmer, Gordon Cramp, Angelo Cinque
Based on the UK comedy duo
MORK & MINDY (Stafford Pemberton)
1980-1981 £10 $16
1980 (64pg)
Comic Strips: Mork Joins the Club (6fc), Cliff Hanger (6fc)
Photo Features and Photo Cover
1981
Writer: Charles Pemberton , Art: Edgar Hodges
Photo cover
Based on the US TV comedy series starring Robin Williams and Pam Dawber
MORPH Amazing Adventures of (World/Purnell)
1980-1984 £6 $10
Based on the BBC TV series
MOSCHOPS (World)
1983 £5 $8
MUMFIE (World)
1996 £5 $8
'Britt Allcroft's Magic Adventures of..'
Created by Britt Allcroft from the works of Katherine Tozer writer Britt Allcroft and John Kane
MUMMIES ALIVE (Grandreams)
1998 (64pg) £5 $8
Stories adapted from original Mummies Alive scripts
Includes stills (fc) from the series
Based on the animated TV series
MUM'S OWN
1993 £8 $13
UK girls comics reprints, circa. 1955-65
MUNCH BUNCH (World/Studio Publications Ipswich Ltd)
1981-1984 £5 $8
1981(64pg) (Studio Publications Ipswich Ltd)
Art: Angela Mitson and Ken Spink
©1982 (World)
Art: Angela Mitson
©1983 (64pg) (Studio Publications)
Art: Angela Mitson, Malcom Barter, Stephanie Birch
Based on the animated TV series
MUPPET SHOW (Brown Watson)
1978-1979 £12 $19
©1977 (64pg)
Comic Strips (2x8fc): Its The Muppet Show

Muppet Babies 1987

Music Star 1976

My Little Pony 1999

Photo cover
©1978
Comic Strips: The Muppet Show, The Show Must Go On, Pigs in Space
Photo cover
Based on the Jim Henson TV series
MUPPET SHOW Jim Henson's (Muppet Press/Grandreams)
1980
©1979 £10 $16
Designed by Bruce McNally, Les Skinner and John Stevenson
Comic Strips: The Muppet Panto - Kermirella, The Muppets Holiday Haunts, Disco Frog
Photo cover
Based on the Jim Henson TV series
MUPPETS Jim Henson's (Muppet Press/Grandreams)
1981-1985 £10 $16
©1980
Editor: Jocelyn Stevenson - Comic Strips: The Mild Bunch
Photo cover
©1981
Typography: Les Skinner - Editor: Jocelyn Stevenson
Comic Strip: A Night to Remember
Art: Manhar Chauhan, Bruce McNally, Les Skinner, Sue Venning
Photo cover
©1982
Cover Art: Sue Venning
Comic Strips (fc): Funfight at the K.O. Corral (13) The Muppets Holiday Haunt (10)
Art: Manhar Chauhan, Bruce McNally, Les Skinner, Sue Venning
©1983
Comic Strips (fc): Muppets at Sea (23) E.C. The Extra-Celestial (5)
Writer: Dick DeBartolo-Art: Manhar Chauhan
Art: Manhar Chauhan, Bruce McNally, Les Skinner, Sue Venning, Graham Thompson
Also features Muppet photo pin-ups (fc)
Photo cover
Based on the Jim Henson TV series
MUPPET BABIES Jim Henson's (Grandreams)
1986-1988 £8 $13
©1985
Comic Strips: The Haunted Nursery, The Big Space Adventure
Editor: Sid Jacobson-Writer: Stan Kay-Art: Marie Severin
Marvel (Star Comics) reprints
©1986
Comic Strips: Kermit and the Beanstalk
Editor: Sid Jacobson-Writer: Stan Kay- Pencils: Marie Severin-Inks: Jacqueline Roettcher
The Dream Machine (21) Writer: Stan Kay-Art: Marie Severin
Marvel reprints
1988
No comic strips featured
Based on the animated TV series
MUSIC SCENE (Fleetway)
1974 (72 pg) £10 $16
Features: Slade, Cat Stevens, Black Sabbath, Marc Bolan, Roxy Music, Deep Purple, David Bowie, Alice Cooper, Strawbs, Genesis, Gilbert O'Sullivan, ELP, The Who, Led Zeppelin, Moody Blues, Elton John, Small Faces
Pin Ups: Alice Cooper, Rod Stewart, Robert Plant, Maggie Bell,

David Bowie, Eric Clapton, Marc Bolan, Elton John
MUSIC STAR (Fleetway)
1970's £10 $16
1974
Features: David Cassidy, Donny Osmond, Michael Jackson, Slade, Sweet, David Bowie, Noddy, T Rex
1975
Features: Michael Jackson, Osmonds, David Cassidy, Rolling Stones, Suzi Quatro
1976
Features: Bay City Rollers, David Essex, Mud, Queen, Rod Stewart, The Osmonds, Slade, Alvin Stardust, David Cassidy
MY CARTOON ANNUAL (Opal Quill)
1984 £4 $7
MY FIRST ANNUAL (Purnell)
1970's-1980's
1970's £4 $7
1980's £3 $5
©1980 - Writer: Barbara Hayes
MY GUY (Fleetway/IPC)
1970's-1980's
1970's £8 $13
1980's £6 $11
1981 (128pg)
Photo Stories: How to Make a Husband, Girl of My Dreams, Ghost Story, What're We Going to do About Harry?
Features: Charlies Angels quiz, The Royals, TV Hunks (includes Lewis Collins, Martin Shaw, David Soul, John Travolta etc.), Peter Powell
Pin Ups: Bob Geldof, Sting, Ian Mitchell, Erik Estrada, Gerry Sundquist, Rex, Johnny Cougar, Oliver Tobias, David Easter, Lewis Collins, Terry Sharpe, Ray Lake, David Bowie, Peter Blake, Nikki Richards, Leo Sayer, Chris Quentin, Trevor Eve, David Essex, Peter Powell
1982
Photo Stories: The Personel Touch, The Final Chapter, Free As a Bird,
Pin Ups: Rex Smith, David Bowie, Johnny Logan, Jean Jacques Burnel, Jimmy Baio, Cliff Richard, David Essex, Leif Garrett, Andy Gibb, Shakin Stevens, Ranking Roger, Gary Numan, Sting, Andy Summers, Steward Copeland, Joe Jackson, Chris Atkins, Bruce Jenner, David Hodo, Scott Graham
Feature: Paul Weller
1983 (112pg)
Pin Ups: Midge Ure, Phil Lynott, Dave Wakeling, Neil Rooney, Steve Norman, Mike Holoway, Roger Taylor, Shakin Stevens, Adam Ant, Jermaine Jackson, Chris Atkins, Steve Strange, Gus Goad, David Sylvian, David Essex, Dennis Waterman, Gerry Sundquist, Billy Idol, Gary Numan, Mick Bass
Feature: Elvis
1984 (96pg)
Pin Ups: Adam Ant, Lee Jones, Les Nemes, Steve Strange, Chas Smash, David Van Day, Simon Le Bon, Terry Hall, Nick Heyward, Cliff Richard, Gary Numan, Julian Cope, Junior, Jim McInven, Kevin Rowland,
Feature: Bucks Fizz, Duran Duran, David Sylvian
Based on the UK girls teenage magazine
MY LITTLE PONY (Grandreams/World)
1985-1999

New Avengers 1978

New Kids on the Block 1992

No Hiding Place 1967

1985-1989	£8	$13

1985 (Grandreams)
1987-1990 (World)
1988 (64pg) (fc)
Picture Strips: Shady's Secret, Gingerbread's Gingerbread Joke*

1990-present	£5	$8

1990 (64 pg) (fc)
Writer: Pat Posner
Picture Strips (2x8): The Pirate Party, Sorbet Surprise and the Sly Sorceror
1999 (64pg)
Writer: Pat Posner, Art: Adrian Phillips
Based on the Hasbro Characters

MY NURSERY RHYME (World/Opal Quill)
1970's-1984

1970's	£4	$7
1980's	£3	$5

1984 (Opal Quill)
Art: Lee Brown

NEIGHBOURS (Grandreams/World/Hamlyn)

1990-1992	£5	$8

©1989 (Grandreams) (64pg) (fc)
Editor: Melanie J. Clayden, Writer: John Kercher
1989 (World)
Writers: Brenda Apsley, Clive Hopwood and Nick Pemberton
1990 (World)
Writer/Editor: Clive Hopwood
©1990 (Grandreams) (64pg) (fc) Special
Features: Kristian Schmid, Sally Jensen, Annie Jones, Stefan Dennis, Rachel Friend, Mark Stevens, Jessica Muschamp
©1990 (World) (64pg) (fc) Special
Features: Craig McLachlan, Jessica Muschamp, Ian Smith, Anne Charleston, Paul Keane, Annie Jones, Guy Pearce, Anne Haddy, Stefan Dennis, Vivien Gray
1991-92 (Hamlyn)
Based on the Australian TV soap

NELLIE THE ELEPHANT (World)

1991	£4	$7

Writer: Geoffrey Alan-Art: Stan Freeman

NEW AVENGERS (Brown Watson)

1978-1979	£12	$19

©1977 (64pg) (fc)
Comic Strips: Fangs for the Memory (8), Hypno Twist (6)
Art: John Bolton
Photo features on the cast
Photo cover
Based on the TV series starring Patrick MacNee, Joanna Lumley and Gareth Hunt

NEWCASTLE UNITED (CrystalSpirit)

1995	£3	$5

NEW KIDS ON THE BLOCK (Marvel/World)

1991-1992	£5	$8

©1990-©1991 - Special (Marvel)
1991-92 - Official Annual (World)
1991 (64pg) (fc/tc)
Writer: Tommy Jay with Kim Glover
Designers: Hilary Edwards, Liz Auger and Bob Swan
1992 (64pg) (fc)
Writer: Tommy Jay with Kim Glover

Designers: Marc Abbott & Stuart Young
Based on the U.S. boy band

NEW MUSICAL EXPRESS 1974 Hot Rock Guide (Fleetway)

1974	£12	$19

Features: David Bowie, Pink Floyd, Roxy Music, Stones Special, Slade, Yes, Nazareth, Alice Cooper and Lou Reed
Based on the UK rock newspaper/magazine

NEWS CHRONICLES Annual (News Chronicles)
1950's-1960's

1950's	£12	$19
1960's	£10	$16

NEWS OF THE WORLD Football Annual (World)
1940's-1970's

1950's	£12	$19
1960's	£10	$16
1970's	£8	$16

1972 (108pg)
Edited by: Frank Butler
Features/Features: George Best, Ron Harris, Ron Davies, Gordon Banks, Richie Benaud, Johnny Leach

NICK BERRY Special (Grandreams)
1988

©1987	£5	$8

Based on the UK actor/singer

911 (Grandreams)

1998	£4	$7

Based on the UK boy band

NODDY (Grandreams/Pedigree)
1950's-present

1950's	£20	$32
1960's	£15	$24
1970's	£10	$16
1980's-present	£8	$13

1995 (World)
Consultant Editor: Gillian Baverstock
Education Advisor: Godfrey Hall
New Illustrations: Andrew Geeson
2000 (Pedigree)
'The Bumper Noddy Annual'
Based on the Enid Blyton character

NODDY SOUND Bumper (Pedigree)

2000	£5	$8

©1999
Features seven buttons which when pressed make sounds related to the stories

NOEL EDMONDS Multi Coloured (Brown & Watson)

1980	£10	$16

©1979 (64pg)
Pin Ups: Three Degrees, Leo Sayer, Rod Stewart, The Jam, Blondie, Abba, John Travolta, Andy Gibb, Elvis Costello, Boomtown Rats, Kevin Keegan, Racey, Darts
Based on the BBC TV personality

NO HIDING PLACE (World)

1967	£12	$19

©1966
Based on the ITV detective series

NOSEY BEARS (Marvel/Grandreams)

1989	£4	$7

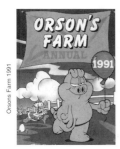

Based on the toy range
NOW I KNOW Walt Disney's... (Fleetway)
1974 (72pg)   £8 $13
Features: Peter Pan, Lady and the Tramp, Goofy, Sleeping Beauty, Jungle Book, Seven Dwarfs, Aristocats, Pinocchio, Brer Rabbit, Mowgli, Robin Hood
Based on the Disney characters
NUMBER TWO Album (Lion Publishing)
1974   £10 $16
©1973
Comic Strips: The Street Arabs Friend (6 bw)
Story: Chad Varah-Art: Norman Williams
Originally published in 'Eagle' annual
Highland Fling (3bw) - Art: Harold Johns
Barry Nearly Cops It! (2bw)
Story: Thelma Sangster-Art: Harold Johns
The Hiding Place, reprinted from 'Pilot'
An extract from the book by Corrie Ten Boom, published by Hodder and Stoughton
Beyond the Moon first appeared in 'Decision Magazine'
Ike and the Big Journey and Space Race Game are reprinted from 'Adventurers'
The Street Arab's Friend is reproduced from a booklet available from Dr Barnardo's
Highland Fling, Barry Nearly Cops It!, A Great Guy, Plusword and all the Smart Alec cartoons reprints 'Plus'
The Interview with Stan Smith, by Richard Bewes, first appeared in 'Link Magazine'
Puzzles: Mr A S Tompkin, Art: Rachel Beckingham and Diane Matthes
NUTTY NODDLE (Fleetway)
1964   £10 $16
©1963
OASIS Special 100% Unofficial (Grandreams)
1998   £3 $5
©1997 (64pg) (fc)
Writer: Mick St Michael and Ian Welch
Photo features
Based on the UK rock band
OH BOY! (Fleetway)
1978-1980's
1978   £10 $16
1979-1982   £8 $13
1979 (128pg)
Features: Eric & Woody (Bay City Rollers), Fonzie & Suzie Quatro, Rod Stewart, David Soul
1980 (128pg)
Romance comic strips (bw), photo-strips and features
Pin Ups (fc): Phil Lynott, Shaun Cassidy, Scott Baio, Marc Bolan, Elvis Presley, Boomtown Rats, David Essex, Leif Garrett, Queen
1983   £10 $16
Includes Adrian Paul modelling photo*
1984   £8 $13
1985 (96pg)   £20 $32
Cover features: Model/Actor Adrian Paul
Features: Spandau Ballet, Nick Heyward
Pin Ups: Lee Curreri, Bucks Fizz, Men at Work, Gene Antony Ray, Orange Juice, Altered Images, Edwyn, David Essex, Nick Rhodes
OKAY ADVENTURE Annual (Popular Press/Boardman & Co.)

1955-1958   £15 $24
Features: The Last Stand of Major Wilson, Invisible Justice etc.
OLDIE Annual (Bloomsbury)
1994   £5 $8
©1993
Edited by Richard Ingrams
Based on the UK magazine
OOR WULLIE (D.C. Thomson)
1941 - present (bi-annual)
1941   £350 $560
1951-1953   £100 $160
1955-1959   £50 $80
1960-1965   £20 $32
1967-1971   £10 $16
1973-1979   £8 $13
1981-1989   £6 $10
1991-present   £5 $8
OREGON TRAIL (Stafford Pemberton)
1979   £8 $13
Comic Strip (fc): The Trap (6)
Rod Taylor photo cover
Contents include photos (fc) from the Western TV series
ORSON'S FARM (Ravette Books)
1991   £5 $8
Writer Gordon Volke
From the creator of Garfield - Jim Davis
ORVILLE (Grandreams)
1987   £4 $7
©1986
Writer: Felix Culper
Based on the Keith Harris puppet character
OSMONDS
1974-1978
1974   £12 $19
1975-1978   £10 $16
1975 Annual (World)
1976 -1978 'Osmonds Yearbook'
Based on the US Pop Group
OUR BOYS COWBOY Annual
1950's   £12 $19
OUR OWN SCHOOLBOYS (World)
1950's-1960's
1950's   £10 $16
1960's   £8 $13
OUR OWN SCHOOLGIRLS (World)
1950's-1960's   £8 $13
1950's   £10 $16
©1956 (128pg)
Text Stories: Detention Insurance, Writer: Agnes Booth
Ginnie's Island Adventure, Writer: Lillian Murray
Gymkhana, Writer: Sylvia Little
The Horse that Didn't Like Grass, Writer: Sybil Burr
Pat's First Cruise, Writer: Joan Selby Lowndes
Bikes and Bisons, Writer: John Maurice
Lucky Day for Maureen, Writer: Arthur Nettleton
The Drove by Night, Writer: Dawn Sparkes
At The Sign of the Peacock, Writer: Catherine Morris
Terry, Tom and Cocoa, Writer: Stella Miles

The Adventure at Tarpon Springs, Writer: Doris Taylor
The Lost Cat, Writer Agnes Booth
Surprise for Daphne, Writer Beryl C. Lawley
Comic Strips: Fairdene on the Farm (6bw), The Missing Heir (6bw)
1960's   £8 $13
©1961 (128pg) (bw)
Frontispiece (fc): Party Games
Comic Strips (2x6): A Rooster For Rover, Skater's Waltz
Text Stories: A Conspiracy of Silence featuring Sally Baxter Girl
Reporter by Sylvia Edwards, Wendy's Magic Lamp featuring Shirley
Flight , Air Hostess by Judith Dale, Tour of Peril featuring Julie Ross
Travel Courier by Trudi Allen
Writers: Betty E. Spence, A.O. Pearson, Theo Lynch, Susan Jolly,
Lillian Murray, Wyn Davis, Agnes Kennett, Annette Painter, Joyce
Stranger
OUTER LIMITS (World)
1966-1967
1966   £15 $24
1967   £12 $19
Dell reprints
Based on the TV sci fi series
OUTLAWS (Purnell)
1961   £10 $16
Writer: Philip Davies-Art: Simonetti and Leo Rawlings
Comic Strips (8bw): Silent Witness, The Garnett Gang, The Fastest
Gun
Text stories: Battle at Rimrock Station, Vengeance Trail, Dance of
the Buffalo, 'Ed Barcas... Gunfighter!', The Brothers, Scarbrand, The
Great Steffani, Fugitive Doctor,10,000 Dollars Reward
Based on the TV Western series
PARSLEY (Polystyle)
1972   £8 $13
Including The Herbs
Based on the BBC puppet animation series
PARTRIDGE FAMILY (World)
1973-1976
1973   £12 $19
1974-1976   £10 $16
1975 (80pg) (fc/tc)
Comic Strips (UK): Easy Come, Easy Go (6fc)-Art: Edgar Hodges,
Shirley Goes On Strike (6fc)-Art: Melvyn Powell
Text Stories: A Shock For Shirley, Partridge Pilgrimage, The
Partridges Take A Vacation, Laurie's Secret, Danny's Dial-A-Date
Service, A Girl In A Million, A Man's Best Friend
Includes photo features on, David Cassidy, The Osmonds and the
Jackson Five (bw)
Photo cover
Based on the TV series starring David Cassidy and Shirley Jones
PATCHES (DC Thomson)
1980's-1990's   £5 $8
1984
Pin Ups: Todd Carty, Kids from Fame (2)
PATHFINDER for ALL SCOUTS (Purnell/Thames Publishing)
1950's-1960's
1950's   £10 $16
1960's   £6 $10
1961
Art: John Challen
PAUL DANIELS Magic Annual (World)

1983-1984   £5 $8
©1982 (64pg) (fc/tc)
Art: Melvyn Powell, David Brian, Paul Green
Photo cover
Based on the UK magician
PAUL YOUNG (Grandreams)
1986   £5 $8
Based on the UK pop singer
P.C. 49 (Juvenile/Preview/Dakers)
1951-1955
©1950-P.C. 49   £25 $40
By Alan Stranks
'Author of the Famous Radio Series'
Art: F.G. Moorsom
1952-On Duty with P.C. 49   £20 $32
1953- On the Beat with P.C.49   £20 $32
1953-Eagle Strip Cartoon Book No.1   £15 $24
Eagle reprints
1954- Eagle Strip Cartoon Book No.2   £15 $24
Eagle reprints
1955 - P.C. 49 Annual   £15 $24
All prices with dustjacket, Half price without dj, Art: Worsley
Based on the radio/comic character
PELLEPHANT (Brown Watson)
1970's
N/D No. 1   £5 $8
PELLEPHANT and His Friends (Brown Watson)
1970's
©1975   £5 $8
Also n/d edition
PENNY (IPC/Fleetway)
1980's   £4 $7
Based on the UK girls comic
PENNY CRAYON (Marvel)
1991   £4 $7
Based on the BBC animated TV series
PEPPER STREET (D C Thomson)
1987   £3 $5
Based on the animated TV series
PERISHERS (World)
1980-1981 (64pg)   £8 $13
Includes Daily Mirror newspaper strips drawn by Dennis Collins and
written by Maurice Dodd
Based on the animated TV series and newspaper comic strip
PERSUADERS
1973   £10 $16
Comic Strips: Hot Ice, Avalanche, Skyjack
Text Story: Strictly for the Birds
Photo cover
Based on the TV series starring Roger Moore and Tony Curtis
PET SHOP BOYS ANNUALLY (World)
1989 (64pg)   £5 $8
Features: Chris Lowe - The Sunglasses, Its a Sin, Actually - The
Sleeve, Neil Tennant - The Marvel Comics Years, The Fan Club,
Travel, What Have I Done to Deserve This, Neil - The Suits and
Coats, Making Records, Rent, Chris Lowe - The Milton Keynes
Staircase, Always on My Mind, It Couldn't Happen Here - The Film,
Heart, History, Reviews, Discography

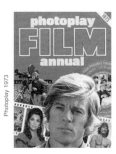

Photoplay 1973

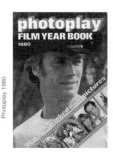

Photoplay 1980

Pigeon Street 1982

Based on the UK pop band
PETER ANDRE (Grandreams)
1998-1999 (64 pg) (fc)   £3 $5
©1997
Writer: Belinda Jones - Designer: Jason Bazini
Photo Features
©1998
Writer: S. Denim-Designer: Jason Bazini
Photo features
Based on the UK pop singer
PETER PAN (World)
1960's   £5 $8
Based on the J M Barrie character
PHANTOM (World)
1968-1969   £10 $16
Based on the comic strip character
PHILLIP SCHOFIELD (World)
1993   £3 $5
Based on the UK TV personality
PHOTO LOVE (Fleetway)
1980's   £5 $8
1985 (80pg)
Star Profile: Paul Young
Pin Ups (fc): Martin Kemp, Paul Young, Sting, Shakin Stevens, Mike Nolan
PHOTOPLAY FILM Annual (Argus Press)
1971-1975   £10 $16
1971 (80pg)
Cover features: Paul Newman
Features: Jon Voight, David Lean, Christopher Lee, Vincent Price, Peter Cushing, Dustin Hoffman, Barbra Streisand, Christopher Plummer, Susan George, A Last Valley (Movie), Jack Lemmon, Cromwell (Movie), Steve McQueen, Clint Eastwood, Julie Andrews, Goldie Hawn, John Wayne, Lee Marvin
Pin Ups: Dustin Hoffman, Barbra Streisand, Faye Dunaway, James Coburn, Paul Newman & Joanne Woodward, Marilyn Monroe, Jack Lemmon, Steve McQueen, Glen Campbell, Omar Sharif, Clint Eastwood, Julie Andrews, Goldie Hawn
1973 (80pg)
Cover features: Robert Redford
Features: Barry Newman, Brigitte Bardot, Claudia Cardinale, Liza Minnelli, Dustin Hoffman, Sophia Loren, Peter O'Toole, Hywel Bennett, Keith Michell, Simon Ward, Clint Eastwood, Charlton Heston, Robert Redford, Lady Caroline Lamb, Robin Hood (Movie), Steve McQueen, Frenzy (Movie), John Wayne
Pin Ups: Glenda Jackson, Jo Ann Pflug, Sean Connery, Paul Newman, Clint Eastwood, Susannah York, Robert Wagner, Charlton Heston, Michael Caine, Jill St. John, Elizabeth Taylor, Richard Burton
1974
Cover features: Roger Moore & Jane Seymour
Features: Liv Ullmann, Jan-Michael Vincent, Richard Burton, Peter Finch, Robert Shaw, Ali MacGraw, Robert Redford, Steve McQueen, Roger Moore, Burt Reynolds, Jane Fonda, Jane Seymour, John Wayne, Christopher Lee, Barbra Streisand
Pin Ups (fc): Jan Michael Vincent, Burt Reynolds, Peter Finch and Glenda Jackson, Barbra Streisand, Michael Caine, Lesley Anne Down, Oliver Reed, Gene Hackman, Barry Newman, John Wayne and Ann Margret, Paul Newman, James Cann, Jacqueline Bisset,

Britt Ekland, Roger Moore
1975
Features: Clint Eastwood, Richard Burton, Sophia Loren, Robert Redford, Al Pacino, Bruce Lee, Roger Moore, Barbra Streisand, Lucille Ball, Julie Andrews, Steve Warner
Scenes from the films: Caravan to Vaccares, An Investigation into Murder, The Exorcist, The Black Windmill, Vampira, Zardoz, Mame, Serpico, Dillinger, The Tamarind Seed, The Abdication, The Three Musketeers, The Great Gatsby
Pin Ups: George Segal, Robert Redford, David Essex, Al Pacino, Lucille Ball, Veronica Carlson, Roger Moore, Charlotte Rampling, James Coburn, Rod Taylor, Barbra Streisand, Julie Andrews, Omar Sharif, Burt Reynolds
Based on the UK movie magazine
PHOTOPLAY FILM Year Book (IP)
1976-1980   £8 $13
1976 (72pg)
Features: Peter Sellers, The Godfather (Part II) (Movie), Barbra Streisand, Robert Redford, The Great Waldo Pepper (Movie), Susannah York, James Caan, Warren Beatty, Oliver Reed
Pin Ups: Barbra Streisand, Paul Newman, Lee Marvin, Richard Burton, Robert Redford, James Caan, Robert Wagner & Natalie Wood, Clint Eastwood, Burt Reynolds, Roger Daltrey, Charles Bronson, Roger Moore, Faye Dunaway, Ann Margret, Kirk Douglas
1978
Features: Kris Kristofferson, Lynne Frederick, Susan George, Lesley Anne Down, Jenny Agutter, Michael Caine, The Deep (Movie), Nick Nolte, Jessica Lange, Sylvester Stallone, Marthe Keller, Martin Sheen, Al Pacino, Clint Eastwood, Roger Moore, Helen Reddy, A Bridge Too Far
Pin Ups: Michael Caine, Nick Nolte, Liza Minnelli, Barbra Streisand, Barbra Bach, Lee Marvin, Robert Shaw, Starsky & Hutch, Clint Eastwood, Jane Fonda
1979
Features: Tatum O'Neal, John Travolta, Jane Fonda, Casablanca
Pin Ups: Charles Bronson, Kris Kristofferson, Ali MacGraw, John Thaw, Dennis Waterman, William Katt, Oliver Reed
1980
Soft cover featuring Clint Eastwood
Features: Dracula (Movie), Bear Island (Movie), Roger Moore (Moonraker movie), Meteor (Movie), Clint Eastwood, Michael Caine Movies, Christopher Reeve
Pin Ups: Clark Gable, Valerie Perrine, Robert de Niro, Sophia Loren, Clint Eastwood, Ian McShane, John Travolta, Jacqueline Bisset, Elliott Gould, Oliver Tobias
Based on the UK movie magazine
PICKLE Annual
1960   £12 $19
Photo cover
Based on Dennis The Menace U.S. TV series
PICTUREGOER FILM Annual (Odhams)
With dustjackets
1940's-1960's
1950-1960   £25 $40
1958
Includes Marilyn Monroe and Jayne Mansfield
PICTURE SHOW
1940's-1960's
1950-1960   £15 $24

Pingu 1995

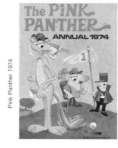

Pink Panther 1974

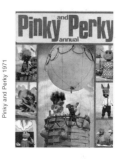

Pinky and Perky 1971

PIGEON STREET (Grandreams)
1982-1983
©1981 and ©1982 (64pg)   £5 $8
Based on the Childrens BBC animated TV series
PINGU (World)
1990's   £5 $8
Based on the BBC TV puppet animation series
PINK (Fleetway)
1970's-1980's
1970's   £8 $13
1974 (128pg)
Comic Strips: Jilly's Night of Joy (6tc), The Star School of Secrets
(8bw), Dear Dad (3bw), One Dark Night (3bw), Janey and the End
of the World (3bw), The Dance Contest (3bw), Me and Madame
(8tc)
Features: Gary Glitter, Slade, Colin Blunstone, Cat Stevens, David
Cassidy, David Lambert, Andy & David Williams, The Jacksons
Pin Ups: Colin Blunstone, Jerry Shirley, Rod Stewart, David Bowie,
Noddy Holder, David Cassidy, New Seekers, White Plains, Michael
Jackson, The Osmonds, Elton John, Donny Osmond,
1978 (128pg)
Comic Strips: Patty's World (2bw), The Eyes of Simon Storm
(10tc/bw), Fever! (2bw), My Love for Larry (3bw), The Bird (2bw), Its
Dreams that Keep You Going! (6bw), Running Out of Time (3bw),
Who's Guilty, Now? (3bw), Sugar Jones (3bw)
Features: Bay City Rollers, Elton John, Mud, Flintlock, David Essex,
Slik, USA Pop, Stevensons Rocket
Small Features: Starsky & Hutch, Ben Murphy, Osmonds,
Pin Ups: Mud, Bay City Rollers (4pg), Flintlock, Slik, Stevensons
Rocket
1979 (128pg)
Comic Strips (bw) and features
Features: Shawn Cassidy, Starsky & Hutch, Leo Sayer, Mud, The
Jam
Pin Ups: Shaun Cassidy, Bay City Rollers, Leo Sayer, Mud
1980's   £6 $10
1981 (128pg)
Comic Strips (bw) and features
Pin Ups: Leif Garrett, Shaun Cassidy (double-page), Greg Evigan,
Dollar, Joey Travolta, Leo Sayer, Bryan Ferry
Photo cover features Lesley Ash
1982 (96pg)
Comic Strips (bw) and features
Features: Andy Gibb, The Police
Pin Ups: Johnny Logan (double-page), Andy Gibb
Based on the girls teenage magazine
PINK PANTHER (World/Brown Watson)
1970's   £8 $13
1974 (World)
Comic Strips: Pink on the Range, The Pink Sphinx, Ape Suzette,
The Pink Trespanther, Pink Pilot, Rock a bye Pink, Le Quiet Squad,
Pink Blueprint, The Smart Art Thief, Pink Predictor, The Purloined
Pink Lemonade,Pink Shoelacer
©1976 (Brown Watson)
Featuring The Inspector
Comic Strips (fc): Pink Panther - Code of the West, A Pink in the
Neck, Pink-A-Boo, The Great Pink Hunter, The Pink Baron Flies
Again, Pink Passenger to Pinkbuktoo, Little Pink Riding Hood, Tally
HoHo the Inspector - Case of: The Staircase Clue, Case of: The

Rerun Crime, Case of: The Sinn Twins
Based on the animated TV series
PINKY & PERKY (Purnell)
1960's-1970's
1960's   £10 $16
1970's   £8 $13
©1974 (60 pg) (fc)
Picture Strips: Shock Treatment, The Day the Swing Broke, By
Candlelight, The Canoe Race, Not Quite True, A Noise That
Annoyed
Based on the ITV marionette characters
PIP, SQUEAK AND WILFRED
1950's   £25 $40
Based on the Daily Mirror cartoon strip
PIPPIN (Polystyle)
1960's-1980's
1969 (96pg) (fc)
Comic Strips: The Pogles, Bizzy Lizzy, The Woodentops, The
Moonbeans, Trumpton, Camberwick Green, Joe,
Endpapers: Gordon Davey
1970's   £10 $16
©1971 (80pg) (fc)
Cover Art: Jim Eldridge
Comic Strips: The Herbs, Mary, Mungo & Midge, Andy Pandy,
Trumpton, The Pogles, The Woodentops, Bill and Ben, Chigley,
Bizzy Lizzy, The Moonbeans
1975
Comic Strips: Chigley, Woodentops, Moonbeans, Fingerbobs, Mr
Benn, Barnaby, Mary Mungo & Midge, Trumpton, Teddy Edward,
The Herbs, Andy Pandy, Pogles
©1977
Cover Art: Fred Robinson
Comic Strips and text stories featuring:
Andy Pandy, The Moonbeans, Barnaby, Mary, Mungo and Midge,
Bagpuss, Camberwick Green, Sooty and Sweep, Chigley and
Trumpton, Rubovia, Weebles,
Along the River, Stories From the Bible: The Story of Peter.
1980's   £8 $13
1980
Andy Pandy, Barnaby, Sooty & Sweep, Ivor the engine, Timbuctoo,
Moonbeans, Camberwick Green, Toytown, Marry Mungo & Midge,
Rubovia,
1981
Comic Strips: The Moonbeans, Timbuctoo, Barnaby, Sooty &
Sweep, Ivor the Engine, Munch Bunch, Mary Mungo & Midge,
Camberwick Green, Andy Pandy, Barnaby,Rubovia
©1983
Picture Strips: Ivor the Engine, The Munch Bunch, Mr Benn, The
Moonbeams, The Wombles, Tat the Cat, Pippa's Playgroup,
Moschops, The Amazing Adventures of Morph, Timbuctoo by Roger
Hargreaves, Bible Story, Gordon Murray's Trumpton,
Mary, Mungo and Midge
Based on Childrens BBC TV characters
PIXIE (Fleetway)
1970s   £8 $13
1975
Comic Strips: Goodbye, Dolly (5tc), Pixie Potter and her Merry
Magic (2tc), Marion of Sherwood (5fc), Hansel & Gretel (16bw), Mini
Ha Ha (1fc), Motor Car Fun (2fc), Vote for Sue (32bw), Black Beauty

Planet of the Apes 1976

The Pogles 1970

Police 1983

---

was Young (4fc), Ricky Rascal (7tc), Highland Lassie (10tc),

PIXIE AND DIXIE with MR JINKS (World/Brown Watson)

1960's-1970's		
1960's	£15	$24
1970's	£10	$16
1975		

Comic Strips: Taming the Tabby, Forty Hoodwinks, The Old-Youngsters
1977 (Brown Watsoon)
Based on the Hanna-Barbera cartoon characters

PIXIE AND DIXIE Television Storybook (PBS)

1963	£12	$19

Comic strip reprints and text stories (bw)
Based on the Hanna-Barbera cartoon characters

PLANET OF THE APES (Brown Watson)

1975-1977	£10	$16

©1976
Comic Strips: Pit of Doom, Ship of Fools
Based on the TV series starring Roddy McDowall

PLAY AWAY (Grandreams)

1980's	£3	$5

Based on the BBC pre-school series

PLAYBOX (Fleetway)

1909-1956		
1950-1956	£20	$32

PLAYDAYS (World)

1990's	£3	$5

1994 (64pg)
Editor: Margaret McCarthy, Design: Liz Auger
Writers: Clare Bradley, Kristina Stephenson, Christina Takkides
Art: Kristina Stephenson, Teresa Foster, Sue Cony, Susie Poole and Ken Morton
Text Stories: Thomas the Rhymer by Louise Fryer, Princess Tilly and the Dragon by Eileen Doyle, King Greenfingers by Kathleen J Dean, The Grimpy Court Jester by Angela Neville*
1995
Design: Liz Auger
Based on the BBC TV pre-school series

PLAYGROUP (Fleetway)

1980's	£4	$7

1987 (80pg)
Comic Strip characters include: Jenny & Ginger, Sammy the Squirrel, Rob Rabbit, Magic Roundabout, Mr Small
Text Stories: Magic Roundabout

PLAYHOUR (Fleetway/IPC)

1955-1986		
1955	£25	$40
1956-1959	£20	$32
1960-1965	£15	$24
1965 (96pg)		

Comic Strip characters include: Sonny and Sally, Bunny Cuddles, Mimi and Marmy, Mr. Toad, Tommy Trouble, Leo the Friendly Lion, Sooty & Sweep, Wink and Blink, Billy Brock, The Talking Bird

1966-1969	£10	$16
1970's	£8	$13
1972 (96pg)		

Comic Strip characters include: Moony from the Moon, The Magic Roundabout, Sonny and Sally, Nutty Noddle, Dozey Dormouse,

Bunny Cuddles, Rolf Harris and Coojeebear, Mimi and Marmy, Mr. Toad, Tommy Trouble, The Puss-Cats, Little Gregory Grasshopper, Leo the Friendly Lion
1975
See 1972
1979 (80pg)
Comic Strip characters include: Wizard Weezle, Pinkie Puff, The Dolly Girls, Sonny and Sally, Mimi and Marmy, Mr Small, Little Bo Peep, Pixie Pip, Willie Wisp, Bunny Cuddles, Mr Toad, The Magic Roundabout, The Beans, Bobtail Bunny, Tommy Trouble, Moony from the Moon, Num Num, Sally and Jake

1980's	£5	$8
1981		

See 1972
1984 (80pg)
Comic Strip characters include: Pinkie Puff, Puss Cat Family, The Dolly Girls, Nutty Noodle, Wink and Blink, Mimi and Marmy, The Broken Doll, Mr Popple, The Beans, Dozey, Mr Toad, TV Boy, Sally and Jake, The Jumblies, Wizard Weezle
1986
Comic Strips: See 1972 plus Mr. Men
Based on the preschool UK comic

PLAYLAND (Polystyle)

1970s	£10	$16
1971		

Features children's TV favourites -
Clangers, Sooty & Sweep, Tingha & Tucker, Hector's House, Babar, Parsley the Lion, Camberwick Green, and Hatty Town
1972
Features children's TV favourites -
Clangers, Sooty & Sweep, Hector's House, Parsley the Lion, Camberwick Green, Toy Town, Tales of the Riverbank, Crystall Tipps & Alistair, Sir Prancelot and Hatty Town
Based on the UK comic

PLAY SCHOOL (World/Grandreams)

1970's-1980's	£3	$5

©1984 (Grandreams)
Art: Paul Johnson, Jan Brychta, Claire Beaton, Joanna Isles, Nancy Retley Jones, Tom Brooks and Joanna Cheese
©1985 (Grandreams)
Art: Paul Johnson, Jan Brychta, Stella Farris, Peter Wane, Joanna Cheese and Amanda Paulter
Based on the BBC TV pre-school series

PLAY SCHOOL Omnibus (Grandreams)

1982	£3	$5

Editor: John Barraclough-Art editor: Nigel Money

PLAYWAYS (Lutterworth Press)

1962	£10	$16

POGLES

1969-1972	£8	$13

Based on BBC TV Watch With Mother series

POLICE (Stafford Pemberton)

1982-1983		
©1982	£8	$13

Based on the UK pop band featuring Sting

POLICE ACADEMY (Marvel)
1992
Based on the animated TV series

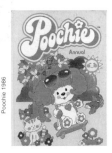

Poochie 1986

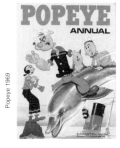

Popeye 1969

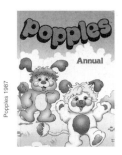

Popples 1987

POLLY POCKET

1994-1996	£3	$5

1994 (64pg) (World)
Writer: Judith Laverly, Editor: Brenda Apsley
Illustrations: Arkadia, Designer: Rob Sharp
Comic Strips: Gymkhana, Goes to Africa, Cafe Caretaking, Starlight Castle Search,
©1995 (48pg) (fc) (Grandreams)
Comic Strips: Secret Garden, All That Glitters, Bianca's Party
Art: Glenn Rix and Paul Green
Based on the girls toy range

PONY CLUB (Purnell/World)

1950's-1980's

1950's	£10	$16
1960's	£8	$13
1970's-1980's	£5	$8

Editor: Genevieve Murphy

PONY IN MY POCKET (World)

1990's	£3	$5

PONY MAGAZINE (Purnell)

1970s (with dj)	£8	$13
1970's (without dj)	£4	$7

1975 (96pg) (bw)
Editor: Michael Williams
Text Story Writers: Sally Dudley, Caroline Akrill, Elizabeth Hawthorne, Besse Leese, Anne English, Mary Holmes, Nina Ananins, Josephine Pullein-Thompson
Art: Nicola Palin, Elaine Roberts, Ellen Gilbert, Nicola Beckett, Heidi Best, Janet and Anne Grahame Johnstone, Nina Annanins, Christine Bousfield
1976 (96pg) (bw)
Half price without dustjacket (fc)
Compiled by the Editor of 'Pony' Michael Williams
Comic Strip: Problem Pony (1)
Photo features and text stories (bw)

POOCHIE (Grandreams)

1986

©1985	£4	$7

Based on the Mattel toy range

POP CLUB

1979	£8	$13

Features Paul McCartney and Led Zeppelin

POPEYE (Adprint/Purnell/Brown Watson/ Pemberton/World/Grandreams)

1960-1980's

1960	£15	$24
1961-1965	£12	$19
1966-1969	£10	$16

©1968 (World)
Comic Strips: Physical Fitness Programme, Striking Out Sis, Space Egg, Sailor's Rights, The Ol' Swimming Hole
Art: Bud Sagendorf

1970 on	£8	$13

1972 Popeye Annual No.1
©1972 (Brown Watson)
Number One
Comic Strips (tc/fc): Popeye and the Capsule of Knowledge, Popeye and the Generation Gap, Popeye and the Space Monsters, Popeye and the Bride - Art: Bud Sagendorf

©1974 (Brown Watson)
Comic Strips (tc/fc): Popeye the Sailor in
Popeye's Railroad, Bully for You, Mushroom Doom, The Pushover, The Last of the .....?, A Fat Plot, Green Grows the Spinach, A Damsel in Distress, The Sea Monster, Sea Hag in The Stupid Solution, Professor O G Wotasnozzle in The People Changer
Art: George Wildman
1980 (Stafford Pemberton) (64 pg) (tc)
Cover Art: Paul Green
Popeye and the Princess,The Sea Hag's Spell, The Saga of Superstuff, Who Gots Swee'Pea? Comes the Revalooshun!, Genius Juice, Life of the Party
1981 (Stafford Pemberton) (64 pg) (fc)
Cover Art/Endpaper: Paul Green
Comic Strips: The Swamp County Meteorite Site Heavyweight Fight (23) - Popeye#140 reprint
Ghost Mine by Bud Sagendorf (8),
Thimble Theatre Presents.. Popeye in the...Maddening Mystery of the Disappearing Daredevils of the Colossal Carnival Circus!!! (22) Popeye #141 reprint

POP GROUP (World)

1970's	£10	$16

1977 (80pg)
Features: Queen, The Rubettes, Slade, KC and the Sunshine Band, Bay City Rollers, Roxy Music, Mud, The Shadows, Steeleye Span, Abba, Showaddywaddy, ELO, The Who, 10cc, Stylistics
Pin Ups: Bay City Rollers, Steeleye Span, 10cc, Showaddywaddy, The Glitter Band, Abba, Sailor, O'Jays, Slade, Smokey Robinson and the Miracles, Pilot, Beatles, Status Quo, Mud, Roy Wood, Mott the Hoople, Queen, The Supremes, The 3 Degrees, Stylistics, The Rubettes, The Osmonds, Kenny, The Rolling Stones, Jackson 5
1978 (64pg) (fc/fc)
Photo features include: E.L.O., Wings, Smokie, Beach Boys, Showaddywaddy, Doobie Brothers, Abba, Poco, Osibisa, The Who, Steeleye Span, Gallagher & Lyle, Jethro Tull, Mud, Dr. Hook, The Carpenters, Rolling Stones, Santana, Status Quo, Chicago, Tavares, Hollies, Thin Lizzy, Cockney Rebel, Procul Harum, Osmonds, Four Tops, Bob Marley, Bee Gees, Rory Gallagher, Manfred Mann's Earth Band, Hot Chocolate, Peter Frampton, Rubettes
Photo cover featuring Queen, Mud and Smokie

POPPLES (Marvel)

1987-1989	£5	$8

1987 (64pg)
Comic Strips and Text Stories
1989 (64pg)
Comic Strips (fc): One Baby's Zoo! (10), The Kitten Napper! (7), Talking Teddy? (5), Treasure Hunt! (9), Popples (5)
Based on the toy range

POP SUPERSTARS (Opal Quill)

1984-1985	£7	$11

1984
Features: Human League, Spandau Ballet, Culture Club, Soft Cell, Style Council, Nick Heyward, Duran Duran, Men at Work, O M D, Altered Images, Heaven 17, Michael Jackson, Bow Wow Wow, Wham, The Beat, Depeche Mode, Icehouse, Thompson Twins, ABC, Tears for Fears, Orange Juice, Malcolm McLaren, Fun Boy 3, Dexy's Midnight Runners, Eurythmics, Yazoo, Ultravox
1985
Features: Thompson Twins, Howard Jones, Eurythmics,

Popswop 1976

Portland Bill 1985 St Michael

Pow 1970

Kajagoogoo, Limahl, Lotus Eaters, Billy Joel, Nick Heyward, Culture Club, Style Council, Pretenders, Michael Jackson, Duran Duran, Paul Young, Tracey Ullman, Madness, Nik Kershaw, Ultravox, Bananarama, Echo and the Bunnymen, Spandau Ballet

POPSWOP (World)

1973-1977	£10	$16

©1973 (96 pg)
Features on: Ben Murphy, David Cassidy, The Osmonds, Marc Bolan, Elton John, Slade, Marie Osmond, Rod Stewart, the New Seekers, David Bowie, The Sweet, David Essex
Pin Ups (sp fc): Donny Osmond, David Cassidy, Marty Kristian, Michael Jackson, Rod Stewart, New Seekers, Ben Murphy, Sweet, Cliff Richard, Alice Cooper, Elton John, The Osmonds, David Bowie, Marc Bolan, The Faces
Based on the UK pop magazine

POP WEEKLY

1960's	£12	$19

1969 Features Cliff Richard

PORTLAND BILL The Adventures of (World/Purnell)

1980's	£5	$8

Based on the Childrens BBC TV puppet animation series

PORTLAND BILL (St Michael)

1985		
©1984	£5	$8

Based on the Childrens BBC TV puppet animation series

POSTMAN PAT (Polystyle/World)

1980's - present		
1980's	£5	$8

1986 (World)
©1989 (Polystyle)

1990's		
1992 (World)	£3	$5

Stories and features written by Brenda Apsley
Art: Ray Mutimer and Edgar Hodges
1996 (World)
writer Brenda Apsley
Art: Ray and Christine Mutimer
Based on the ITV puppet animation series

POTSWORTH & CO (World)

1992 (64pg) (fc)	£4	$7

Based on the Hanna-Barbera character

POUND PUPPIES (Grandreams)

1980's	£5	$8

Based on the toy range

POW! (Odhams)

1968-1972		
1968	£15	$24

Includes Spider-Man #1, Strange Tales (Nick Fury) # 135 reprints

1969	£12	$19
1970-1972	£10	$16

1970 (80pg)
Comic Strips: At the Mercy of Baron Strucker (12fc), The Nervs (3fc), The Swots and the Blots (3tc), The Cloak v Cloakwoman (2tc), Escape into Space (5tc), Wee Willie Haggis (3tc), Percy's Pets (3tc), The Swots and the Blots (4fc), The Cloak v Blubberman (3fc), The Amazing Spiderman - When Falls the Meteor! (18tc), Grimly Focndish (4tc), Sammy Shrink (2fc), Fantastic Four - Death of a Hero! (13fc)

Based on the UK comic

POWER RANGERS TURBO Saban's Official (Grandreams)

1998-1990	£3	$5

©1997
Editor: Tony Lynch, Designer: Dave Saunders
©1998
Editor: Tony Lynch, Designer: Jason Bazini
64 pg colour photo features
Based on the TV series

PREMIER BOOK For Boys Dean's(Dean)

1960-1969		
1960-1965	£8	$13
1966-1970	£6	$10

©1969 (128pg) (bw)
Frontispiece (fc illustration)-from 'Charlie Boy'
Comic Strip: Thief In The Night (4)-Writer: Edmund Burton
Text Story Writers: Philip M. Pethick, Edmund Burton, Edgar Barrett, Richard Lyne, Ronald Horton, Hector Barrie, B. Leonard

PREMIER BOOK For Girls Dean's (Dean)

1960s		
1960-1965	£8	$13
1966-1970	£6	$10

PRINCESS Gift Book For Girls

1960-1970's	£8	$13

Based on the UK girls comic

PRINCESS (Egmont World)

2000	£3	$5

Features Disney characters

PRINCESS TINA (IPC/Fleetway)

1968-1979		
1960's	£12	$19
1970's	£8	$13

1975 (128pg)
Text Stories: The Accident, Writer: Helen Vintner
The Picture on the Wall, Writer: Angela R Griffiths
Comic Strips: Patty's World (6tc), Life with Tina (4tc), Super-Girl Sandra (2x2tc), Barbie - The Model Girl (2bw & 6tc & 4tc), The Happy Days (6bw), Chariman Cherry (5bw & 3tc), The Trolls (3tc & 4tc), Milly The Merry Mermaid (2tc & 2bw), Patty's World (6tc), Wuthering Heights (11bw)
1979 (96pg)
Comic Strips: Moira Slave Girl of Rome (20tc), Milly the Merry Mermaid (2x2tc), The Happy Days (8tc), The Trolls (2x4tc), The Happy Days (4tc)
Features: Prince Charles (1pg feature & pin up)
Based on the UK girl's comic

PRINCESS TINA BALLET Book (Fleetway/IPC)

1969-1970's	£10	$16

No.1 ©1968
No.4 ©1971 (70pg)
Features include: Stars of the Kirov, Contrasts from the Ballet Rambert, The Wizard of Oz, Ballet Imperial, The Spanish Nureyev, Giselle, Facade, Cinderella Goes Touring
Pin Ups: Alison Howard, Deirdre O'Conaire, Christine Aitken
Large format photo features (fc)

PRINCESS TINA PONY Book (IPC/Fleetway)

1960's-1970's	£8	$13

1969 (64pg) (fc)

Comic Strip: Molly Must Not Ride (7)
1971 (80pg) (fc)
1974 (84pg) (fc)
Endpaper Art: Harry Bishop
1979 (80pg) (fc/tc)
PRODIGY Special Totally 100% Unofficial (Grandreams)
1999
©1998   £3 $5
Based on the UK rock band
The PROFESSIONALS
1979-1985
1979   £10 $16
1980-1985   £8 $13
©1978 (Brown and Watson)
Comic Strips: Sight of Something Bigger, The High Flier
©1979 (Grandreams)
Comic Strips: Oh to be in England, Strike Force
©1980 (Grandreams)
The Scapegoat, This time R.I.P.
1982 (Stafford Pemberton) (80pg)
Comic Strips (fc): When the Chips are Down, The One That Got Away
Includes photo features (fc)
1983 (Stafford Pemberton) (64pg)
Comic Strips: Race Against Time (8fc), Sticky Ending (8fc)
Includes photo features and pin ups
1984 (Stafford Pemberton) (64pg)
Comic Strips (2x8 fc): Influence, Week-End by the Sea
Photo cover
©1984 (Purnell) (64 fc) (fc/bw)
Comic Strips (fc):Traitor, Stagefright
Photo cover
Based on the TV series starring Martin Shaw and Lewis Collins
PROJECT SWORD (City)
1968 (96pg)   £20 $32
Comic Strips (fc): Project Sword-The Beetle (10), Project Sword Moon Crawler (6), Project Sword Apollo Rocket (7), Project Sword Booster Rocket (8), Project Sword Moon Prospector (6), Project Sword Hovertank (7), Project Sword Survey Vehicle (8)
Includes Zero X Mark 101 cutaway and photo feature on the Project Sword personnel
PROTECTORS (Polystyle)
1974   £10 $16
Based on the Gerry Anderson TV series starring Robert Vaughn and Nyree Dawn Porter
PUFFALUMPS (Grandreams)
1988   £3 $5
PUPPY IN MY POCKET (World)
1980's-1990's
1980's   £5 $8
1990's   £3 $5
Based on the toy range
The QUEST (Brown Watson)
1978
©1977 (64pg)   £8 $13
Comic Strips (6x2fc): Blood on the Plains, Make Me a Hero
Includes photo features from the TV series (fc/bw)
Photo cover
Based on the TV Western series starring Kurt Russell and Tim

Matheson
QUESTION OF SPORT (Marvel/World)
1981, 1990   £5 $8
©1980 (World)
1990 (64pg) (Marvel)
Editor Sheila Cranna - Design: Gary Gilbert
Based on the BBC TV sports quiz show
RADIO Annual (Stamford Publishing)
1984 (80pg) (fc)   £5 $8
'Your Independent Radio Annual'
Features: Paul McCartney, Duran Duran, Madness, Altered Images, Human League, Toyah, Ultravox, Shakin' Stevens, Bucks Fizz
Comic Strip: Radio Treasure Trail (6)
The annual was published in many editions with the same contents but different independent radio stations logos featured on the cover. An feature is dedicated to each radio station in the respective annual. These include: Radio Hallam, 225 Hereward Radio, Beacon Radio 303, Radio Tees, Radio Aire 362, Red Rose 301, Essex Radio, Downtown Radio, 235 Penine Radio and Chiltern Radio
RADIO CAROLINE
1960's   £10 $16
Based on the pioneering UK pirate radio station
RADIO FUN Book (Amalgamated)
1940-1960
1940   £200 $320
1950-1955   £15 $24
1956-1960   £10 $16
Based on the UK comic
RADIO LUXEMBOURG Book of Record Stars (Souvenir/World)
1960's
No.1-©1961   £20 $32
No.2-4   £15 $24
©1965-No 4 (158pg) (bw)
Introduction: The Beatles-Editor: Jack Fishman
Photo features include: Public Thoughts On My Private Life - Elvis Presley (4), It's Tough At The Bottom Says Georgie Fame (5), Cilla, Kathy and Me by Dusty Springfield (2), I'm The Dean Of Hollywood - Dean Martin (2), I Was A Never-Was by P.J. Proby (6), Sticks And Stones With The Rolling Stones (6), Roger Miller Shows you how to be King Of The Road (3), The Daddy Of Them All by Chuck Berry (2), The Other Side Of The Camera by Cliff Richard (4), The Trail From Tulsa by Gene Pitney (4), Music That Will Never Die by Jim Reeves (4), Help! (6-Beatle film)
Features by: Tom Jones, Trini Lopez, Bobby Vinton, Louis Armstrong, Manfred Mann, Roy Orbison, The Animals, Jerry Lee Lewis, Muriel Young, Herman (Peter Noone), Dave Clark, Brenda Lee, Jimmy Savile, The Bachelors and The Searchers
Beatles photo included on cover (fc/bw)
Based on the Independent radio station
RADIO ONE (City)
1969   £12 $19
Based on the BBC radio station
RAGDOLL Annual (Egmont World)
2000   £3 $5
Features Teletubbies, Tots TV, Rosie and Jim and Brum
RAGGY DOLLS
1980's-1990's

Raiders of the Lost Ark 1982

Rambo 1988

Razzmatazz 1985

RE

1980's	£5	$8
1990's	£3	$5

1992 (64pg)
Includes comic strips, text stories and puzzles
Based on the Childrens ITV animated series
RAIDERS OF THE LOST ARK (Marvel/Grandreams)
1982

©1981	£8	$13

Cover Art: Howard Chaykin
Comic strip adaptation (fc): Raiders of the Lost Ark
Based on the movie starring Harrison Ford
RAINBOW Annual
1924-57
Later known as 'Rainbow Annual'

1950-1957	£15	$24

Based on the UK comic
RAINBOW (Stafford Pemberton/World)
1981-1990's

1981	£8	$13
1982-1989	£5	$8
1990's	£3	$5

1981 (Stafford Pemberton)
Writer: Diana Stokers-Art: Wendy Bickers
Photo cover
1990 (World) (64pg) (fc)
Writer: Clive Hopwood
1992 (World) (fc)
Writer: Michael Butcher-Art: RWS Graphics
Based on the ITV children's series
RAINBOW BRITE (Grandreams)
1984

©1983 (64pg)	£5	$8

Picture Strips (3x2fc): Starlite's Tail Shampoo, Roses For The
Princess
Based on the toy range
RAINBOW FAVOURITES (Cliveden Press)

1989	£3	$5

Rainbow Annual compilation
RAINBOW GUIDE (World/Guide Association)

1990's	£3	$5

1995 (World)
1996 (GA) - present
1997
Editor/Designer: John & Hilary Halam
Alphabet Studio, Manchester
Based on the Girl Guides
RAINY DAYS Walt Disneys (Fleetway)

1976	£6	$10

Comic Strips feature: Mickey & Friends, Goofy, Donald Duck, Pluto
RANGER (Fleetway)

1967-1969	£12	$19

Based on the UK comic
RAMBO (World)

1987-1988	£5	$8

1988 (64pg) (fc)
Comic Strips: Custrel's Last Stand (6), The Traitor (8), Gun Run (6),
Underground Attack (6)
Based on the animated TV series

RANGERS Football Club (Inglis Allen)

1990-present	£3	$5

1997-No.7 (56pg) (fc/bw)
Editor: John C. Traynor-Writer: Douglas G. Russell
Photo features
RATTTIES (Grandreams)
1989

©1988 (64pg) (fc)	£4	$7

Stories adapted from the original TV scripts by Mike Wallis and
Laura Milligan
Layout/Art: Sharon Morgan and John Barber
Based on ITV children's series featuring the voice of Spike Milligan
RAWHIDE (Dean)
1960's

1961	£15	$24
1962-1965	£12	$19
1966 on	£10	$16

©1960 (128pg)
Cover/Contents Art: Leo Rawlings
Writer: Bill Pembury
Text stories (tc) with painted frontpiece (fc)
Based on the TV Western series starring Clint Eastwood
RAWHIDE Television Storybook (New Town Printers)

1961	£10	$16

RAZZMATAZZ (Fleetway)

1985	£7	$11

Features: Madness, Police, Bucks Fizz
Comic Strips: The Culture Club Story, The Duran Duran Story
Pin Ups: Limahl, Howard Jones, Junior, Big Country, Madness,
Marilyn, Kim Wilde, Gary Numan, Nick Heyward and Thompson
Twins
Based on the ITV music show
REAL GHOSTBUSTERS (Chad Valley/Marvel)
1989-1992

©1988/89	£10	$16

©1988/1989 (Chad Valley) (fc)
Comic Strips: The Spook From Outer Space! (12) - Writer: Ian
Rimmer, Art: Phil Gascoine and Dave Hine, Haunted Melodies (4)-
Writer: Sue Flaxman, Art: Kev Hopgood and Dave Hine,
Supernatural Bowl! (5), Writer: Jane Fabian, Art: Steve Parkhouse
and Dave Harwood, Monster Movie! (5), Writer: John Carnell, Art:
Anthony Williams and Paul Marsall, Spook Mechanic! (3), Writer:
Graeme Watson, Art: Martin Griffiths and Dave Elliott, Blimey! It's ...
Slimer (2x1pg), Writer/Art: Bambos
Text Stories: The Return of Mr. Stay Puft!
Writer: John Freeman-Art: Mike Collins and Lew Stringer
Jaws of the Beast!
Writer: Nick Abadzis and Steve White-Art: Anthony Larcombe
(these two text stories are reprinted in the Marvel annual)
The Green Ghosts!, Writer: Richard Alan-Art: Anthony Williams

1989-1992	£8	$13

1989 (fc)
Cover Art: Anthony Williams and John Burns
Endpaper: Andy Lanning, David Harwood and John Burns
Editor: Richard Starkings
Comic Strips: Noises in the Night (1), Writer: Richard Alan, Art:
Brian Williamson and Tim Perkins, Sarah Sangster's Spectre! (4),
Writer: Ian Rimmer- Art: Andy Lanning and Dave Harwood, The
Spook from Outer Space! (12)

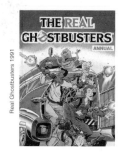

Real Ghostbusters 1991

Rentaghost 1983

Ritchie Rich 1974

See ©1988/1989 annual
Office Bound (3), Writer: Dan Abnet, -Art: Brian Williamson,
Spooked Out! (4), Writer: John Freeman, Art: Anthony Williams
Text Stories: Ghosbusters Busted!
Writer: Ian Rimmer-Art: Anthony Williams and Tim Perkins
Also see 1988/89 annual
1990 (64pg) (fc)
Cover Art: Andy Lanning, Dave Harwood and John Burns
Endpaper: Bambos and John Burns, Editor: Helen Stone
Comic Strips: Bustmans Holiday (2), Writer: John Carnell, Art:
Anthony Larcombe, Roller Ghoster! (4), Writer: John Carnell
Art: Brian Williamson and Dave Harwood, 'Phone Phantom (1),
Writer: John Carnell, Art: Anthony Larcombe, Stonehenge Revenge!
(5), Writer: John Carnell, Art: Phil Elliott and Bambos, Dead and
Breakfast! (3), Writer: John Carnell, Art: Dougie Braithwaite and
Dave Harewood, Blimey! It's...Slimer! (1), Writer: Bambos, Art:
Bambos, Loch Ness! (5), Writer: John Carnell, Art: John Geering
and Dave Harewood, Equal Frights!, Writer: John Carnell, Art:
Anthony Larcombe
Text Stories: The Dexter's Chain-Store Massacre!, Writer: Ian
Rimmer, Art: Martin Griffiths
The Green Ghosts!, Writer: Richard Alan, Art: Anthony Williams
Winston's Diary, Writer: Dan Abnett, Art: Tony O'Donnell and Dave
Harwood, Demon Bowler!, Writer: John Freeman, Art: Andy
Wildman and Dave Harwood
1991 (64pg) (fc)
Cover Art: Andy Lanning, Dave Harwood and John Burns
Endpaper: Cam Smith, Editors: Helen Stone and Jenny O'Connor
Comic Strips: Video-Nasty (4), Writer: Ian Rimmer, Art: Brian
Williamson and Cam Smith, Too Many Spooks Spoil The Broth (3),
Writer: Ian Rimmer, Art: Andy Wildman and Stephen Baskerville
Bus-Busters! (4), Writer: Ian Rimmer, Art: Tony O'Donnell, Slimer's
Putrid Panto (1), Art: Bambos, The Blob! (4), Writer: John Carnell
Art: Brian Williamson and Dave Harwood, The Root Of All Evil!,
Writer: John Carnell, Art: Brian Williamson and Cam Smith (3)
Text Stories: Dummy Run!, Story: Ian Rimmer, Art: John Marshall
and Dave Harewood, Ghost Writing!, Writer: Dan Abnett, Art: Cam
Smith, Chocolate Fudge Up!, Writer: Rebecca Owen, Art: John
Marshall and Stephen Baskerville, Mystery Of The Mist, Writer: Ian
Rimmer, Art: Andy Lanning and Stephen Baskerville
1992 (64pg) (fc)
Cover Art: Andy Lanning, Stephen Baskerville, John Burns
Endpaper: Anthony Williams, Stephen Baskerville
Editor: Helen Stone
Comic Strips: Centaur of Attention (5): Writers-Dan Abnett, Steve
White, Art-Andy Wildman, Lesley Dalton, The Curse of the Ancient
Mariner(6): Writer: Glenn Dakin, Art: Anthony Williams, Cam Smith
Slimer (1): Art: Bambos, The 7 Deadly Sins (5): Writer: Glenn Dakin,
Art: Brian Williamson, Stephen Baskerville, Mayhem For Melnitz (5),
Writer: Ian Rimmer, Art:Tony O'Donnell, Lesley Dalton
Text Stories: Ghoul in One: Writer-Ian Rimmer, Art-John Marshall,
Stephen Baskerville, Ghost Plane!: Writer-Ian Rimmer, Art: John
Marshall, Stephen Baskerville
Based on the animated TV series
RECORD BREAKERS (BBC)
1981   Need price
Based on the BBC TV series
RECORD STARS
1960's   £10 $16

1962-No.1   £12 $16
1963 on   £10 $16
RECORD MIRROR & DISC (World)
1977   £10 $16
Features: Queen, Hot Chocolate, Sweet, David Essex, Roxy Music,
Cockney Rebel, Sparks, Gary Glitter, Wings, Elton John, David
Bowie, Bay City Rollers, 10cc, Showaddywaddy, David Cassidy,
Mud, Abba, Marc Bolan, John Lennon
Pin Ups: MOTT, Roy Wood, Elton John, Steve Harley, Kenny, Pilot,
Alex Harvey, Showaddywaddy, Rod Stewart, David Essex, Slade,
David Bowie, David Cassidy, Bryan Ferry, Smokie, Queen
Mud, Hot Chocolate, Leo Sayer, Mike Batt, Marc Bolan, Gary Glitter
& Band, 10CC, Rubettes, Abba, Wings
REDCAP
1965   £10 $16
Based on the ITV series
RENTAGHOST (Stafford Pemberton)
1983   £5 $8
Features contributed by: Edward Brayshaw, Ann Emery and Michael
Staniforth
Based on the Childrens TV series
RETURN OF THE SAINT (Stafford Pemberton)
1979-1980   £7 $11
1979 (64pg) (fc)
Comic Strips (fc): A Packet of Trouble (7), Roberts Return (6),
All You Need is a Good Agent (6)
Includes photo pin-ups of Ian Ogilvy and photo feature on Leslie
Charteris
Photo cover
Based on the TV series
RICHIE RICH The Poor Little Rich Boy featuring Little Dot and
Little Lotta (Brown Watson)
1974
©1973 (80pg) (fc/tc)   £10 $16
Comic Strips: Richie Rich in, A Gem of a Mistake, Little Picnic
Family, What's A Friend For?, Every Rich Way, Able Gable, Cadbury
Rides Again, The Million Dollar Robbery, The Kid Who Has
Everything, Little Dot in The Only Way, Fitness Fan, Why Is Dot?
Little Lotta in, Why Can't I Have A Dog?, The Defender
Text Story: Richie Rich and the Magic Rod
Harvey Comic reprints
RIDERS OF THE RANGE Eagle (Juvenile/Thames/Hulton)
1952-1962
1952 (with dustjacket)   £15 $24
1953-1956 (with dustjacket)   £12 $19
1957-1960   £10 $16
1961-1962   £12 $19
1952-1956 (Juvenile/Thames)
Dustjacket art: Frank R. Grey
1957-1960 (Hulton)
Cover art: Frank Humphris
1961-1962 (Hulton)
Cover art: Harry Bishop
n/d 1953 - '2nd Round-Up' (100pg)
'Devised and written by Charles Chilton
Author and Producer of the Famous Radio Feature' By special
arrangement with 'EAGLE'
Comic Strips (4lw): The Case of the Murdered Prospector, Rustler
Under Suspicion, Luke's Good Deed

Riders of the Range 1957

Ripleys 1974

Rod Hull and Emu 1978

Includes five plates (fc)
RIDING (World)
1970's	£5	$8

RIGHT SAID FRED (Grandreams)
1992	£3	$5

Based on the UK pop group
RING RAIDERS (Grandreams)
1990-1991 (64pg) (fc)	£6	$10

Based on the animated TV series
RIN TIN TIN ADVENTURE Stories (Adprint)
1960	£12	$19

RIPCORD
1965	£12	$19

Based on the TV series
RIPLEY'S BELIEVE IT OR NOT (World)
1974-1976, 1992
1974-1976	£8	$13

1974 (80pg)
Comic Strips (fc): True War Stories - The Red Knight Of Germany (10),The Lost Battalion (9) - Art: Don Heck
The Incredible Sea Hunt Of Sub E-11 (13)
Includes 30 full page 'Ripley's Believe It Or Not' newspaper strips (fc/tc)
1975
Comic Strips (fc): The Last Kamikaze (9), Hand to Hand (5), Miracle of the Marne (4), Dead Man's Ambush (2), The Balloon Buster (5)
1992	£5	$8

Based on the newspaper strip
ROAD RUNNER (World)
1970's
1976 (64pg) (fc)	£7	$11

Comic Strips: Say Uncle (8fc), Basket Brawl (5fc), Spell of Speed (7fc), Museum Peace (6fc), The Mean Machine (6fc), Music Hath Harms (6fc), The Green Goodguy (6fc), Lighting Legs (6fc), Run Beep Run (4fc), The Cool Caper (4fc)
ROBBIE FOWLER (Grandreams)
1997
©1996 (64pg) (fc)	£3	$5

Writen by Robbie Fowler and Tony Lynch
Based on the Liverpool soccer player
ROBBIE WILLIAMS Special (Grandreams)
2000
©1999	£4	$7

Based on the UK pop singer
ROBIN (Hulton/Odhams)
1954-76
1954	£20	$32
1955-1959	£15	$24
1960-1965	£12	$19
1966-1969	£10	$16
1970-1976	£8	$13

Based on the UK pre school comic
ROBIN (Grandreams)
1986
1986 (80pg)	£3	$5

Not related to the original comic
ROBIN HOOD (Amalgamated)

See: THE ADVENTURES OF ROBIN HOOD
ROBIN OF SHERWOOD (Grandreams)
1986	£5	$8

Michael Praed photo cover
Based on the TV series
ROBOCOP-The Series (Grandreams)
1995
©1994 (48pg)	£5	$8

Editor: Barrie Tomlinson
Comic Strips: Robocop (The Series), The Grim Reaper!, Night of the Cat!
Based on the TV sci-fi series
ROBO MACHINE featuring THE GOBOTS (World)
1986-1987 (64pg)	£8	$13

Based on the animated TV series
ROCK ON! (Fleetway)
1980 (76pg)	£8	$13

Photo features based on the rock music magazine
ROCKY LANE Western Comic Annual (Miller)
Featuring Rocky Lane and his horse Black Jack
n/d 1958-1961
No.1	£15	$24
No.2-4	£12	$19

Card covers
1960 - No.3 (98pg) (bw)
Comic Strips: Rocky Lane in The Looters of the Lawless Range (18), Dee Dickens in The Ghost, The Prospector, The Elixir Of Youth (3x4), Rocky Lane in The Bloody Gap Plot! (11)-Art: Giordano & Alascia, Jeeter and his Talking Horse Preposterous in A Night Time Fable (4), Rocky Lane and the Hand of Death (18), The Sneak Rustlers 'A Black Jack Story'(7), Black Jack's Hitching Post (1), Big Bow and Little Bow (4), Rocky Lane in The Stagecoach of Doom (7), Rocky Lane in The Chief's Blunder (7)
Fawcett/Charlton reprints
Text Stories: The Three Deuces by Walter Farmer, Wits Against Gun by Eando Binder
Feature: The Man Who Tamed Abilene-Art: Mario DeMarco
Photo/art cover (fc)
Based on the Republic Pictures' movie/TV western star
ROD HULL AND EMU (Look-In/ITP/Stafford Pemberton)
1970's	£6	$10

1975 (Look-In/ITP)
1978 (Stafford Pemberton)
Based on the childrens ITV series
ROGER MOORE ADVENTURE Book (Panther/Souvenir))
1966	£8	$13

ROGUE TROOPER (Fleetway)
1991 (96pg)	£8	$13

Editor: Peter Hogan with assistance from Richard Burton
Frontpiece: Dave Gibbons
Comic Strips: Decoys (6fc), Writer: Michael Fleisher, Art: Christopher Weston, Blinded (8bw) - Writer: G. Finley-Day, Art: Steve Dillon, The War Game (4bw) - Writer: T. M. Hebden, Art: Jaimie Ortiz, The Undeath Project (16fc), Writer: M. Fleisher, Art: Smith Perkins, 60 Hours that Shook the World (5bw) Writer: P. Milligan, Art: R Jones, Bio Death (8bw), Writer: M Fleisher, Art: Steve Dillon, Death Valley (8bw), Writer: G. Finley-Day, Art: Cam Kennedy, Circus Daze (7fc), Writer: Michael Fleisher, Art: John Hickleton

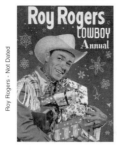

Text Stories:Marching as to War, Writer: John Smith, Art: Chris Weston
Based on the 2000AD comic strip
ROLAND RAT (Grandreams)

1984-1987	£3	$5

No. 1 - 1984
Based on the TV puppet character
ROOBARB & CUSTARD

1980's	£5	$8

Based on the animated TV series
ROSIE AND JIM (World)
1990's

1994	£3	$5

Writer: Nicola Baxter
Art: Edgar Hodges, David Brian, Peter Nicholls, Gill Whelan, Sara Silcock & Helen Prole
Based on the Childrens TV puppet series
ROVER BOOK for Boys (D.C. Thomson)
1926-1942, 1950, 1956-1959

1926	£150	$240
1950 (Scarce)	£50	$80
1956-1958	£25	$40
1959 (Scarce)	£30	$48

ROY OF THE ROVERS (Fleetway/EgmontWorld)
1958-94, 2000
Becomes YEARBOOK1993-1994 (Fleetway/World)

1958 - Football Annual	£30	$48

Painted Frontispiece by G Keane
'GOAL! Roy Race nods in another winner!'
B/w strips, stories and features. Illustrated four colour sections and comic strips include - The Road to Wembley (endpaper)Cups that Count, National Colours and Badges of the Four Home Counties, Caps for the Soccer Stars, League Club Badges, Colours Worn by World Cup Teams, More of Soccer's Trophies, Roy Race's Score-A-Goal Game (back endpaper)
Comic Strip (8 pg): Take a Tour Round Melchester Stadium with Roy Race as Your Guide

1959	£20	$32
1960-1965	£15	$24

1963 'Tiger Roy of the Rovers All Sports Annual' - A Five Star Annual
Comic Strips: Soccer Christmas (6tc), Too Scared to Bat! (6bw), Billy Tries To Please (1bw), Trainer Trouble (16bw), Boxing Gloves for the President (9bw)
1964 'Tiger Roy of the Rovers Annual'
Comic Strips: Melchester Rovers v Film Stars United (8tc), Tubby's Weight Problem (9bw), Team Wreckers - An Exciting Story from Roy's Schooldays (9bw)

1966-1969	£10	$16
1970-1979	£8	$13
1980-1989	£6	$10
1990-1994, 2000	£5	$8

1979 (Fleetway) (128pg)
Comic Strips (tc/bw): Mike's Mini Men, Roy of the Rovers, Simon's Secret, Tommy's Troubles, Roy Race's School Days, The Safest Hands in Soccer, The Hard Man, The Football
1984 (Fleetway) (128pg)
Comic Strips: Roy of the Rovers (8fc), Mike's Mini-Men (30lw), Durrel's Palace (6tc), Mighty Mouse (6lw), The Hard Man (6tc),

Tommy's Troubles (6lw)
Includes back endpaper (lw) of Melchester Rovers European Cup Winners 1969 team
1989 (Fleetway)
1990 (Fleetway) (112pg)
Comic Strips: Roy of the Rovers (fc), Rick Stewart in Goalkeeper (tc), Billy's Boots (tc), Hamish and Mouse (bw), The Moon-Rock Kid (lw), Jack of United (lw), Jimmy of City (lw)
1991 (Fleetway) (112pg)
Comic Strips: Roy of the Rovers (fc), Rick Stewart - Goalkeeper (tc), Hot-Shot Hamish and Mighty Mouse (tc), Iron Boy! (tc), Billy's Boots (bw), The Challenge Match (lw), Jack of United (lw), Jimmy of City (lw)
1993 (112pg)
Comic Strips: Roy of the Rovers (fc), Gary's Golden Boots (fc), Goalkeeper (tc), Hamish and Mouse (tc), Billy's Boots (bw), Byrd of Paradise Hill (lw)
1994
Comic Strips (fc): Roy of the Rovers, Buster's Ghost, Andy Steel Playmaker
2000 (Egmont World) (64pg) (fc)
Special Millenium Souvenir
Roy Race... THE LEGEND
Comic Strip: Roy of the Rovers (18), Writer: Ian Rimmer
Art: Barrie Mitchell
Based on the UK soccer comic strip
ROY OF THE ROVERS Football Champions! (Fleetway)

1990-1991 (64pg)	£8	$13

©1989
Comic Strips (fc): Brian Clough - Goalscorer and Manager (5), The Kevin Keegan Story (6)
Includes photo features (fc/bw) and Roy Race intro
ROY ROGERS ADVENTURES (Dean)
1950's-1960's

No.1 - ©1957	£15	$24
No.2 on	£12	$19

©1959 (No.3)
Art: Leo Rawlings
Based on the Western movie actor
ROY ROGERS' BUMPER BOOK (Adprint)
1950's

1954	£20	$32
1955 on	£15	$24

1954 (96pg) (fc/tc)
Photo cover (fc)
Features text stories and colouring, activity and puzzle pages
Two variant covers exist. One version has 'King of the Cowboys' printed along a wooden fence
Based on the Western movie actor
ROY ROGERS COWBOY ANNUAL (World)
1952-1960s

1952	£20	$32
1953-1959	£15	$24
1960-1963	£12	$19

Based on the Western movie actor
ROY ROGERS' STORIES (Adprint)
1956-1960's

1956 (No.1)	£20	$32
1957-59	£15	$24

Rupert 1974

Rupert 1976

Rupert 1979

1960 on £10 $16
1956 (80pg) (fc/tc)
Writer: John Jamieson-Art: Reg Foster with Peter Alvarado
Text stories
Photo cover
RUGBY WORLD (Pedigree)
2000 £3 $5
RUGRATS Nickelodeon (Sapling/EgmontWorld)
1997-present
1997 (Sapling) £6 $10
Comic Strips: The Cranky Hank (6), Tooth Truth (6)
2000 (Egmont World) (64pg) £5 $8
Comic Strips: Circus Surprises, Jungle Explorers, Decorating Disasters
Based on the animated TV series
RUPERT (Express/Pedigree)
1937-present
Cover Art: Alfred Bestall - final cover 1973, Alex Cubie, John Harrold
Writers: Alfred Bestall, James Henderson, Ian Robinson
Picture Strip Art: Alfred Bestall, Alex Cubie, John Harrold
Softback covers (©1942-©1949)
©1936 (with dustjacket) £2500 $3400
1950-1953 £100 £160
©1949
'Rupert'
Picture Strips: Rupert and Ninky, Rupert and the Young Imp, Rupert's Magic Top, Rupert's Island Adventure, Rupert and Uncle Grizzly, Rupert and the Twins, Rupert and the New Pal, Rupert, Algee and the Bee, Rupert and Pong-Ping's Party
©1950
'Adventures of Rupert'
Picture Strips: Rupert's Silver Trumpet, Rupert and Margot's House, Rupert and the Jumping Fish, Rupert and the Gooseberry Fool, Rupert and the Paper Plane, Rupert and the Three Guides, Rupert and the Travel Machine, Rupert and the Big Bang, Rupert and the Empty Cottage
©1951
'The New Rupert Book'
Picture Strips: Rupert and Dr Lion, Rupert and Ting-Ling, Rupert and Mr Punch, Rupert and the Lucky Man, Rupert's Elfin Bell, Rupert and the Runaways, Rupert's Queer Path, Rupert's Dull Day
©1952
'More Rupert Adventures'
Picture Strips: Rupert and the Mare's Nest, Rupert and the Sea-Sprites, Rupert and the Elephants, Rupert and the Arrows, Rupert, Beppo and the Caravan, Rupert and the Snuff-Box
1954-1956 £80 $128
©1953
'More Adventures of Rupert'
Picture Strips: Rupert and Miranda, Rupert and the Green Buzzer, Rupert, Algy and the Cannibals, Rupert and the Missing Pieces, Rupert in Mysterland, Rupert at Rocky Bay
©1954
'The New Rupert'
Picture Strips: Rupert and the Friendly Sea-Lion, Rupert and the Sketch Book, Rupert and the Castaway, Rupert and the Backroom Boy, Rupert and the Dragon Pills
©1955
'Rupert'

Picture Strips: Rupert and the Poll Parrot, Rupert and the Blue Firework, Rupert and the Autumn Primrose, Rupert and the Unknown Journey, Rupert and the Cough Drop
1957-1959 £70 $110
©1956
'The Rupert Book'
Picture Strips: Rupert and the Blue Moon, Rupert and the Bandit's Cave, Rupert and Unlucky Simon, Rupert and the Flying Sorcerer
©1957
'Rupert' - continues title until present day
Picture Strips: Rupert and the Crackerjack, Rupert and the Pine Ogre, Rupert and the Lion Rock, Rupert and the Wind Whistle
©1958
Picture Strips: Rupert and the Water-Lily, Rupert and the New Bonnet, Rupert and the Ice Flowers, Rupert and the Spring Adventure, Rupert and the Train Journey
1960-1966 £90 $144
(Magic painting intact - half price if painting completed)
©1959
Picture Strips: Rupert and the Copper Bird, Rupert and the River Rescue, Rupert and the Butterflies, Rupert and the Hazel Nut, Rupert and the Toy Scout
©1960
Picture Strips: Rupert and the Crystal, Rupert and Morwenna, Rupert and Ozzie, Rupert and the Diamond Leaf
©1961
Picture Strips: Rupert and the Hearth-Rug, Rupert and the Pepper Rose, Rupert and the Black Spark, Rupert and the New Boat, Rupert and Greyrocks Cove
©1962
Picture Strips: Rupert and the Dragon Fly, Rupert and the Robins, Rupert and Niagra, Rupert and the Bad Dog, Rupert and the Coral Island
©1963
Picture Strips: Rupert and the Birthday Present, Rupert and the Golden Acorn, Rupert and the Lost Cuckoo, Ruperet and the Inventor, Rupert and the Cold-Cure
©1964
Picture Strips: Rupert and the Dover Sole, Rupert and the Distant Music, Rupert and the Compass, Rupert and the Dog-Roses, Rupert and the Rock Pool
1966-1968 £60 $96
(Magic painting intact - half price if painting completed)
©1965
Picture Strips: Rupert and the Gaffer, Rupert and the Winter Woolley, Rupert and the Old Hat, Rupert and Rusty
©1966
Picture Strips: Rupert and the Magic Ball, Rupert and the Secret Boat, Rupert and the Billy Goat, Rupert and the Spring Chicken
©1967
Picture Strips: Rupert and the Lost List, Rupert and the Jackdaw, Rupert and Floppity, Rupert and the Carved Stick
1969 £25 $40
©1968
Picture Strips: Rupert and the Truant, Rupert and the Fiddle, Rupert and the Fire-Bird, Rupert and the Rolling Ball
1970-1975 £20 $32
©1969
Picture Strips: Rupert and the Whistlefish, Rupert and the Old

Ruprt 1994

Rupert 2000

Russ Abbot 1983

Chimney, Rupert and the Snowball, Rupert and Raggety, Rupert and the Fishing Rod
©1970
Picture Strips: Rupert and the Outlaws, Rupert and the Blunderpuss, Rupert and the Paper-Fall, Rupert and the Sky-Boat
©1971
Picture Strips: Rupert and the Gomnies, Rupert and the Popweed, Rupert and the Early Bird, Rupert and the Windlings
©1972
Picture Strips: Rupert's Deep Sea Adventure, Rupert and the Learner, Rupert and the Rugger Match, Rupert and Gwyneth
©1973 - Two variant covers exist
White face and hands
Brown face and hands (very scarce)
(Only 3-8 copies are known to exist)
A copy sold at auction in 1999 for £16,500
Picture Strips: Rupert and the Bouncers, Rupert and the Housemouse, Rupert and the Waterfall, Rupert and the Flying Boat
©1974
Picture Strips: Rupert and the Iron Spade, Rupert and Jenny Frost, Rupert and the Secret Path, Rupert and the Little Bells
1976-1979   £15 $24
©1975
Picture Strips: Rupert and the Little River, Rupert and the Thinking Cap, Rupert and the Broken Plate, Rupert and the Blue Star, Rupert and the Winter Sale
©1976
Picture Strips: Rupert and the Jumping Men, Rupert and Young Kevin, Rupert and the Hot Water, Rupert and the Windy Day
©1977
Picture Strips: Rupert and the Winkybickies, Rupert and the Fire-Lighter, Rupert and Septimus, Rupert and the Silent Land
©1978
Picture Strips: Rupert and the Rivals, Rupert and the Squire, Rupert and the Boffit, Rupert and the Secret Shell, Rupert's Odd Party
1980-1989   £10 $16
©1979
Picture Strips: Rupert and the Penguins, Rupert and the Moon Moths, Rupert and the Ice Skates, Rupert and the Capricorn
©1980
Picture Strips: Rupert and the Flavours, Rupert and the Mixed Magic, Rupert and the Blizzard, Rupert and the Ocean Office
©1981
Picture Strips: Rupert and the Castle Trap, Rupert and the Wicked Uncle, Rupert and the Buzzing Box, Rupert and the Wrong Sweets, Rupert and the Silent Dog, Rupert and the Baby Cloud
©1982
Picture Strips: Rupert and Pong-Ping, Rupert and the Umbrella Boy, Rupert and the Gemlins, Rupert and the Snow Puzzle, Rupert and the Red Box
©1983
Picture Strips: Rupert and the Black Circle, Rupert and the Dragon Race, Rupert and Santa Paws, Rupert's Autumn Adventure
©1984
Picture Strips: Rupert and the Two Moons, Rupert and the Wee Man, Rupert and the Igloo, Rupert and the Wonderful Kite, Rupert and the Cuckoo Clock
©1985

Picture Strips: Rupert, Bill and the Pearls, Rupert at Pong's Party, Rupert and the Unknown Journey, Rupert and the Snowstorm, Rupert and the Pirate Boys, Rupert and the Windmill
©1986
Picture Strips: Rupert and the Strange Airman, Rupert and Rika, Rupert and the Worried Elves, Rupert and the Dragon Mystery, Rupert and the Mulp Gulper, Rupert and the Iceberg
©1987
Picture Strips: Rupert and the River Pirates, Rupert and the Worg Seeds, Rupert and the Lotus Isle, Rupert and Hamish, Rupert and Old Tom's Trove
©1988
Picture Strips: Rupert on Um Island, Rupert and the Go-Cart, Rupert and the Sleeping Village, Rupert, Beppo and the Kite, Rupert and Terry's Return, Rupert and Podgy's Christmas
1990-present   £8 $13
©1989
Picture Strips: Rupert and the Boomerarrow, Rupert and the Knight, Rupert and the Thaw, Rupert and the Power Flower, Rupert and Algy's Misadventure, Rupert and Rika's Return
©1990
Picture Strips: Rupert and Little Yum, Rupert and the Sea Queen, Rupert and the Eastern Isle, Rupert and the Little Train, Rupert and Willie's present
©1993 - No. 58 'The Daily Express Annual' (96pg)
Writer: Ian Robinson, Art: John Harrold
Picture Strips: Rupert and Ottoline, Rupert and the Chinese Creeper, Ruper and Rosalie's Adventure, Rupert and the Sands of Time, Rupert and the April Fool
©1999 - No.64 (Pedigree) (112pg)
'Rupert The Express Annual'
Writer: Ian Robinson, Art: John Harrold
Picture Strips: Rupert and the Forset Throne, Rupert and the Gold-Rush, Rupert and the Skylark, Rupert and the Apple Trees, Rupert and the Christmas List

RUSS ABBOT'S MADHOUSE (Grandreams)
1983-1984
©1982   £4 $7
Comic Strips: Cooperman in Feet First, Hey, Big Spender, Vince Prince, The Scoutmaster's Guide to Scouting, A Photo Frame Up, It's a Dog's Life, Classroom Capers, The Bells are Ringing, The Lone Raider, Monster Mirth or Stein of the Times, Phone-In Fun, The Scoutmaster
©1983   £3 $5
Comic Strips: Jim'll Jinx It, Vince Prince in All Ads up!, Basildon Bond in Code and Chips, Cooperman in A Stitch in Time, Vince Prince in The Audition, A Storm in a Bath Tub, Jim'll Jinx It, The Scoutmaster in Good Advice, Vince Prince at the Seaside, Geronimo in Conning the Conductor, The Scoutmaster in Be Prepared, Basildon Bond in A Brief Encounter, Boggles in The Mail Music Get Through, Barratt Holmes in the Martian Mystery, Basildon Bond in Concrete Evidence
Based on the ITV comedy series

RYAN GIGGS Special (World)
1995   £3 $5
Writers: Ray Goldsworth and Rob Holden
Based on the Manchester United soccer star

RYAN GIGGS Official Annual (Grandreams)
1996

Sandie 1974

Sapphire & Steel 1981

Schoolboys 1974

SC

©1995   £3 $5
Based on the Manchester United soccer star
The SAINT (World/PBS)
1968-1970, 1973
1968   £15 $24
1969-1970   £12 $19
©1969 (96pg) (fc/tc)
Comic Strips (2x6) (tc): Simon Templar, The Saint in The Rocket
Renegade, Cave of Death
Text Stories: A Saintly Trip (fc), The Saint Goes Nap (tc), The Saint
Takes a Hand (fc), Highways Robbery (fc), The Saint and the
Skeleton (fc), Snowball of Death (tc), Trust the Saint (fc)
Photo cover (part)
1973 (PBS)   £10 $16
Based on the TV series starring Roger Moore
SAINT Television Storybook (PBS)
1972
©1971 (64pg)   £10 $16
SALLY (Fleetway)
1970's   £5 $8
Based on the UK girls comic
SANDIE (Fleetway)
1970's   £5 $8
Based on the UK girls comic
SAPPHIRE AND STEEL (World)
1981 (64pg)   £10 $16
Text Stories: Bid Time Return, Rogue Robot, Chamber of Horrors,
Star Gazing, Finger of Blood, Picture Cover
Based on the TV sci fi series starring Joanna Lumley and David
McCallum
S.A.S. (Grandreams)
1984-1985   £5 $8
©1983 (64pg)
Editor: John Barraclough-Researcher/Writer: Peter Newark-Art: Tony
Jozwiak
Comic Strips: Falklands Campaign (6bw), Battle of Mirbat (6fc),
Seige Busters (6fc)
©1984 (64pg)
Researcher/Writer: Peter Newark
Comic Strips (6x2fc) :The Phantom Major, Colonel 'Paddy' Mayne
SATURDAY SOCCER SCENE ANNUAL (Grandreams)
1981   £4 $7
SCEPTRE Girl's Story Annual (Purnell)
1960 (512pg)   £8 $13
SCHOOLBOYS' Annual (World)
1968-1980
1968-1974   £5 $8
1970 (128pg)
Editor: Mae Broadley-Art: John Leeder, David Brian, David Fryer,
Stephen Livesey
1973
Editor: Mae Broadley-Art: EdgarHodges, John Leeder, Alan Lindsell,
David Fryer
1974 (80pg)
Editor: Mae Broadley, Art: Edgar Hodges, S Livsey, A Linsdell and
Paul Crompton
Text Story: The Silent Witness, Writer: O. Lloyd Jones
The Trophy, Writer: John Blaylock

The Hero, Writer: Con Rougier
Professor Phizz and the Long Arm of the Law, Writer A Robertson
Jewel in Space, Writer: J M Winyard
1975-1980   £3 $5
1977 (80pg)
Editor: Mae Broadley-Art: Edgar Hodges, Paul Crompton, Glenn Rix,
John Millington, Paul Green
1980
Art: Edgar Hodges, Glenn Rix, Paul Crompton, Mel Powell, Annabel
Spenceley. C Horrocks
SCHOOLBOYS' TREASURE Book
1950's   £8 $13
SCHOOL FRIEND (Fleetway House/Fleetway)
1927-1981
1950-1959   £15 $24
1960-1969   £10 $16
1962 (128pg)
'A Sunshine Annual'
Comic Strips: Penny and the Maypole Riders (tc), Chula-The
Lantern Girl (fc), Judy's Daring Channel Swim (tc), The Masked
Ballerina (fc), Princess Anita and the White Stag (tc), Dilly the Carol
Singer (tc), Tracy and the Fashion Secrets (fc), Mystery on the
Mountain(tc), Student Nurse Gillian Saves the Christmas Party (tc)
Text Stories: The Ghostly Skater, Linda's Hairdressing Rival by Mary
Moore, Girl in the Back Seat by Dorothy Waters, The Wandering
Sands by Denise Kerry, Pete and the Cat Thief by Evelyn Day, Jill
had a Word for It! by Penelope Desmond, Sugar Plum Fairy by
Esme Nolan
1963 (128pg)
Comic Strips: Tracy on Location (fc), Popsy (tc), Babs and the
Family (tc), Secret of the Sky (tc), A Present for Princess Lola (tc),
Pat of the Dolphins (tc), Dolores and Donk (tc), Mystery at
Brookdean School (tc)
Text Stories: A Pony for Penny by Patricia Wild, A Climb for Dorinda
by Cecil Danby, Girl of the Frozen North by Kay Vernon, The Mixed
Foursome by Ida Melbourne, Padmini the Beautiful and Brave, The
Courage of Delia Lawson by Ronald Horton, The Dress by John
Challis
Includes a feature by TV presenter Muriel Young
1964 (Fleetway) (128pg)
Comic Strips: Tracy on the Road, Dilly Dreem, The Sparrows of
Angel Street, A Dazzling Display, The Tomboy Next Door, Camera-
Mad Carol
Text stories: Lucky Black Horse by Cecily Danby
The Loneliest Girl in Town by Christine Landon
The Girl who went back to 1066 by Evelyn Day
Tropical Magic by Janet McKibbin
The Midnight Feast by Gwen Perrott
Ladybirds Alibi by Frances Cowen
The Fisherman's Daughter by Percy Clarke
Mysterious Neighbours by Hilary Bailey
All because of Cora by Francis Lindsay
1970-1979   £8 $13
1972 (IPC) (128pg)
Comic Strips: The Ugly Duckling (25tc), Lisa and the Great Trek
(6tc), Gail Gulliver (15bw), Bessie Bunter (2tc), Gorgeous Greta
(10tc), Monkey Business-featuring Sindy doll (3tc), Mini Ha Ha (1fc),
The House of Dolls (5tc), Hazel Nutt (1tc)
Text Stories: Back In Time, The Badger Boy, Dance of the Dragon,

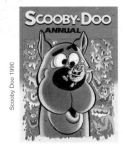

Scooby Doo 1990

Scorcher 1975

Score 1977

The Four Leaved Shamrock, The Silent Three and the Z-Ray Lamp, Peggy Calls the Tune

1980-1981	£5	$8

Based on the UK comic

SCHOOL FUN (IPC)

1985	£3	$5

SCHOOLGIRLS Annual (World)

1970s-1980s	£3	$5

SCOOBY-DOO (Brown Watson/World/Marvel)

1970's-1990

1970's	£10	$16
1980-86, 1990	£8	$13

Scooby Doo Where Are You...? - Brown Watson editions
©1979 (Brown Watson)
Comic Strips: Phantom of the Racetrack (4tc), Super Sea-Dog (6fc), Scooby Doo: 'Dog-Napped' (3fc), It's Magic! (4fc), The Big Dig Mystery (6tc)
©1980 Scooby Doo Cartoon Annual (World)
Cover Art/Endpaper: Phil Woodall
Comic Strips: Dazzling Duds (4fc), The Golden Ghost (5fc), The Ghost of King Neptune (10bw), The Frightful Scarecrow (5bw), Menace of the Man-Mummy (10bw), The Phantom of Youth (15bw), Coast-To-Coast Ghost (4bw), Fester and the Jester (10bw), The Faceless Phantom (10bw)
Writer: Mark Evanier-Art: Dan Spiegle
©1981 (World) (80pg)
Comic Strips (fc): The Boogie Man, Happy Haunting Ground, The Haunted Riverboat, Ghost of Dracula, The Treasure of Sierra Fantasma, The Gorgeous Ghost
©1982 (64pg)
Cover Art: Melvyn Powell-Endpaper: Paul Green
Comic Strips: That's Snow Ghost (12), Hand From the Wall (5), The Swamp Witch! (14)
Scooby-Doo Where Are You? reprints
©1983 (64pg) (fc)
Cover Art: Melvyn Powell-Endpaper: Paul Green
Comic Strip: Night for a Fright (25)
Scooby-Doo Where Are You? reprint
Text Story Art: Paul Green
©1984
Comic Strips: Napoleon Lives! (13)
Reprint from Scooby-Doo Mystery Comics #23
The Phantom Funnyman (12)
Text Story Art: Paul Green
1986 (64pg) (fc)
Cover Art: Melvyn Powell-Endpaper: Paul Green
Comic Strips: Mystery of the Ghosty Goose (20)
Reprint from Scooby-Doo Mystery Comics #19
The Gypsy's Curse (13)
Reprint from Scooby-Doo Mystery Comics #22
Text Story Art: Paul Green
1990 (Marvel)
Comic Strips (fc): The Mysterious Gorilla, The Spooky Suit, The Phantom Diver
1991 (Marvel) (64pg)
Editor: Harry Papadopoulos, Art: Caroline Steeden
Comic Strips: The Ghost of King Neptune (10fc), Coast to Coast Ghost (4fc), The Horrible Hound Sound (6fc), The Spook Who Loved Lemonade (5fc),

Based on the Hanna-Barbera animated series

SCOOP (D.C. Thomson)

1980's	£5	$8

1982 (128pg) (fc/bw)
'Sports Annual'
Comic Strips: Cannonball (7tc), Hyperman (8tc), This Goalie's Got Guts! (7tc), Speed Kings (7fc/tc), Buster (6tc), Joe Judd (7tc)
Pin Ups (fc): Kevin Keegan, Steve Ovett, Steve Davis, Trevor Francis, Desmond Douglas, John McEnroe, Randy Mamola & Kenny Roberts, Ian Botham, Diego Maradona, Kenny Dalglish, Andy Irvine, Ray Clemence, Blokhin, Zoff, Zico, Rummenigge, Tony Sibson, Pat Jennings, Eric Bristow, Mike Hazelwood, Trevor Brooking & Son, Daley Thompson
Soccer/Sports annual

SCORCHER (Fleetway)

1971-1983

1971	£8	$13
1972-1979	£6	$10

1975 (160pg) (bw/tc)
Comic Strips: Lags Eleven, Sub, The Celtic Story, Billys Boots, Barry Binns, Bobby of the Blues, Nipper
1978 (128pg) (fc/bw)
Comic/Picture Strips: Stars of the World Cup (5), Manager Matt (2x1), Billy's Boots (6), Bobby of the Blues (10), Lags Eleven (6), The Story of the League Championship (4), The Amazing Strollers (11), Nipper (6 fc), Hot Shot Hamish (6), Jack and Jimmy (3)
Star Spot Pin Ups: Phil Parkes, Leighton James, Paul Sturrock, Malcolm MacDonald

1980-1983	£5	$8

1981 (96pg)
Comic Strips: Billys Boots (fc), Jimmy Jinks (tc), Nipper (8tc), Jack & Jimmy (10bw), The Kevin Keegan Story (5fc), Hot Shot Hamish (7fc), Alf's Albion (11bw), Bobby of the Blues (8tc)
Based on the UK soccer comic

SCORE

1972-1982	£5	$8

1977 (128pg)
Comic Strips: Jack of United, Trouble Shooter, Peter the Cat, The Challenge Match, Jimmy of City
Based on the UK soccer comic

SCOUT (Pearson/World/Boy Scouts Association)

1950's-1980's

1950's	£15	$24
1960's	£8	$13

1962 (Pearson)
Editor: Rex Hazlewood
1969 (196pg)
Endpapers: Brian Gough
Text stories by: Joyce Stranger, John Sweet, Robin Williams, Falcon Travis, Leighton Houghton, David Harwood, K M Peyton, Eric Cameron, Richard Ringley, Murray Collier, Peter N Walker
Art: Pete Harrison, Jack Trodd, Curly

1970's	£5	$8
1980's	£3	$5

1980 (World)
Editors: Peter Brooks and Bill Bruce-Cartoons: David Easton
1988 (64pg) (World)
Edited by Ron Jeffries
Text Stories: Sea Scouts to the Rescue, Writer: Colin McKay, Art:

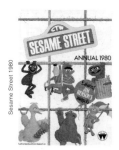

Doug Mountford
A Night of Mystery, Writer: Dave Wood, Art: Peter Harrison
The Official Scout Annual
SCOUT PATHFINDERS (Thames/Purnell)
1960's-1970's
1960's	£8	$13
1970's	£6	$10

1967 - Art: Phil Gascoine
SCRAMBLE (Swan)
1940's-1951
1950-1951	£15	$24

SCREEN TEST
1974 £8 $13
Based on the Childrens BBC TV quiz show starring Michael Rodd
SESAME STREET (World/Marvel/Grandreams)
1980, 1993-present
1980 (World)	£8	$13
1993 - present	£5	$8

©1992 (64pg) (fc)
Art: Nancy Stevenson, Carol Inouye, Dennis Hockerman, Nancy Cunningham, Melinda Fabian, Patrick Girouard, Marsha Winborn, George Martin, Paul Richer, Rodica Prato, Fred Schrier, Ellen Appleby, Bill Davis, Larry Difiori, Ajin, Ann Wilson, Tom Brannon, Rick Brown, Jerry Smath, Tom Tucker, Kristin Johnson, Mary Eubank, Tom Herbert
©1999 (64pg) (fc)
Cover art: Bruce McNally
Comic Strip: Goodbye Natasha (2)
Art: Joe Ewers
Art: Tom Leigh, Maggie Swanson, Tom Brannon, Lulu Delacre, Sally Vitsky, Brad McMahon/Eddie Young, Joe Ewers, Ellen Appleby, Tommy Stubbs, Lawrence DiFiori, David Dees, Joe Mathieu, Katherine Osbourne, Paul Richer
SEXTON BLAKE - VALIANT Book of TV's (Fleetway)
1969 £15 $24
Based on the ITV Detective series
SGT BILKO (World)
1960-1962
©1959	£20	$32
©1960-1961	£15	$24

©1961 (96pg) (fc)
Comic Strips: How To Get Rich In Real Estate (24), Omens Rapidans (26) - U.S. reprints
Text stories writer: Douglas Enefer
Based on the TV comedy series starring Phil Silvers
SHAKIN STEVENS Special (Grandreams)
1984
©1983 £6 $10
Writer: John Miller, Layout/Design: Nigel I. Money
Lots of photo features and discography
Based on the Pop Star
SHE-RA PRINCESS OF POWER (World)
1987-1988 £8 $13
1987 (64pg) (fc)
Cover Art: Ron Smethurst
Comic Strip: The Curse of the Lion People (6) - Art: Ron Smethurst
Text Stories Art: Paul Green, Melvyn Powell, Glenn Rix#
Based on the filmation animated TV series and toy range

SHERLOCK HOLMES (World)
1980
©1979 £8 $13
Cover art: Edgar Hodges
Comic Strip (fc): The Hound of the Baskervilles
Art: Glenn Rix, Paul Crompton
SHERLOCK HOLMES & DR. WATSON (Grandreams)
1980
©1979 £8 $13
Art: Carlos Cruz
Comic Strips: The Case of the Deadly Spectre (8bw), The Case of the Jade Immortal (8fc), The Case of The Kris of Death (5fc), The Case of The Missing Mummies (8bw)
Text Story: The Case of the Cat Burglar, The Case of The Suspect Swami
Features: Victorian Villains, Victorian Detectives
Photo cover
Based on the TV film
SHIVER AND SHAKE (Fleetway)
1973-1986
1973	£6	$10
1974-1979	£5	$8
1980-1986	£3	$5

Based on the UK comic
SHOE PEOPLE (World)
1988 (64pg) (fc) £3 $5
Art: Rob Lee
Features stories and picture strips
Based on the animated TV series
SHOOT (APL/IPC)
1960's-present
1968	£10	$16
1969-1979	£8	$13
1980-1989	£5	$8
1990-present	£3	$5

Photo features on all the top names of the year!
Based on the UK soccer magazine
SIMON DEE
1968 £10 $16
Based on the UK DJ and chat show host
SIMON & SIMON (World)
1983 (64pg) £8 $13
Based on TV Detective series
SINDY (Fleetway/Grandreams/Pedigree)
1971, 1983-present
1971	£10	$16
1983-1989	£8	$13

1983 (Fleetway) (80pg)
Comic Strip & Text stories - Sindy's Disaster Day, What Harry Did, Sindy's Little Monster, Ghost Ballerina, Alpine Danger, The Highwaymen, Zanna of the Jungle
Features: Famous Sayings from Sindy, Fun Things to make, Sindy takes you to some Haunted Places, Drawing People, Sindy makes your own Cut Outs, Kings & Queens,
1984 (Fleetway)
Comic Strips: Sindy's Clean Up Day, Sindy meets the Abominable Snowman, Black Beauty by Anna Sewell, Sindy's Rival, The Misfit, Sindy's Strange Tennis Game

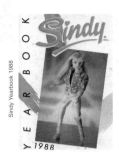

Sindy Yearbook 1988 — YEARBOOK 1988

Sixer 1978

Six Million Dollar Man 1980

Features: Special Collection Sindy, Make a Desk Tidy, Let's Have a Party, How to be a Witch, Tell your own Fortune, How to Crochet a Flower Belt, Sindy's Favourite Four (Gary Numan, Simon Le Bon, Shakin Stevens, Thereze Bazaar)
1985
©1984 (Grandreams) (64pg) (fc)
1st Grandreams annual
Editor: John Barraclough-Writer (comic strip/text stories): R.A.G. Clarke-Writer (features): Beryl Johnston-Art: Kim Raymond & Chris Higham (Temple Art)
Comic Strips (3x8): Sindy Tops the Pops, Sindy's Cornish Adventure, Sindy Saves the Riding School, Sindy's Snow Maidens, A Friend Indeed to a Friend in Need, Sindy's Giddy Aunt, Sindy Finds the Cure, Sindy takes a Hand
Features: Pop Gossip, The Emanuels (Fashion), Beauty feature, Pop Gossip (Wham), Sindy's Show Jumping Game
1986 (Grandreams)
©1985
Artwork - Kim Raymond & Hugh Thornton Jones (Temple Art)
Comic Strips: Sindy's Snow Maidens,
1988 Year Book (Grandreams)
Comic Strip: Super Sindy in Class Act (8)
Part Time (3bw)-Complete the story and colour
Features - Spring Surprise, Star Profile (Palamino), Sindy Cassette Labels, Five Star File, Summer Fun, Horoscope Glamourous Girl, Hot Gossip, Sindy Abroad, Autumn Shades, Room for Improvement, Michael J Fox, Ballet Dancer, Nick Berry (alias Wicksy from Eastenders), Party Time
1990-1997   £5 $8
1996 (Pedigree) (48pgfc)
Photo features and games
Based on the girls doll and comic
SIR PRANCELOT (Purnell/Stafford Pemberton)
1970's   £12 $19
1972 (Purnell)
Writer: Jocelyn Phillips.
Art: Toni Goffe
1976 (Stafford Pemberton)
Based on the BBC TV animated series
SIX GUN HEROES
1960's
No 1-5   £10 $16
SIX MILLION DOLLAR MAN (World/Stafford Pemberton)
1977-1980   £8 $13
1977 (Stafford Pemberton) (64pg) (fc)
Comic Strips: A Broken Promise, Mistaken Loyalty, Boot Are Made For Skiing - Art: Melvyn Powell
Photo cover
1978 (64pg) (fc)
Comic Strips: Exhibition, Combination, Foiled
1979 (64pg) (fc)
Comic Strips: Seams Suspicious, Set to Kill
Photo cover
1980 (64pg) (fc)
Comic Strips: The Laser Gun, Turning a Blind Eye, The Dummy Death-Ray
Based on the TV sci fi series starring Lee Majors
SIXER Annual For All Cub Scouts (Purnell)
1960's -1970's

1960's   £8 $13
1970's   £5 $8
N/D (1976)
Editor: Jack Cox - Text Stories:The Goose Chase by Peter Lawrence, Chicken Cub by John Sweet, The Man in Goatskins by John Havenhand, The Ambush by John Marsh
N/D (96pg)
Text Stories: Marbrouk the Puny One by Kelman Frost
The Squeeze - A Robin Hood Writer: Roland Pertwee
Wilderness Ways by Arthur Catherall - Art: Roland Davies
A Fox to Remember by John Onslow
Based on the Boy Scouts
SIXER Annual For All Wolf Cubs (Purnell)
1950's-1960's
1950's   £10 $16
1960's   £8 $13
1960 - Art: R Wilson
Based on the Boy Scouts
SKATEBOARD (Brown Watson)
1979
©1978 (64pg)   £6 $10
SKELETON WARRIORS (World)
1996 (64pg) (fc)   £3 $5
Writer: Mike Butcher-Art: Rob Sharp
Comic Strip: That Shrinking Feeling! (6)
Based on the animated TV series
SKIPPY THE BUSH KANGAROO (World)
1970-1973   £12 $19
1970
©1969 (96pg) (fc/tc)
Text stories, features and games
Photo cover
Based on the Australian TV series
SKY SPORTS SPORTS Annual (Pedigree)
2000   £3 $5
SKY DANCERS Official Annual (Grandreams)
© 1996 (64pg) (fc)   £3 $5
Comic Strips: Sky Clone Chaos!, The Harp of Flight!, The High and Mighty!
SLICK FUN Album (Swan)
1949-1955
1950-1955   £15 $24
SMART GIRL Annual (Odhams)
1960's   £8 $13
Based on the UK fashion magazine
SMASH! (Odhams/Fleetway)
1967-1976
1976 (softcover)
1967   £12 $19
1968-1969   £10 $16
1970-1976   £8 $13
Featured Comic Strips: Bad Penny, Grimly Feendish, Tuffy McGrew, The Man from BUNGLE, The Swots and the Blots, The Nervs, Its the Rubber Man, Charlies Choice, Ronnie Rich, Joe Innocent, Percys Pets, Danger Mouse, The Legend Testers, The Curse of the Ka
Based on the UK comic
SMOOSHEES (Fleetway)

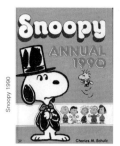

Snoopy 1990

Sooty 1975

Space 1999 1976

1989 £3 $5
Art: Geoff Shirley and Brian Gough
Based on the toy range
SMURFS (Stafford Pemberton/Grandreams)
1980-1981, 1998
1980 £8 $13
Text Stories: The Smurf meets a Baby Duckling, The Smurfs and the
Toys, The Smurfs and the Windmill - Art: Peyo
1981 £8 $13
Comic strip (fc): The Smurfs Sports Day - Art: Peyo
©1997 (Grandreams) £5 $8
Comic Strips: The Smurf Eggs, The Smurf Garden -
Art: Peyo
Based on the cartoon characters
SNOOPY (Ravette)
1990 (fc) £10 $16
Comic Strips by Schulz
Comic Strips (x3): Peanuts featuring Good ol' Charlie Brown
Text Stories: You're a Hero Charlie Brown, Sally's Christmas Party,
Scuba Diving Snoopy
Writer: Golden Volke
Based on the newspaper comic strip
SOCCER STARS (APL/IPC/Pedigree)
1996-2000 £3 $5
From the maker's of Shoot
SOCCER SUPERSTARS (APL)
1995 £3 $5
SONIC THE HEDGEHOG Official Yearbook (Grandreams)
1993
©1992 £6 $10
Comic Strips: Sonic the Hedgehog in Cartoon Concerto, Sonic the
Hedgehog in Speed Demonz, Shinobi in The Dark Circle, Sonic the
Hedgehog in Double Sonic
Based on the computer games character
SOOTY (Daily Mirror/Purnell/World)
1950's-present
1950's £25 $40
1960-1965 £15 $24
1966-1969 £10 $16
1970's £5 $8
1980's-present £3 $5
Daily Mirror annuals called 'Sooty's 1st Annual', 'Sooty's 2nd Annual'
etc
©1974, 1983 (Purnell)
1992 (World)
Art: Gina Hart and John Cooper
1993 (World) (64pg) (fc)
Writer: Clive Hopwood - Art: Jonathan Howard
©1995 (Grandreams) (48pg) (fc)
Writer: Beryl Johnston - Art: John MacGregor
1997 (World) (64pg) (fc)
Writer/Designer: A Shot in the Dark-Art: Jeff Harrison
Picture Strips (3x3): Weekend Weather, Too Busy, Christmas Magic
Photo Strip: Home Alone (7)
Photo cover
1998 (World)
Writers: John Broadhead and Joyce McAleer, Art: Alan Willow
Photo cover
Based on the Childrens TV series

SOOTY & CO (Grandreams)
N/D (1990's) (48pg) (fc)
Writer: Beryl Johnston - Art: John MacGregor
Based on the Childrens TV series
SPACE ANNUAL, Peter Fairleys (TV Times Publication)
1970
©1969 £10 $16
Photo features
SPACE FAMILY ROBINSON - LOST IN SPACE (World)
1967 (96pg) (Scarce) £20 $32
SPACE KINGLEY
1953 £30 $48
The Secret Squadron
SPACE 1999 (World/Whitman)
1976-1980
©1975 £8 $13
©1975 (64pg)
Comic Strips: Adam and Eve, Mark II (6fc) - Art: John Burns
A Woman's World (6tc) - Art: John Burns
Photo Text Stories: The Great Brain Robbery, Curse of the Dead
Features interviews with Martin Landau, Barbara Bain and Barry
Morse - Photo Cover
©1976-1978 £7 $11
©1976 (80pg)
Comic Strips: The Meeting Point (6fc)
Another Chance, Mindprobe (6x2 bw)
Includes photo stories and character profiles (fc/bw)
Large format
©1977 (64pg)
Cover art: Edgar Hodges
Comic Strips (tc): This Green Unpleasant Land... (8), Challenge! (6)
Photo Text Stories (fc): Enter the Metamorph, A Means for Revenge,
One Man's Meat, The Beast of Bokassa
Includes character profiles and pin-ups (fc)
1979 (Scarce) £10 $16
©1979
Comic Strips: Another Chance, Mindprobe!, Meeting Point
Based on the Gerry Anderson TV series
SPACE BABY (Fleetway)
1989 (64pg) £3 $5
Writer/Art: Peter Kingston
Space Baby created by Mike Young
Based on animated designs by Dave Edwards
SPACE INVADERS (World)
1983 (64pg) £4 $7
Sci Fi text stories and features
SPACE PRECINCT (Grandreams)
1996
©1995 (48pg) (fc) £4 $7
Photo cover
Based on the Gerry Anderson TV series
SPACEWAYS (New) Comic Annual (Boardman/Moring)
1955-1956
1955 £15 $24
1956 £12 $19
Titled 'The New Spaceways Comic Annual No.1'
Art: Denis McLoughlin
Swift Morgan, Roy Carson reprints

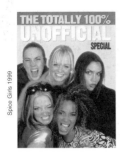

Spice Girls 1999

Spider Man Not Dated

Spiderman 1981

SPARKY Book (for Boys & Girls) (D.C. Thomson)
1968-1980
1968   £15 $24
1969-1975   £10 $16
1976-1980   £8 $13
1979 (126pg) (fc/tc)
Comic Strips include: The Sparky People, Mr. Ackroyd, Puss an'
Boots, Hungry Horace, Dreamy Daniel, Thingummy Blob, Ali's Baba,
Brainless, Superwitch, Baron Von Reich's-Pudding, Arfer, L Cars,
Peter Piper, Some Mummies Do 'Ave 'Em
Sci-Fi Strips (fc): The Great Atomic Camera of Pluvius II ((7),
Birdman of Alsace (6)
Based on the UK comic
SPEED & POWER Look and Learn (Fleetway)
1979 (80pg)   £5 $8
SPEED (Fleetway)
1981 (128pg)   £5 $8
Comic Strips: Topps on Two Wheels, Quick on the Draw, The
Ragged Racer, The Battling Birdmen, Speedboy, £1,000,000
Challenge
Also includes photo features and text stories
SPEEDSPORTS (World)
1979 (64pg)   £5 $8
SPICE GIRLS Special Totally 100% Unofficial (Grandreams)
1998-1999
©1997 (64pg) (fc)
Writers: Teresa Maughan, Mick St. Michael and Ian Welch
©1998 (64pg) (fc)
Writer: Joseph Adair - Designer: Teresa Maughan
The name 'Spice Girl' doesn't appear in the title or contents due to
copyright law
Photo features
Based on the UK girl band
SPIDER-MAN (World/Marvel-Grandreams/Marvel)
1975-1987, 1990-1992
1975 (World) (80pg)   £12 $19
Features Punisher
Amazing Spider-Man #129-131, Tales to Astonish #57 reprints
1976-1979   £10 $16
1976 (World)
Features Black Panther
Amazing Spider-Man #1, 8, Marvel Team-Up #20 reprints
1977 (World)
Features Doc Savage & Punisher
Spider-Man Giant Size #3-4 reprints
1978 (World)
Comic Strips: The Amazing Spider Man! - The Parents of Peter
Parker (36fc) - Writer: Stan Lee & Larry Lieber, Art: Mickey Demeo
Turning Point featuring the Return of Dr Octopus! (23fc)
Writer: Stan Lee, Art: Steve Kitko
Originally presented in Spiderman #11 (April 1964)
1979 (World)
Cover Art: John Romita Jr and Frank Giacoia
Comic Strips: The Web and the Flame (features Human Torch)-
Writer: Stan
Lee-Art: Mike Esposito and T Mortellaro
Amazing Spider-Man Annual #4 reprint
1980-1987, 1990-1992   £8 $13
©1979 (Marvel/Grandreams)

Comic Strips: Stegron Stalks The City! (17), War of the Reptile-Men!
(15), Amazing Spider-Man #165-166 reprints
Text Stories: A Sting in The Tail (5)-Guest stars The Scorpion, Fun-
House Of Fear (5)
Features: Spidey's Villains (5), Stan Lee - The Creator Unmasked
(3), Mock
cover 'Stan Lee' Art: Evi DeBono (tc)
©1980 (Marvel/Grandreams)
Comic Strips: Where Were you When the Lights went Out?-Art: Bill
Manto, Sal Buscema and Mike Esposito
Still Crazy After all These Years-Writer: Bill Mantlo-Art: Jim Mooney
& Mike Esposito - Peter Parker # 20-21 reprints
©1981 (Marvel/Grandreams)
Comic Strips (fc/tc): The Wings of The Vulture (20), From the
Depths of Defeat (20)
Features The Vulture and Kraven the Hunter
Writer: Stan Lee -Art: John Romita
Amazing Spider-Man #48-49 reprints
Text Story (UK): The Electric Sting (10)-features The Scorpion and
Electro (fc/tc)
Cover features Spider-Man, Electro, The Vulture, Kraven the Hunter
and The Scorpion
©1982 (Marvel/Grandreams)
N/D - price £2.50
Comic Strips: Vengeance is Mine-Writer: Ralph Macchio-Pencils:
Jim Mooney-Inks: Mike Esposito
Peter Parker Annual #4 reprint
©1983 (Marvel/Grandreams):
Comic Strips (2x18fc/tc): The Night Gwen Stacy Died, The Goblin's
Last Stand - Amazing Spider-Man #121-122 reprints
Text Stories (2 x8fc): Source of the Sleeper,
Hunter's Moon-featuring Kraven the Hunter
Also includes photos from the live action TV series (fc)
©1984 (Marvel/Grandreams)
Comic Strips: But the Cat Came Back-Writer: Roger Stern-Art: John
Romita Jr & Jim Mooney
Goin' Straight-Writer: Roger Stern-Art: John Romita Jr & Jim
Mooney - Amazing Spider-Mam #226-227 reprints
©1985 (Marvel/Grandreams)
N/D - price £3.25
Comic Strips: Spiderman Versus Doctor Octopus-Writer: Stan Le-
Art: Steve Ditko
A Savage Sting has.... The Scorpion (featuring Captain America)-
Writer: Tom DeFalco-Pencils: Herb Trimpe-Inks: Mike Esposito
Amazing Spider-Man 33, Marvel Team-Up #106 reprints
1990
Art: Todd McFarlane
Based on the Marvel comics characters
SPIDER-MAN (World)
1997-1998   £5 $8
1997 (64pg) (fc)
Endpaper art: Jon Rushby
Comic Strips: Day of the Chameleon (23)-Writer: Nel Yomtov-
Pencils: Alex Saviuk-Inks: Rob Stull
Freely adapted from a story and screenplay by John Semper
Spider-Man Adventures reprint
The Spider-Shadow (10)-Writer: Glenn Dakin-Art: Brian Williamson
The Besreker Machine (12)-Writer: Alan Cowsill-Art: Jon Rushby
and Brian Williamson
Text Story: Deadly Night Shift- Writer: James Hill-Art: Adrian Phillips

Star Lord 1981

Starsky & Hutch 1980

Star Trek 1974

Feature: Animating Spider-Man - The creative team behind the animated show
Fact Files: Spider-Man, The Chameleon, Mysterio, Green Goblin, Venom
1998 (64pg)
Comic Strips: The Hobgoblin: Bad Luck & Trouble (20fc)-Writer: Nel Yomtov-Pencils: Alex Saviuk-Inks: Rob Stull
Freely adapted from a Writer: John Semper and the teleplay by Larry Brody
Takin It to the Streets (22fc)-Writer: Nel Yomtov-Pencils: Alex Saviuk Inks: Rob Stull
Freely adapted from a story and teleplay by Stan Berkowitz
Into the Mystic (5fc)-Writer: Nel Yomtov-Art: Andy Kuhn
Spider Man Adventures reprints
A special origin of Spiderman feature
Based on the animated TV series

SPIDER WOMAN (Marvel/Grandreams)
1984
©1983   £8 $13
Comic Strips: Beware the Spider Woman - Bounty Hunter (17fc)-Writer: Michael Fleisher-Art: Frank Springer & Mike Esposito
Bring on the Clown (17fc)-Writer: Michael Fleisher-Pencils: Frank Springer-Inks: Mike Esposito
Doctor of Madness-(featuring The Hulk) (17fc)-Writer: Steven Grant-Pencils: Carmine Infantino-Inks: Alan Gordon
Sider-Woman #21 reprints
Based on the Marvel Comics character

SPLASH (World)
1987-1988   £3 $5
1987
Features: Tears for Fears, Duran Duran, Wham, Eurythmics, Dire Straits, Howard Jones, Aha, U2
1988
Art: Terry Kennett, Stephen Lings, David Mostyn, David Murray, Linda Smith

STARBURST (Marvel/Grandreams)
1982-1983   £12 $19
©1982 (Not Dated - Cover Price £2.50)
Editor John Barraclough-Writer: Alan Murdoch-Cover Art: John Bolton
Features Horror Film Reviews from the thirties to the seventies
Based on the UK sci fi fantasy magazine

STAR FLEET (World)
1984 (64pg) (fc/tc)   £6 $10
Art: Paul Green and Phil Woodall
Photo cover
Based on the Japanese puppet series

STAR LORD (Fleetway)
1980-1982
1980   £10   £16
Comic Strips: Strontium Dog
1981-1982   £8 $13

STAR MAIDENS (Stafford Pemberton)
1978   £8 $13
Based on the UK TV sci-fi series

STARSKY & HUTCH (Stafford Pemberton)
1978-1980 (64pg)   £8 $13
1978
Comic Strips: Gunrunners, Framed, A Tangled Web

1979
Comic Strips: Armed Robbery (5fc), Holiday Job (5fc)
1980
Comic Strips: Starsky Sees Stars (fc), Five Minutes for a Life! (8fc), Where's the Casth (7fc)
All include photo features on the cast
Based on the Police series starring David Soul and Paul Michael Glasier

STAR TREK (World/StaffordPemberton/Grandreams)
1968-1979
1968 (Scarce)   £20   £32
1969-1970   £15 $24
1971-1975   £10 $16
1976-1979   £8 $13
1972 (World) (80pg) (fc)
Comic Strips: The Voodoo Planet (25), The Youth Trap (25), The Legacy of Lazarus (24)
1977 (World) (80pg) (fc)
Cover Art: Edgar Hodges
Comic Strips: Sceptre Of The Sun (2 parts)
Reprint from Star Trek #10
The Psychocrystals (2 part) - Reprint from Star Trek #34
Features Art: Edgar Hodges, Paul Green, John Millington, David Hart
Large format
1978 (64pg) (fc)
Cover Art (incorporates photos of Kirk and Spock): Edgar Hodges
Endpaper: Paul Crompton
Comic Strips: Our Captain Is Missing!(23) - Star Trek #38 reprint
Prophet Of Peace (23) - Star Trek #39 reprint
Features Art; Paul Green, John Fasnacht, John Millington
©1978 (64pg) (fc)
Cover Art: Edgar Hodges
Comic Strips: Sport of Knaves (22)
No Time Like The Past (22), Writer: G. Kashdan, Art: Al McWilliams
A World Against Itself (13), Writer: Arnold Drake, Art: Al McWilliams

STAR TREK THE MOTION PICTURE
1979   £8 $13

STAR TREK: NEXT GENERATION (Marvel)
1992
©1991   £8 $13
Mini -series Marvel Comic reprints

STAR TV & FILM ANNUAL (Odhams)
1960's   £10 $16
1967
Roger Moore cover
1968
Features: Stephanie Powers (The Girl from UNCLE), Tom Jones, Doctor Dolittle (Rex Harrison), Batman & Robin, Tommy Steele, Michael Bentine, James Bond (You Only Live Twice), Cliff Richard, Julie Andrews, Eric & Ernie, Ursula Andress, Johnny Morris, Val Doonican, Cilla Black, Monkees, Julie Felix, Jimmy Saville, James Coburn, Nancy Sinatra, Alf Garnett, The Long Duel (Yul Brynner), Caroline Mortimer, Rolf Harris
Morecambe & Wise photo cover

STAR & TV FUN (Odhams)
1968   £10 $13
Morecambe & Wise photo cover

STAR WARS (Brown Watson/Grandreams/World)

Stars Wars 2000

Stingray 1966

Strike Force 1983

1978-1982, 1986, 1998-1999
1978 £10 $16
1979-1982, 1986 £8 $13
©1979
'Marvel Presents' (Grandreams)
Comic Strips (tc/fc): Day of the Dragon Lords!
The Sound Of Armageddon!-Writer/Editor: Archie Goodwin-Art: Carmine Infantino & Terry Austin
Includes 'Why I Wanted To Act' by Carrie Fisher
©1981 (Marvel/Grandreams)
Comic Strips: Droid Duel-Writer: Archie Goodwin-Art: Carmine Infantino and Gene Day
The Third Law-Writer: Larry Hama-Art: Carmine Infantino and Carlos Garzon
Death Probe-Writer: Archie Goodwin-Pencils: Carmine Infantino-Inks: Day and Stone
©1985
Featuring Ewoks
1998-1999 £5 $8
1998 (World) (64pg) (fc)
Designer: Simon Connor-Compilers: John Broadhead and Joyce McAleer
Photo tribute to the original film series
1999 (World) (fc)
Designer: Simon Connor - Writer/Editor: Dan Whitehead
Based on the original film
STAR WARS - THE EMPIRE STRIKES BACK (Grandreams)
1981-1982 £8 $13
©1981 Annual No. 2 (64pg)
Comic Strips: Crimson Forever! (3 chapters)
Writer: Archie Goodwin-Art: Al Williamson, Tom Palmer, Walt Simonson
The Dreams of Cody Sunn-Childe! (22fc)
Writer: Wally Lombego-Pencils: Carmine Infantino-Inks: Tom Palmer
STAR WARS - RETURN OF THE JEDI (Grandreams)
1983-1984 £8 $13
©1983 (64pg)
Comic Strips: In the Hands of Jabba the Hutt! (14fc), The Emperor Commands! (16fc), Mission to Endor! (16fc), The Final Duel (16fc)
©1984 (Marvel/Grandreams)
Cover Artwork: Jerry Paris
Comic Strips (fc): Chanteuse of the Stars (20), The Big Con (20)
Ellie (22) - Editor: Louise Jones - Writer: Jo Duffy
Pencils: Ron Frenz-Inks: Tom Palmer
Marvel reprints
STAR WARS EPISODE 1 - THE PHANTOM MENACE
(Egmont World)
2000 (64pg) (fc) £5 $8
Writers: John Broadhead and Joyce McAleer
Design and Layout: Simon Connor
Photo features and stories
STAR WARS SPECIAL EDITION (BHS)
N/D 1980's £8 $13
'Empire Strikes Back', "Return of the Jedi' Annual compiliation
STEPS Special Totally 100% Unofficial (Grandreams)
2000
©1999 (48pg) (fc) £3 $5
Writer: Joe Adair-Designer Sue Bartram
Based on the UK dance/pop group

STINGRAY (City/Ravette/Fleetway)
1966-1967, 1993-1994
©1965 £20 $32
©1965 (96pg)
Comic Strips (fc): Night Raid, Pacific Disasters, The Great Robbery, The Treasure Map, Marineville Attack!
©1966 £15 $24
©1992-©1993 £8 $13
1993 (Fleetway) (63pg)
Cover Art: Steve Kyte - Editor: Alan Fennell
Design: Cally Stewart
Comic Strips (full colour): Creatures of the Lake (16), A Trip to England (16), The Treasure of Loch Fionn (14)
TV Century 21 reprints featuring Art: Ron Embleton
Profiles: Troy Tempest, Marina and Phones, Titan and Agent X2 Zero, Commander Shore and Atlanta, Terror Fish
Includes Specifications of Stingray cutaway by Graham Bleathman
©1993 (Ravette) (62pg)
Comic Strips (fc): Stingray (5), Marineville Fact File No 1-17 (17) - Writer: Alan Fennell - Art: Keith Page
Technical illustrations of Marineville, Terror Fish, Titanica, Hydromic Missiles and Pacifica by Graham Bleathman
Based on the Gerry Anderson TV series
STINGRAY 'Television Storybook' (PBS)
1966
©1965 £15 $24
Based on the Gerry Anderson TV series
STOPPIT AND TIDYUP (Grandreams)
1990
©1989 (64pg) (fc) £3 $5
Art: Steve Box and Terry Brain
Based on the ITV animated series
STREETHAWK (World)
1986 (64pg) £4 $7
Comic Strip: The Night of the Hawk (6)
Based on the action adventure TV series
STREET SHARKS (Grandreams)
1997
©1996 £3 $5
Art/Design: Arkadia
Comic Strip: A Little Bit of the Action
Based on the animated TV series
STRIKE FORCE
1980's £6 $10
Based on the Spelling Goldberg action adventure TV series
STRIKER
1974-1978 £5 $8
Based on the UK soccer comic
SEE: Gary Lineker's Striker Annual
SUE DAY
1962 £8 $13
SUN Annual For Boys (World)
1970's
1972 £5 $8
Editor: Mae Bradley - Art: Steve Livesey, Edgar Hodges, David Brian, Alan Linsdel
Text Stories: Boomerang by Tony Haynes, The Visitation by David Gittens, The Feats of Onry by Fred Rogerson, The Cunning One by

Sun Book for Boys 1974

Super Heroes 1980

super Heroes 1981

L B Lux, Incident in Serengeti by David Gittens
Picture Strip: The Remarkable Voyage of the Shenandoah
1974
Editor: Mae Broadley - Art: Edgar Hodges, John Leeder, Paul Crompton
Text Stories: The Clever One by Derek Neville, A Feat of Endurance by Anthony Wootton, Journey in the Mist by Wentworth Andrews
Picture Strip: The War in Lincoln County
Includes features on Arlo Guthris, Al Stewart and Gordon Lightfoot
1976
Editor: Mae Broadley - Art: Paul Crompton, John Warren, Tony Lomas, David Hart
Text Stories: Hijack to the Big Time by Christopher Hard, A Crusoe of the Cosmos by W Price, This Freedom by Ian Gordon
Picture Strip: I'm the Greatest (Muhammed Ali)
Includes feature on Elton John

SUN SOCCER Annual (Ring)

1972-1990's

1972-1979	£7	£11
1980-1990s	£5	£8

1981 (Ring) (96pg) (fc/bw)
Star Gallery featuring player profiles include: Bryan Robson, Mickey Thomas, John Gregory, Milija Aleksic, Gordon McQueen, Alan Hansen, Osvaldo Ardiles and Kevin Keegan

SUNNY STORIES

1956

©1955	£10	£16

SUPERADVENTURE (Atlas/Top Sellers)

1958-1972

1958-1959	£50	£80
1959-1960	£30	£48
1960-1961	£25	£40
1961-1962	£20	£32
1962-1965	£15	£24
1967-1969	£12	£19
1970	£15	£24
1971-1972	£10	£16

DC Comics reprints featuring Batman, Superman, Superboy, Supergirl, Aqua Man, Flash, Jimmy Olsen, Tommy Tomorrow, Johnny Quick, Congo Bill, Green Arrow, Legion of Super Heroes
N.B. 1958-1965 split year listing

SUPERBOY (Atlas)

1953-1968

1953-1954	£60	£96
1954-1955	£40	£60
1955-1958	£30	£48
1958-1961	£25	£40
1961-1966	£20	£32
1967-1968	£15	£24

Based on the DC Comics reprints featuring Superboy, Rex the Wonder Dog and Detective Chimp
N.B. 1953-1966 split year listing

SUPERCAR (Collins)

1962-1964

1962	£25	£40

'Mike Mercury in Supercar'

1963-1964	£20	£32

Based on the Gerry Anderson puppet series

SUPERCAR 'A Big Television Book' (World)

1963

©1962	£15	£24

SUPER CINEMA (Fleetway House)

1950's

	£15	£24

1954 - Errol Flynn front cover
1955 (164pg) (tc)
Dramatised photo features include: Trouble In Store (Norman Wisdom), Wings of the Hawk (Van Heflin), Rob Roy (Richard Todd), Appointment in Honduras (Glenn Ford), Tumbleweed (Audie Murphy), The Kidnappers (Duncan Macrae), Conquest of Cochise (Robert Stack), Hell Below Zero (Alan Ladd), The Runaway Bus (Frankie Howerd), Star of India (Cornel Wilde), It Came From Outer Space (Richard Carlson), River Beat (Phyllis Kirk)
Pin Ups: Hugh O'Brian, Broderick Crawford, Audrey Hepburn, Aldo Ray, Jose Ferrer, Burt Lancaster, Rod Cameron
Cover artwork (fc): Richard Todd in Rob Roy (Walt Disney-RKO)

SUPERCOLOURED COMIC Annual (Boardman)

1950-1952 (Scarce)	£40	£60

SUPER-DC Bumper Book (Top Sellers)

1970

Includes Superman, Batman reprints and text stories (UK)

SUPERGIRL (St Michael/Octopus)

1985

©1984	£7	£11

Adapted by Wendy Andrews
Photo storybook
Based on the film written by David Odell

SUPER GRAN (Grandreams)

1986

©1985 (64pg)	£3	£5

Comic Strips (2x8bw): The Aztec Angel, Spring-Heeled Scunner
Text stories writer: Forrest Wilson
Photo cover
Based on the Tyne Tees TV series and books by Forrest Wilson

SUPER HEROES Annual (Brown Watson/Grandreams/Marvel)

1978-1981, 1989-1992	£8	£13

©1978 (Brown and Watson) (Marvel Presents)
Comic Strips: The Mighty Thor - A Spectre from the Past!, Writer: Gerry Conway, Art: John Buscema and Dick Giordano (18tc/fc)
The Amazing Spiderman - Whodunit! (17fc), Writer: Len Wein, Art: Sal Buscema
The Silver Surfer - The Flame and The Fury! (19fc/tc), Writer: Stan Lee, Art: John Buscema
©1979 (Marvel Presents)
Comic Strips: The Mighty Thor- To Hela and Back (tc/fc)- Writer/Editor: Len Wein, Art: John Buscema & Tony DeZuniga
The Silver Surfer - Gather, Ye Witches (fc)
Writer: Stan Lee, Pencils: John Buscema, Inks: Dan Adkins
Prince Namor, The Sub-Mariner - The Sea That Time Forgot (fc/tc)- Writer: Roy Thomas-Pencils: Marie Severin-Inks: Joe Gaudioso

1981	£10	£16

©1980 (Marvel)
Comic Strips: The Uncanny X-Men in "X-Men" & When Mutants Clash (tc), Writer: Stan Lee, Pencils: Jack Kirby, Inks: Paul Reinman
Ms. Marvel in Bridge of No Return (fc)
Writer: Chris Claremont, Art: Jim Mooney & Joe Sinnott

1989-1992	£8	£13

1989 (96pg) (fc)
Editor/Designer: John Freeman

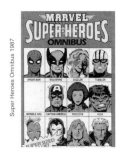

Cover pencils: Martin Griffiths, Inks: Simon Coleb
Endpaper: Jeff Anderson
Comic Strips: Spider-Man and his Amazing Friends in The Triumph of the Green Goblin (20) - Writer/Adaptation from NBC TV teleplay: Dennis Marks, Pencils: Dan Spiegle, Inks: Vince Colletta
Spider-Man and his Amazing Friends #1 reprint
Fantastic Four in Back to the Basics (22) - Writer & Pencils: John Byrne, Inks: Bjorn Heyne, The Uncanny X-Men in Prison of the Heart (12), uncredited
The Incredible Hulk in Vicious Circle (22)-Writer: Peter David-Art: Todd McFarlane, Incredible Hulk # 340 reprint
Fantastic Four & Spider-Man in Clobberin' Time (6), Writer; Sholly Fisch, Pencils: James Fry, Inks: Mark McKenna
Cover features Spider-Man, Iceman and Fire-Star
1990
Editor: John Freeman
Cover Art: Martin Griffiths, Inks: Simon Coleby
Comic Strips: The Incredible Hulk in Call of the Desert (18)
Editor: Dennis O'Neil-Story & Pencils: John Byrnes-Inks: Bob Wiacek
Spider-Man Meets Doc Ock! (2), Captain America in Story (8)
Editor: Al Milgrom-Story & Art: Norm Breyfogle
The Thing and the Avengers in Full House..Dragons High (17)
Editor: Roger Stern, Writer: Peter Gillis-Pencils: Frank Miller-Inks: Bob McLeod
Fantastic Four in Synchronicity (7) - Editor: Al Milgrom-Story: Mark Borax-Art: Norm Breyfogle
1991 (64pg) (Marvel)
Editor: Andy Seddon
Cover: Art Wetherall, Rob Sharp
Comic Strips: The Invincible Iron Man - Fallout (22fc), Writer: David Michelinie, Pencils: John Romita, Ink: Green, Stone and Layton
The Fantastic Four - Death in a Vacuum! (14fc), Writer: Bill Mantlo, Art: Greg Brooks
Mother of the Bride (12fc), Writer: Jo Duffy, Art: John Bolton
Text Stories: War Beneath the Wars, Writer: John Tomlinson, Pencils: John Marshall, Inks: Stephen Baskerville
Poster: Classic X Men, Art: Arthur Adams
Based on the Marvel Comics characters
SUPER HEROES (London Editions)
1982-1984   £10 $16
1982
Cover Art: Alan Craddock
1983 (64pg) (fc)
Cover art: Alan Craddock, Endpaper: Bryan Talbot
Comic Strips: Justice League of America in Adam Strange-Puppet of Time (32)
Writer: Cary Bates, Art: Dick Dillin & Frank McLaughlin
The Atom in Mimiature War of the Bat-Knights (10), Writer: Bob Rozakis, Art: Alex Saviuk & Francisco Chiaramonte, Batman in Night of the Stalker (14), Writer: Steve Englehart, Plot/Pencils: Vin & Sal Amendola, Inks: Dick Giordano
Text Story: Wonder Woman in the Eye of the Eagle, Writer: Kelvin Gosnell
1984
Cover Art: Alan Craddock, Endpaper: Bryan Talbot
Based on the DC Comic characters
SUPER HEROES Omnibus (Marvel)
1987-1988

©1987   £8 $13
Comic Strips (fc): The Fury of X-Factor
Writer: Tom Defalco-Pencils: Rick Leonardi-Inks: Bob Layton
Amazing Spider-Man #282 reprint
Metamorphosis Oddity-Plot/Writer: David Michelinie-Pencils: Mark Bright-Plot/Inks: Bob Layton-Iron Man # 217 reprint
Call of the Desert-Story & Pencils: John Byrne-Inks: Bob Wiacek
Incredible Hulk # 314 reprint
To Tame a Tumbler!-Writer: Bill Mantlo-Pencils: Herb Trimpe-Inks: Jack Abel-Captain America #291 reprint
Psylocke-Writer: Chris Claremont
Pencils: Alan Davis-Inks: Paul Neary-Uncanny X-Men # 213 reprint
Based on the Marvel Comics characters
SUPER HEROES SECRET WARS (Marvel/Grandreams)
N/D
Comic Strips (fc): Secret Wars (23)
Writer: Jim Shooter-Pencils: Michael Zeck-Inks: John Beatty
Spider-Man and Alpha Fight (3), The Collected Spiderman (28)
Writer: Louise Simonson-Pencils: Paul Neary-Inks: Sam De La Rosa
Based on the Marvel Comic
SUPER LEAGUE Sky Sports Official Annual (World)
1998   £3 $5
SUPERMAN (Atlas/Top Sellers/Egmont/Fleetway/Grandreams)
1951-1990's
1951   £150 $240
1952   £80 $128
1953-1954   £50 $80
1954-1955   £40 $60
1955-1960   £30 $48
1960-1963   £25 $40
1962-1966   £20 $32
1967-1968   £15 $24
1969-1972   £12 $19
1972 (Brown Watson)
Superman Annual No. 1
1972 N.B. 1955-1966 split year listing
1973/1974-1978 - See SUPERMAN & BATMAN
1979-1983   £10 $16
1980 (Egmont) (64pg) (fc)
Cover: Paul Green
Comic Strips: Solomon Grundy Wins on a Monday (16)-Writer: Gerry Conway-Art: J L Garcia Lopez and Bob Oksner
Lightning Strikes.... Thunder Kills (17)-Writer: Gerry Conway-Art: Curt Swan and Bob Oskner
The Tatto Switcheroo (5)-Writer: Martin Pasko-Art: J L Garcia Lopez & Vince Colletta
A Monster Named Lois Lane (14)-Writer: Cary Bates-Art: Curt Swan & Bob Oksner
Includes one page feature 'Can You Draw Superman?' featuring the many faces of Superman as drawn by Curt Swan
1981 (London Editions)
Comic Strips: The Riddle of Little Earth Lost
Writer: David Michelinie-Art: Jose Luis Garcia Lopez-Adam Strange Consultant: Jack C. Harris
The Hero Who Hated the Legion-Writer: Cary Bates-Art: Mike Grell
The Prive Life of Clark Kent-Writer: E. Nelson Bridwell-Art: Curt Swan & Garcia Lopez
The Made to Order Menace-Writer: Elliot Maggin-Art: Curt Swan & Murphy Anderson

Superman 1979

Superman & Batman 1974

Superstars 1979

1984-1989   £8 $13
1984 (London Editions) (64pg) (fc)
Cover Art: Bryan Talbot-Endpaper: Alan Craddock
Comic Strips: Superman and Hawkgirl in: The Stars, Like Moths...!
(17)-Writer: Roy Thomas-Plot & Art: Jim Starlin
Superman in: The Secret Guardian of Smallville! (20)
Writer: Cary Bates-Art: Curt Swan & Bob Oksner
Superman and Green Lantern in: Between Friend and Foe! (17)-
Writer: Marv Wolfman
Plot & Pencils: Jim Starlin-Inks: Steve Mitchell
Feature (2): The Phantom Zone Explored by Dave Prockter
1990's   £5 $8
1993 (London Editions) (64pg) (fc)
Cover Art: Brian Bolland-Endpaper: Dave Gibbons
Comic Strips: The Key That Unlocked Chaos (3 parts)-
Writer: Len Wein-Art: Jim Starlin & Romeo Tanghal
Part One features Superman & Manhunter From Mars, Part Two -
Superman & Supergirl, Part Three - Superman & The Spectre
DC Comics Presents reprint
Superboy in The Slay Away Plan (7), Writer: Cary Bates, Art: Bob
Brown & Murphy Anderson
Includes feature on the comic history of Lex Luthor with Gene
Hackman photo
©1996 (Grandreams) (64pg) (fc)
Comic Strips: Speed Kills (22), Writer/Pencils: Dan Jurgens, Inks:
Art Thibert - Adventures of Superman #463 reprint
The Name Game (22), Writer/Pencils: John Byrne, Inks: Karl Kesel
Superman#11 reprint
To Laugh and Die in Metropolis (17), Writer/Pencils: John Byrne,
Inks: Karl Kesel, Superman#9 reprint
Based on the DC Comics character
SUPERMAN & BATMAN (Brown Watson)
1973-1978   £8 $13
©1977 (64pg)
With Robin The Boy Wonder
Comic Strips: Batman in "This One'll Kill You, Batman!" (20tc/fc),
Writer: Denny O'Neil, Art: Irv Novick & Dick Giordano
Superman in "My Best Friend-- the Super-Spy!" (25fc/tc), Writer:
Elliot S. Magin, Art: Curt Swan & Bob Oksner
Text Stories: Superman - The Master Plan of the Mind Bender (4),
Art: J. Britton
Batman - Wild West's Cowboy Crimes (3), The Riddler's Ransom
Robbery (4), Art: John Bolton
Based on the DC Comics characters
SUPERMAN STORYBOOK Annual (World)
1967-1969
1967   £15 $24
1968   £12 $19
1969   £10 $16
©1968 (96pg) (fc/tc)
Text Stories: Night of the Red Sun- features Lex Luthor (fc), Pink
Elephants- features The Prankster (tc), The Day the Rains Turned
Dry - features The Prankster (tc), Lord of the Deep (tc), Undersea
Invasion (fc), Santa Toyman (fc), Super Witch (fc), Crash Landing
(fc), The Phantom Professor (fc), The Doomed Ship (tc), The
Demon's Music (tc), Brainiac's Mini-Menace- features
Brainiac (fc), The Great God Mars (fc)
Features include: Superman and his Friends, Enemies of Superman
Endpaper artwork based on Curt Swan original includes Superman,

Supergirl, Daily Planet staff, Lana Lang, Lori Lemaris, Mr Mxyzptlk,
Super-Pets, Legion of Super-Heroes and Bizarro 1
All years feature text stories only
Based on the DC Comics characters
SUPERHUMAN SAMAURAI SUPER-SQUAD (Grandreams)
1996
©1995   £3 $5
Edited by Barrie Tomlinson
Comic Strips (fc): TV or not TV! (4), Troubles in Space! (8), Who Put
Out the Lights? (4)
SUPER LEAGUE Sky Sports (World)
1998   £3 $5
SUPERSONICS (IPC)
1979   £8 $13
Features: Billy Idol, David Essex, Shaun Cassidy, Kurt Russel, Bob
Geldof, Johnny Rotten, Paul Simenon of the Clash, The Stranglers,
Bay City Rollers, Michael Jackson, The Jam, The Damned, The
Carpenters
SUPERSTARS (Fleetway/World)
1970's   £7 $11
1978 (64pg) (fc/tc) (World)
Features: Slik, Rod Stewart, Barry Sheen, Twiggy, Chicago, Starsky
& Hutch, Robert Palmer, David Wilky, The Carpenters, Osibisa,
Peter Frampton, Dustin Hoffman, Jack Nicholson, Paul Simon,
Steeleye Span, Barry White, Gene Wilder, Abba, Rick Wakeman,
Bjorn Borg, Sue Barker, Jimmy Connors, Cat Stevens, Bryan Ferry,
Dennis Waterman, Bob Dillon, Joan Armatrading
1979 (64pg) (fc/bw)
Features: Leo Sayer, Farrah Fawcett-Majors, Fleetwood Mac, Bob
Marley, Candi Staton, Muppet Show, Iggy Pop, Cliff Richard, Carly
Simon, Eddie and the Hot Rods, Red Rum, Sylvester Stallone, Nick
Nolte, Bad Company, John Curry, Kris & Barbara, Connery & Moore,
Barry Sheene, Rudolph Nureyev, Niki Lauda, The Fonz, Clint
Eastwood, Sex Pistols, Peter Sellers, Linda
Ronstadt, George Harrison, Crosby Stills and Nash, Neil Diamond,
Jack Jones
SUPERTED (Stafford Pemberton/World/Fleetway)
1980's   £6 $10
1984 (Stafford Pemberton)
Comic Strips: SuperTed in Ghost Town, SuperTed in Atlantis,
SuperTed Texmania
Contributions from: Brian Catchpole, Dave Edwards, Ron Erickson,
Chris Fenna, Fiona Fenna, Roger Ficking, Rob Lee, Robin Lyons,
Sara Markham, Andrew Offiler, Les Orton, Dafydd Parri, Sue Paton,
Rosanne Reeves, Richard Thomas, Phil Watkins, Liz Young, Mike
Young and the staff of Siriol Animation
1985 (World)
1986 (World)
Art: Rob Lee, Andrew Offiler
Comic Strips: SuperTed and the City of Ice, SuperTed and the
Space Witch, SuperTed and the Computer Kid
1989 (Fleetway) (64pg)
Writers: Mike Young and Rob Lee
Art: Rob Lee based on animated designs by Dave Edwards
Paint and trace by Ron Erickson and Frank Coller
Comic Strips (fc): Superted and the Inter-Galactic Poacher
(10),Superted Goes To Spot (10)
Text stories: Cosmic Dust, Spotty's Time Machine
Based on the animated TV series

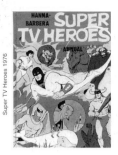
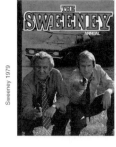

SUPER THRILLER (World)
1958
©1957   £10 $16
Cover: R. W. Smethurst - Frontispiece: Edgar Hodges
Comic Strips (2x8 b/w): Secret City, Sir Launcelot
SUPER TV HEROES Hanna Barbera's (Brown Watson)
1976-1977   £15 $24
©1975
Comic Strips: Birdman and the Galaxy Trio (8tc), Young Samson
and Goliath (5tc), Herculoids Threat of the Cavern Creatures (8fc),
Herculoids The Vapor-Vampire Invasion (6fc), Hold on to Your Mind
(6fc), Birdman Duel at Dawn (6fc), Mighty Mightor Beware!
Skullarva! (4fc), Herculoids Invasion of the Martian Ants (6fc), Moby
Dick Danger in the Deep (4fc), Shazzan Terrors of Turaba (5fc),
Birdman The Solar Scorpions (3tc), Space Ghost The Plague of
Giants (9tc)
Text Story: Mankind in Peril
Based on the animated TV series
SURVIVAL World of (Stafford Pemberton)
1980-1981   £6 $10
1980
Writer/Editor: John Gooders
1981 (48pg)
Writer: Eve Sumner - Designer: Edgar Hodges
Based on the Anglia TV wildlife programme
SUZIE DANDO
1984 (80pg)   £5 $8
Photo features and articles
Comic Strip: Suzie Dando stars in..... The Captive! (7bw)
Based on the gymnast and TV presenter
SWEENEY (Brown Watson)
1977-1979 (64pg)   £8 $13
©1976
Comic Strips: A Necessary Evil (6fc), One Man's Courage (6fc),
Double Trouble (6fc)
Text Stories: The Flying Squad, Knife Edge, Flyaway, Inside Job,
The Hostage, Old Enemy
©1977
Comic Strips: Hyena in London (6bw), Boy Wonder (6fc), Right time,
Right place (4fc)
Text Stories: New Firm, The Banker
©1978
Comic Strips: Double Cross Ambush (6bw), Blow the Fuses (6fc)
Text Stories: Courageous Cops, A Far Too Tidy Corpse, Gold Fever,
Devil or the Deep
All include photo features on the cast
Based on the police series starring John Thaw and Dennis
Waterman
SWEET VALLEY HIGH (Sapling)
1997   £7 $11
Text Stories: Summer Lovin', Model Behaviour, False Possessions,
Mixed Doubles, Sam Enchanted Evening
Based on the TV series and books by Francine Pascal
SWIFT (Hulton/Longacre)
1955-1963
1955   £20 $32
1956   £15 $24
1957-1959   £12 $19
1960-1963   £10 $16

Based on the UK Comic
SWISS FAMILY ROBINSON (World)
1976 (64pg) (fc/tc)   £6 $10
Art: Edgar Hodges, Paul Green
Text stories and features - Photo cover
Based on the TV series
SYLVANIAN FAMILIES Official Annual (World/Marvel)
1988-1991
1988 (World) (64pg) (fc)   £8 $13
Photo text stories and features - Photo cover
1989-1991   £6 $10
©1990 (Marvel) (64pg)
Cover Art: John Burns, Editor: Michael Stuart Phipps, Art: Paul
Gamble, Mario Capaldi
Based on the toy range
TAKE THAT Official Annual
1994-1996   £4 $7
©1993 (48pg)   £4 $7
Writer: Michael Heatley
Editor: Melanie J Clayden-Design/Layout: Louise Ivimy, Sue Bartram
1994 (World) (64pg)
Editor/Writer: Alex Kadis - Design: ArtAtac
©1994 (Grandreams) (48pg)
Editor: Melanie J Clayden-Writer: Michael Heatley-Design by Louise
Ivimy-Photography: Philip Ollerenshaw/Idols
©1995 (Virgin) (48pg)
Cover photography: Peter Ollerenshaw
Editor/Writer/ Design: Tony Horkins, Vici McCarthy and Arthur Brown
Based on the UK boy band
TALES OF THE GOLD MONKEY
1982 (Scarce)   £10 $16
Based on the Indiana Jones style TV series
TALES OF WELLS FARGO (World/Purnell/Peveril/Swan)
1961-1964
1961   £12 $24
1961-World and Purnell versions published in the same year
1962-1964   £10 $16
©1962 'Big TV Bumper Book '
Based on the TV Western series starring Dale Robertson
TALES OF WELLS FARGO TV Storybook
1964
Based on the TV Western series starring Dale Robertson
TAMMY (Fleetway)
1970's-1980's
1970's   £5 $8
1980's   £3 $5
Comic Strips feature: Bella, Bessie Bunter, Masie's Magic, Twangy
Pearl, Sari, Molly Mills, Lulu, Sarah's Seal and Strange Stories
Based on the UK girls comic
TARZAN (World/Brown Watson)
1965-1971, 1973-1980
1965-1971   £8 $13
©1967 (96pg) (fc/tc)
'Edgar Rice Burroughs' - Cover Art: Ron Smethurst
Stories and features: Joe Morrissey, J.H. Pavey, A. Tyson, Mae
Broadley and J. W. Elliot - Art: Edgar Hodges
Comic Strips (fc): The Hunting of the Beast (17), The Insult (8)
Gold Key reprints

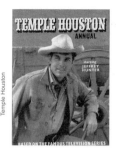

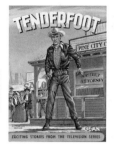

Teletubbies 2000

Temple Houston

Tenderfoot 1962

TE

©1970 (96pg) (fc/tc)
'Edgar Rice Burroughs' - Cover Art: Edgar Hodges
Comic Strip (fc): The Pirates of Kosar (21)
Based on 'Tarzan At The Earth's Core'
Gold Key reprint
1973-1980   £6 $10
©1972 (96pg) (fc/tc) (Brown & Watson)
Comic Strips: Major Disaster (2), Lost in Pellucidar (21), Turchuk
The Mighty (21), The Jungle Pit (8)
Text Stories: Tarzan and the Golden God of Makulu, Tarzan and the
Witch Doctor, Tarzan and the Zoo Trappers
1976 (Brown Watson)
Endpaper: John Bolton
Comic Strips: Origin of the Apeman (48fc)
1978 (World)
Cover Art: Ron Smethurst
Stories and features: Joe Morrissey, J H Pavey, A Tyson, Mae
Broadley and J W Elliot - Art: Edgar Hodges
Comic Strips (fc): The Hunting of the Beast (17), Truchuk the Mighty
(21), Leopard Girl in A Sound of Guns (4)
1968-1970 Based on the TV series starring Ron Ely
TEAM KNIGHT RIDER (Grandreams)
1999
©1998   £3 $5
Editor: Tony Lynch-Designer: Jason Bazim
Photo cover
Based on the action adventure TV series
TEDDY BEAR (IPC/Fleetway)
1967-1981
1967   £12 $19
1968-1970   £10 $16
1970-1975   £8 $13
1976-1981   £5 $8
Based on the UK comic
TEDDY EDWARD
1970's   £6 $10
TEDDY IN MY POCKET (World)
1997   £3 $5
Based on the toy range
TEDDY RUXPIN
1989   £5 $8
Based on the plush toy
TEDDY TAIL'S Daily Mail Annual
1934-1962
1950-1955   £15 $24
1956-1962   £10 $16
TEENAGE MUTANT HERO TURTLES (Grandreams)
1991-1993   £5 $8
©1990 (64pg) (fc)
Writer: Angus Allen - Art: C.L.I.C. Publishing
Comic Strip: New York's Shiniest (8)
1991 (64pg) (fc)
Comic Strips (4 pg x4): Geek Pizza, Day of the Footbots, Sewer
Sub, Monster Problems
©1992
Comic Strips: The Big Splash, Late Pizza, The Ambush
Based on the animated TV series
TEENBEAT - POP TEN

1960's-1970's
1960's   £12 $19
1967
Includes the Beatles
1968
Includes the Monkees
©1969 (102pg)
'By the editor of Teenbeat Monthly Albert Hand'
'Behind the scenes news and views of the stars and their world of
pop'
Features: The Beatles, Rolling Stones, Small Faces, Bee Gees,
Manfredd Mann, Beach Boys, Hollies, Tremeloes
1970's   £10 $16
TELETUBBIES (Egmont World)
1998-present   £3 $5
1998 (64pg) (fc)
Writer: Davey Moore, Art: Jane Swift
1999 (64pg) (fc)
Writer: Simon Nicholson, Art: Jane Swift
Based on the BBC TV pre-school series
TELEVISION ANNUAL (Odhams Press)
1954-1959   £15 $24
TELEVISION CARTOON ANNUAL (World)
1977   £6 $10
Based on Warner Bros Looney Tunes characters
TELEVISION FAVOURITES COMIC ANNUAL (World)
1958   £15 $24
Dell reprints
TELL ME WHY (Fleetway)
1970-1978   £5 $8
1977 (96pg)
Picture Strips: The Shy Scientist (1tc), True Tales of the Old West
(3x1bw),
1978 (80pg) (fc/tc)
Picture Strips (7x2tc): Famous Lives-
Part 1- Hannibal, Part 2 - Giuseppe Garibaldi, Part 3- Peter Paul
Rubens, Part 4 - Sir Walter Raleigh, Part 5 - St. Francis of Assisi,
Part 6 - Alexander the Great, Part 7 - Thomas Wolsey
Based on the UK childrens magazine
TELEVISION CARTOON Annual (World)
1970's   £6 $10
1977
1978 (64pg)
Comic Strips featuring: Foghorn Leghorn & Henery Hawk, Bugs
Bunny, Tweety & Sylvester, Wile E Coyote, Yosemite Sam, Daffy
Duck, Beep Beep
Based on Looney Tunes
TEMPLE HOUSTON (World)
1965   £10 $16
Photo cover
Based on the TV western series starring Jeffrey Hunter
TENDERFOOT (World/Dean)
1959-1961
1959   £12 $19
1959 (World)
Photo cover
1960-1961   £10 $16
1961 (Dean) (128pg)

Writer: Bill Pembury-Art: Leo Rawlings
Text Stories: The Lame Horse, Son of Black Feature, Lawmen of the West, Children of the Woods, Secret of the Mountain, Death on Horseback, Creatures of the West, Strangers in Camp, Robbery at Racoon City, Mystery of Hayden's Hollow, The Young Ranchers, 'Goldy' Gelden
Based on the TV Western series
TERRAHAWKS (World)
1984-1986 £6 $10
©1983 (64pg) (fc/tc)
Comic Strips (fc): Ninestein's Big Drop! (4) - Art: Glenn Rix
The Golden Skeleton Invasion (4)-Art: Phil Woodall
Text stories art: Paul Green, Melvyn Powell and Phil Woodall
Includes photo features from the TV series
Photo cover
©1984 (64pg) (fc)
Comic Strips: When Earth is Enslaved!, Beauty and the Beast
Text stories art: Paul Green
Photo cover
Based on the Gerry Anderson TV puppet series
TERRAHAWKS Story Book (Purnell)
1985
©1984 £6 $10
TERRIFIC (Odhams)
1969
Based on the UK comic £8 $13
TERRYTOON PLAYHOUSE (Purnell)
1964 £12 $19
Features Mighty Mouse, Heckle & Jeckle etc
THANK YOUR LUCKY STARS
1964 (Scarce) £15 $24
Based on the ITV pop music show
THELWELL (World)
1970's-1980's £8 $13
1980 (64pg) (fc/tc)
Thelwell's world of ponies featuring Penelope
Based on the UK cartoonist
THEY THINK IT'S ALL OVER (BBC/Talkback)
1998
©1997 £5 $8
Writers: Simon Sullivant, Bill Matthews, Jim Pullin, Pete Sinclair, Robert Fraser Steele and Harry Thompson
Art: John Aldritch, Kevin Brighton, Nick Davis, Dave Eastburn, Jim Eldridge, Roger Mahoney, Bill Titcombe, David Parkins, Nick Pemberton, Christian Oliver and John Gilliat
Cartoon Strips: Rineker of the Rovers (3fc)
Willie's Boots (4tc), Alan Shearer, Gazza Cap (1fc), Striker Susan (2fc), Believe It Or Not! (1bw), Lord Gower and his Pals (2bw)
Based on the BBC TV sports quiz
THINK OF A NUMBER (Purnell/BBC)
1979 £6 $10
Based on the Childrens BBC TV series starring Johnny Ball
THOMAS THE TANK ENGINE & FRIENDS
(Grandreams/World)
1984-present
1984 £8 $13
1985-1994 £5 $8
©1985 (64pg)

Art: David Palmer (Temple Art)
Writer: Christopher Awdry
©1986 (64pg)
Text Stories and Game Art: David Palmer (Temple Art)
Black & White Art: Owain Bell
Text stories and puzzles
©1993
10th Anniversary Edition (Grandreams)
Cover/Endpaper Art: Owain Bell
Art: David Palmer (Temple Rogers Agency)
1995-present £3 $5
Based on the model animation TV series
3-2-1 (Fleetway)
1985 £6 $10
Based on the ITV game show
THRILLING TALES For Boys
1950's £12 $19
THUNDER (Fleetway/IPC)
1972-1974 £8 $13
1974
Comic Strips (bw): The Forbidden Valley (fc), Adam Eterno, The Spider, Phil the Fluter, Gauntlet of Fate, Cliff Hanger, Dr Mesmers Revenge, Dusty Binns (tc), Royal Flying Corps, The Jet Skaters, Black Max, The Spooks of St Lukes, The Steel Comando (fc), Lightning Storm, Cliff Hanger, Phil the Fluter, Fury's Family
Based on the UK comic
THUNDERBIRDS (City/Century 21/Purnell/Carlton)
1966-1968, 1971-1972, 1993-1994, 2001
1966 £30 $48
1967 £20 $32
1968 £15 $24
1971 £10 $16
1971 (City)
Comic Strips (fc): Thunderbirds in The Menace of the Warlord, Freight-Load of Fear!
Zero X - The Switch-Secret Agent 21 in The Image-Makers-Captain Scarlet in Wave of Destruction-Department S in The Silent Men (tc)-The Greatest Player Ever (tc)
Text Photo Stories (fc): Joe 90 in The Thin Red Wire-Secret Agent 21 in Day of the Fog (tc)-Thunderbirds in The Crab-Captain Scarlet in Decoy to Disaster
1972 (Scarce) £12 $19
©1992 (Grandreams) (64pg) (fc) £6 $10
Comic Strips: Sunprobe (12)
©1993 (48pg) (fc) £6 $10
Comic Strips: Fire Mountain (10)
Also single page comic strip Launch Sequences of Thunderbirds 1-4 and Construction of Thunderbird 5. Technical Data Thunderbirds 1-5
Art: Graham Bleathman
Based on the Gerry Anderson TV puppet series
THUNDERBIRDS 'Television Storybook' (PBS)
1967
©1966 £15 $24
THUNDERBIRDS 2086
1983 £8 $13
Comic Strips (2x8bw): Peril of the Deep, Fall of the Frost Giant
Based on the Japanese animated TV series
THUNDERCATS (Marvel/Grandreams)
1986-1992

Thundercats 1991

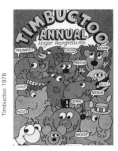

Timbuctoo 1978

T J Hooker 1984

1986	£8	$13

©1985 (64pg) (fc)
Comic Strips: Survival Run! (22)-Writer: David Micheline-Pencils: Jim Mooney-Inks: Brett Breeding
Tears of Sunrise (22)-Writer: David Micheline-Pencils: Jim Mooney Inks: Brett Breeding
Includes character profiles

1987-1992	£7	$11

©1986 (64pg) (fc)
Comic Strips: Siege in Silver and Stone!-
Writer: Jim Micheline-Pencils: Jim Mooney
Inks: Breeding, Morgan & Co.
Jaga Quest!-Pencils: Jim Mooney-Inks: Brett Breeding
Text Story (UK): Way Back...When?-Plot: Simon Furman-Story: Steve Alan-Art: Radbourne and Baskerville
1989
Cover/Endpaper Art: Stephen Baskerville, Geoff Senior, John Burns-Editor - John Tomlinson
Comic Strips: Past Perils Times Two (UK)
Part 1-Writer: Mike Collins-Pencils: Andy Wildman-Inks: Martin Griffiths
Part 2-Inks - Dave Hine
The Fireballs of Plun-Darr!-Writer: Craig Anderson-Pencils - Ernie Colon-Inks - Al Williamson
Text Story:-Thunderdogs Ho!-Writer: Mike Collins-Art: Darren Goodacre
1990
Cover Art: Kirk Etienne, Dave Eliot, John Burns-Endpaper: Dougie Braithwaite, Dave Eliot, John Burns-Portrait Pin-Ups: Art Wetherell and Staz Johnson-Editor: Dan Abnett
Comic Strips: The Price of Pride-Writer: Gerry Conway-Pencils: Jose Delbo-Inks: Janice Chiang
The coming (UK)-Writer: John Tomlinson-Art: Martin Griffiths and Simon Coleby
Text Story: The Last Thundercat's Story
Writer: John Tomlinson-Art: Cam Smith
1991 (64pg)
Cover/Endpaper Art: Frank, Baskerville, Burns-Editorial: Abnett, Papadopoulos
Comic Strip: Trial By Fire-Writer: Steve Alan
Breakdowns: Elwood P Dowdes-Finished Art: Stephen Baskerville
Based on the animated TV series

THUNDER IN PARADISE (Grandreams)

1994 (48pg)	£5	$8

Editor: Melanie J Clayden-Writer: Marco Esposito
Features a profile on Patrick McNee from The New Avengers
Based on Australian TV series starring Hulk Hogan

TIGER (AP/Fleetway)
1957-1987

1957	£20	$32
1958-1959	£15	$24
1960-1965	£12	$19
1966-1969	£10	$16
1970-1980	£8	$13
1981-1987	£5	$8

1983 (128pg)
Comic Strips: Johnny Cougar (8fc), Nipper (4bw), Hot Shot Hamish (6tc), Topps on Two Wheels (4tc), The Slogger from Down Under (14bw), Skid Solo (4bw), Billys Boots (6tc), Death Wish (4bw), File

of Fame (4bw)
Based on the UK comic

TIGER BOOK OF SOCCER STARS (Fleetway)

1972-1975	£6	$10

TIGER BOOK OF SPORTS (Fleetway)

1978-1981	£6	$10

TIGER TIM'S Annual
1922-1954

1950-1954	£20	$32

Based on the UK comic

TIMBUCTOO (Brown Watson)

1978	£10	$16

Based on the characters by Roger Hargreaves (creator of Mr Men)

TINA (IPC/Fleetway)

1960's	£12	$19

See also: PRINCESS TINA
Based on the UK comic

TINGHA & TUCKER TV Annual

1970	£10	$16

Based on the Childrens ITV series

TIN TIN ANNUAL

1962-1963	£20	$32

Based on the Hergè cartoon character

TIP TOP (Epworth Press/AP)
1937-1954

1950-1954	£15	$24

TIP TOP Book for Girl's (D.C. Thomson)

1950's	£15	$24

TISWAS (World)

1981-1983	£6	$10

©1980 (64pg)
Writer: John Gorman, Art: John Millington
©1981 (64pg)
Writer: John Gorman, Art: John Millington
1983 (64pg)
Writer: Ollie Spencer, Art: John Millington
Based on the Children's ITV show starring Chris Tarrant, Sally James and John Gorman

TITANS (World)
1977-1978

1977	£10	$16
1978	£8	$13

Based on the Marvels Comics characters

T.J. HOOKER (Grandreams)
1984

©1983 (64pg)	£8	$13

Comic Strips (2x8bw): Hijack, Masquerade
Includes photo features on William Shatner, Adrian Zmed, Heather Locklear (fc)-Richard Herd and April Clough (bw)
Based on the TV police series starring William Shatner

TOBY (Fleetway)

1977-1979	£5	$8

1979 (80pg)
Picture Strips: Toby and the King Midas, Two Little Scamps and Mustard, 3 Chums & Curly, P. C. Bobby, The Twelve Brothers, Flopsy Flufftail, Grandma Next Door, The Little Prince, Patty and her Magic Puppy, Toby and the Boy Duke, Cherry and Cheeky, Miss Muddle

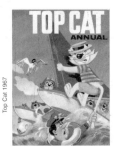

Top Cat 1967

Topo Gigio 1968

Top of the Pops 1975

Based on the pre-school comic
TOM & JERRY (World/PBS/Marvel)
1970's-1990's
1970 's   £6 $10
1975 (World) (80pg)
Comic Strips: The Loco Mover, Hypnotic Eye, Plumb Gummed, Dirty Trickster, Christmas Spirit, Guarded Goodies, Big Spike and Little Tyke, No Fair, Runner Up, Pedigree Pups, Happy Holidays, Jerry and Tuffy, Football Highlight
1977   £8 $13
1977 (PBS)-'World of Tom & Jerry' ©1980 (World)
Comic Strips: Heatwave Antics, Golf Practice, At the Circus, The Melon Seller, Tom the Pieman, The Big Clean Up, Good Deed Day, A Bad Case of Mice-Itis, Droopy
1979 (64pg)
Comic Strips: Not Then (6fc), Surprise Visit (5fc), Switzerland, We Are Here! (8fc), Doors With Flaws (7fc), TV or Not TV (6fc), Who Me? (1fc), Out to Launch (6fc), Luck Who's Talking (15fc), Same Old Thing (6fc)
1980's   £5 $8
©1982 (World) (64pg) (fc)
Cover Art: Melvyn Powell-Endpaper: Paul Green
Comic Strips: A Will and a Way, What's Cooking?, Running Scared
Text Stories Art: Paul Green
©1983 (World) (64pg) (fc)
Cover Art: Melvyn Powell
Comic Strips: Big Spike and Little Tyke, The Space Man, Tom and Jerry, Mouse Musketeers, The Christmas Pet
1990's   £4 $7
©1991 (Marvel)
Editor: Sophie Heath
Based on the MGM Cartoon characters
TOM MERRY'S Own
1950 -1955 $20 $32
TOMMOROW PEOPLE
1979   £8 $13
Based on the Childrens ITV sci-fi series
TONY BLACKBURN POP SPECIAL (World)
1969-1971   £10 $16
No.2 ©1969
Features include Beatles, Status Quo, Clif Richard and much more
No.3 ©1970 (80pg) (fc/bw)
Editor: Angus P. Allan
Features and Pin Ups include: Georgie Fame, Gerald & Arnold, Bee Gees, Donovan, Dave Clark Five, Roger Whittaker, The Beatles, Herman (Peter Noone), Marmalade, The Tremeloes, The Rolling Stones, Sandie Shaw, The Monkees, The Hollies, Frank and Nancy Sinatra, Stevie Wonder
Based on the Radio One disc jockey
TOP CAT (World/Stafford Pemberton)
1960's-1970s   £12 $19
1966 (96pg) (fc) (World)
Comic Strips: On the Beat, On with the Show, Treasure A-La Carte, Doing What Comes Naturally, Playmate for Junior, A Turn for the West, The Golf Break, The Meeyew News, Getting the Facts, Monsters by the Dozen, A Cad in Cats Clothing, The Cat Catcher Caper, Alley Artist
1977 (64pg) (fc) (Stafford Pemberton)
Comic Strips: Music to Meeyow by, The Furest in the Land, Top Cat,

Top Cat, Cats can be Cattish, Time can Travellers, Shindig Alley, Escape Artist, Top Cat, The Need to be Needed, The Meeyow Scow
Based on the Hanna Barbera animated TV series
TOPO GIGIO (Century 21)
1968-1969   £12 $19
©1967 (96pg)
Picture Strips: Topo Gigio Cooks Supper, (4fc), Topo Gigio The Sailor (2fc), Topo Gigio Gets Lost (3fc), Topo Gigio Goes Mushrooming (3fc), Topo Gigio Builds a Sandcastle (4fc), Topo Gigio Has a Bath (3fc), Topo Gigio Goes Camping (3fc), Topo Gigio Grows Carrots (2fc), Topo Gigio Goes Farming (4fc)
Text Stories: Topo's Mysterious Message, Topo and the Cheese Pirates, Topo Hunts for Treasure, Topo's Good Deed, Topo and the Fairy Ring, Topo Visits the Fair, Topo's Bright Idea, Topo's Snowman Party
Based on the hand puppet
TOP SOCCER Annual
1981   £3 $5
TOPICAL TIMES FOOTBALL BOOK (D.C Thomson)
1960's - present
1960's   £10 $16
1960 - 1st Hardback Annual
Bobby Charlton Cover
1963-64 (128pg) (fc/bw)
Picture Strip (b/w): My Eight Fantastic Years by John Charles (6)
Pin Ups include: Pele, Bobby Moore, Terry Venables, Manchester United and Leicester City teams 1963
1970's   £6 $10
1980's   £5 $8
1990's   £3 $5
TOP OF THE POPS-BBC TV (World)
1974-1983, 1992
1974 (96pg)   £10 $16
Features: The Jacksons, Slade, Gary Glitter, Marc Bolan, David Bowie, Alice Cooper, Elvis Presley, Cliff Richard
Pin Ups: Elton John, Alice Cooper, David Bowie, Rod Stewart, Slade, Marc Bolan, Sweet, Osmonds, Gary Glitter, David Cassidy
Small Features: Rolling Stones, The Who, Cliff Richard, Elvis, Beatles, Dave Clark 5, Carly Simon, Cat Stevens
1975 (80pg)   £8 $13
Features: Olivia Newton John, Slade, The Osmonds, Roy Wood, Wings, Carpenters, Rolling Stones
Pin Ups: Nazareth, Status Quo, David Essex, David Cassidy, Gilbert O'Sullivan, Donny Osmond, Mud, Gary Glitter, Roy Wood, David Bowie, Slade, The Carpenters, Alvin StarDust
1976-1983   £7 $11
1976 (80pg)
Features Gary Glitter, Elton John etc
1977 (80pg)
Features: David Bowie, David Essex, The Rubettes, 10 CC. Queen, Steve Harley, Dave Clarke, Peter Shelley, Rod Stewart
Pin Ups: David Bowie, Steve Harley, Leo Sayer, Mac and Katie Kissoon, Roy Wood, Wings, Elton John, Hello, Bryan Ferry, Gilber O Sullivan, Mud, Donny Osmond, Queen, Bay City Rollers, Mick and Alan, The Stylistics, Sweet, Dave Hill, Slade, Electric Light Orchestra, Hot Chocolate, Showaddywaddy, Jim Capaldi, Art Garfunkel, Pilot, Rod Stewart
1978 (64pg) (fc/bw)
Editor: Ken Irwin

Top of the Pops 1992

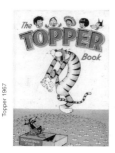

Topper 1967

Transformers 1990

Features: Demis Roussos, Leo Sayer, Tina Charles, Smokie,10 CC, Status Quo, 5000 Volts, Slik, The G Band, Guys 'n' Dolls, Kursaal Flyers, Sailor, Steve Harley, ELO, Be Bop Deluxe, West Coast Sound, Frampton, Marley & Mercury, Abba, Wings, Jethro Tull, David Essex, Queen, Bay City Rollers, Thin Lizzy, The Rubettes, Showaddywaddy, Gallagher & Lyle, Paul Nicholas, Bad Company, Elton John, Sherbet
1982 (64pg)
Features: Blondie, Peter Powell, Simon Bates, Mike Oldfield, The Who, The Jam, Bryan Ferry
Pin Ups: David Bowie, The Police, Ian Dury, Cliff Richard, Elton John, Showaddywaddy, Status Quo, Dexys Midnight Runners, The Beat, Sad Cafe, Sheena Easton, Secret Affair, Thin Lizzy
1983
Features: Kid Jensen, Adam Ant, Midge Ure, Linx, Shakin Stevens, Ian Dury, Elvis Costello, Joe Jackson, Ozzy Osbourne, Carpenters, Madness, Toyah Wilcox, The New Romantics, Spandau Ballet, Duran Duran, Japan, Police, David Bowie, Siouxsie Sioux, Charlie Dore, Chrissie
Pin Ups: Adam and the Ants, Duran Duran, Gary Numan, Electric Light Orchestra, Cliff Richard, Modern Romance, The Jam, Ultravox, Madness, The Pretenders, Joe Jackson, OMD, The Beat, Linx, A Teardrop Explodes, Toyah Wilcox
1992 (64pg)
Features: Madonna, Nicky Campbell, New Kids on the Block, DJ Gary Davies, Vanilla Ice, Anthea Turner, MC Hammer, Bruno Brookes, Bros, Kylie Minogue, DJ Jakki Brambles, DJ Mark Goodier, EMF, Betty Boo, DJ Simon Mayo, Jason Donovan
Pin Ups: Kim Appleby, Janet Jackson, Vanilla Ice, Chesney Hawkes, MC Hammer, Danni Minogue, Bros, Cliff Richard, Pet Shop Boys, Betty Boo, Monie Love,
Based on the BBC TV pop music show

TOPPER Book (D.C. Thomson)

1955 - present		
1955	£100	$160
1956	£60	$96
1957	£50	$80
1958-1959	£40	$60
1960	£30	$48
1961-1965	£20	$32
1966-1969	£15	$24
1970-1979	£10	$16
1980-1989	£8	$13
1990-present	£5	$8

Comic Strips feature: Beryl the Peril, Mickey the Monkey, Ali's Baba, Tricky Dicky, Willie Fixit, Pearl, Pete Pike, Hungry Horace, Send for Kelly, Jack Frost, Desert Island Dick, Video Kid, Jimmy Jinx, Peter Piper, The Scratch Squad, Figaro, The Neals on Wheels, Square Eyes, Tom & Terry, Danny's Tranny, Willie Walker and the Whizzers from Ozz
Based on the UK comic

TOP POP SCENE (Purnell)

1971-1978	£8	$13
1975		

Features: Detroit Spinners, Jim Stafford, Terry Jacks, David Cassidy, 10cc, Roy Wood,Johnny Bristol, Richard Hudson, The Osmonds, Neil Sedaka, Marvine Gaye, Bay City Rollers, Paul & Linda McCartney, Hot Chocolate, The Glitter Band, Showaddywaddy, Sparks, Maggie Bell, Rubettes, Suzi Quattro, Slade, Barry Blue

TOP POP STARS

1960's	£10	$16
1962 Cliff Richard photo cover		
1963 Elvis Presley photo cover		
1964 Clif Richard photo cover		
1965 Includes Moody Blues		
1967 Includes Sonny & Cher, Lulu		
1969 Includes Bob Dylan, Sandie Shaw		

TOP TWENTY (Purnell)

1965	£10	$16

TORCHY the BATTERY BOY 'Gift Book' (Daily Mirror)

1961-1965		
N/D 1960	£20	$32
©1961-©1964	£15	$24

Based on the Gerry Anderson & Roberta Leigh puppet series

TORNADO (Fleetway)

1980-1981	£6	$10

Based on the UK comic

TOTS TV (Grandreams)

1993-1997	£3	$5

1993 - Writer: Robin Stevens-Art: Arkadia
©1993 (48pg)
Writer: Robin Stevens-Art: Arkadia
©1995 (48pg)
Writer: Andrew Davenport-Art: Jo Davies and Louis Vettese
©1996 (48pg)
Writer: David Moore-Art: John Timms
Based on the Childrens ITV series

TOXIC CRUSADERS (Grandreams)

1992 (64pg)	£3	$5

Based on the animated TV series

TOYAH (Grandreams)

1982	£5	$8

Editor: John Barraclough-Writers: Bev Gilligan, Margarette Driscol-Layout/Design: Nigel L Money
Based on the UK pop singer

TOWSER (Fleetway)

1985 (80pg) (fc/bw)	£5	$8

Based on the animated series

TOYBOX (BBC)

2000	£3	$5

T'PAU (Grandreams)

1989 (64pg) £5 $8
Editor: Melanie J Clayden-Writer: John Kercher-Layout/Design: Sharron Morgan and Caroline Robinson
Based on the UK pop group

TRANSFORMERS (Marvel/Grandreams)

1986-1992, 1994		
1986	£10	$16
©1985 (64pg) (fc/bw)		

Editor: Sheila Cranna
Comic Strips (UK): Plague of the Insecticons! (20), Writer: Simon Furman, Art: Collins/Anderson
And There Shall Come... A Leader! (10), Writer: Simon Furman-Art: John Stokes
Text Stories: Missing in Action, Hunted

1987-1991	£8	$13
©1986 (64pg) (fc)		

Trumpton 1968

Tugs 1990

TV 21 1970

Editor: Sheila Cranna
Comic Strips (UK): To a Power Unknown (11), Writers: Ian Mennell,
Wilf Prigmore, Art: Will Simpson
Victory (11), Writer: Simon Furman-Artist: Geoff Senior
Text Stories: The Return of the Transformers, State Games, The
Mission
©1987 (64pg) (fc)
Comic Strips (UK): What's In A Name? (5)-
Writer: Simon Furman, Pencils: Simpson, Inks: Elliot, Vicious Circle!
(10), Writer: Simon Furman, Pencils: Anderson, Inks: Harwood
Ark Duty (7)
Text Stories: Headmaster's Saga (3 chapters)
©1988 (64pg) (fc)
Editor: Chris Francis, Cover Art: Lee Sullivan
Endpaper: Dan Reed, John Burns
Comic Strips (UK): Altered Image! (6), Writers: Simon Furman/Ian
Rimmer, Art: Lee Sullivan
All In The Minds! (11), Writer: Simon Furman, Art: Dan Reed
Peace (6), Writer: Richard Alan, Art: Robin Smith
Text Story: Prime Bomb! (two-part), Writer: Ian Rimmer, Art: Robin
Smith
©1989 (64pg) (fc)
Editor: Chris Francis
Designer: Gary Gilbert, Cover Art: Lee Sullivan
Endpaper: Wetherell/Baskerville/Burns
Comic Strips (UK): Destiny of the Dinobots (6), Writer: Steve Alan,
Art: Andy Wildman, Dreadwing Down! (11), Writer: Simon Furman,
Art: Dan Reed, The Chain Gang (6), Writer: Dan Abnett, Art: Dan
Reed
Text Stories: The Quest, Trigger-Happy!, Writer: Ian Rimmer, Art: Art
Wetherell/Stephen Baskerville
©1990 (64pg) (fc)
Editor: Euan Peters, Designer: Jacqui Papp
Cover Art: Geoff Senior, Endpaper: Jeff Anderson
Comic Strips: Fallen Angel - Part 1 (9fc), Script: Simon Furman, Art:
Geoff Senior, Fallen Angel - Part 2 (11fc), Script: Simon Furman, Art:
Jeff Anderson, Firebug (11fc), Writer: Dan Abnett, Art: Jeff Anderson
Text Stories: The Magnificent Six, Writer: Simon Furman, Art: Staz,

1992	£12	$19
1994 (Grandreams)	£8	$13

The Next Generation
Based on the animated TV series and toy range
TRAPDOOR (Grandreams)

1989 (64pg)	£3	$5

Art: The County Studios
Based on the animated TV Show
TREASURE (Fleetway)

1975 (80pg)	£6	$10

Picture Strips: Onka and the Sleeping Dragon (4fc), The Paper Boat
(4fc), The Animal Army (4fc), The Magic Box (4fc), Hiawatha and
the Secret of the Mountain (6fc), The Legend of Tahiti (6fc)
Includes Art from: Peter Jackson
Based on the childrens magazine
TRIGAN EMPIRE 'Look & Learn Book' (Fleetway)

1974	£10	$16

©1973 (72pg) (fc)
Art: Don Lawrence
Ranger/Look & Learn picture strip reprints
TRIUMPH Book For Boys

1950's	£12	$19

TROLLS

1993	£3	$5

Based on the toy range
TRUMPTON Gordon Murray's (Purnell)

1968-1972	£10	$16

©1967 (80pg)
Writer: Muriel Gray, Art: John Armstrong
Picture Strips: The Mayor's Birthday (fc), Nibs Joins the Circus (bw),
Trumpton's Christmas Party (fc), Jumbo to the Rescue (fc),
Text Stories: When Trumpton's Clock Stopped, The Wonderful
Snowstorm, The Birthday Present, Captain Flack's Secret, The
Voyage of Saucy Sue, The Stolen Fire Engine, Lulu's Strange
Friend, Who Stole The Breakfast, The Flying Bus Shelter, Mrs
Cobbit's Christmas Pudding, The Runaway Donkey,
Based on the Childrens ITV model animation series
TUCKS
1940's-1950's

1950's	£15	$24

Foreword by Enid Blyton
TUCKER'S LUCK (Fleetway)

1984-1985	£8	$13

Based on the BBC TV Grange Hill spin-off
TUGS (Grandreams)

1990-1991	£3	$5

©1989
Art: County studios
Based on the ITV model animation series
TREASURE HOUR SUPER TIME Annual
(Treasure Hour Books)

1969	£8	$13

TV ACTION (Polystyle)

1973-1974	£10	$16

1974 (80pg) (fc/tc/bw)
Endpaper(fc): Pete Duel & Ben Murphy photo from Alias Smith and
Jones
Comic Strips: The Persuaders in The Big Shot (8fc)- The Last
Hostage (7tc), Hawaii Five-O in Take-Over Bid (8tc), Dad's Army
(4tc)-Art: Bill Titcombe, UFO in Operation Babylon (8fc), Droopy
(2fc), Doctor Who in The Hungry Planet (8fc)-Art: Jim Baikie- features Jon Pertwee
Text Stories: Alias Smith and Jones in The Herd is Coming (4lw),
illustrated story features Pete Duel, Cannon in Not Just a Hunch
(3fc)-photo story, Mission Impossible in The Breakout (3bw)-photo
story features
Linda Day George, The Protectors in The Collector (4 bw/fc)-photo
story
Features include: Hawaii Five-O game -with photos(fc), Mission
Impossible-bios of the characters and actors, including full page
photo (fc)- the feature features a bio of Lesley Warren but includes a
photo of Linda Day George
Photo cover features Jon Pertwee, Robert Vaughn, Pete Duel & Ben
Murphy and Jack Lord (fc)
Based on the UK comic
TV ALL STARS

1970	£10	$16

Morecambe and Wise photo cover
TV ANNUAL (Amalgamated Press)

TV Comic 1960

TV Comic 1968

TV Chimps 1977

1950's £15 $24
TV CENTURY 21/TV 21 (City/Fleetway)
1966-1973
1966 £25 $48
1967 £20 $32
1968 £15 $24
1969-1970 £12 $19
1971-1973 £10 $16
©1965 (96pg)
Cover Art features- My Favourite Martian, Burke's Law, Stingray and Fireball XL5
Comic Strips (fc): Burke's Law in Who Killed the Pest Killer (4), Who Killed the Sultan (4)-Fireball XL5 In The Red Planet (5)-Stingray in The Burglars (6), Marineville Traitor (6)-Lady Penelope in Bullion Raid (8)
Text stories feature: Double Two-One Special Agent, My Favourite Martian, Supercar
©1967 (96pg)
Comic Strips (fc):
Thunderbirds - Renegade Rocket (5fc), Fireball XL5 - The Ghost Fleet (6fc), The Munsters (2fc), Zero X - Conflict on Mars (6), 21 Special Agent - The Killer Robots (5fc), My Favourite Martian (2fc), Catch or Kill - The Monster of the Lake (6fc), Wright CHARLIE (2fc), Stingray - Trial of Danger (6fc), Get Smart (2fc), Thunderbirds - Volcano Alert (7fc)
Text Stories feature: Traitor at Marineville, 21 Special Agent - Assignment Destroy USS
1971 (96pg)
Comic Strips (fc): Star Trek in Captives In Space (6fc), Planet of Rejects (8fc)-Land Of The Giants in Soldiers of Doom! (7fc)-Tarzan in Mark of the Leopard (6fc),The Saint meets The Mind-Masters (6fc)-Land Of The Giants in The Giant Maker (6tc)-Forward from the Back Streets (8tc)
Text Stories feature: Land Of The Giants, Star Trek, Tarzan
1972 (80pg)
Comic Strips (fc): Star Trek (5)-Micky's Moonbugs (2x2)-Spider-Man (8)-Homer the Happy Ghost (2x2)-The Ghost Rider (8)-The Ringo Kid (2x4)-The Silver Surfer (8)
Text Story: The Land of the Giants (4)
Based on the UK comics
TV CHIMPS (World)
1977 £8 $13
Based on the PG Tips chimps
TV COMIC (News of the World/Beaverbrook/ TV/Polystyle)
1954-1984
1954 (Scarce) £30 $32
1954
Includes Larry the Lamb and Muffin the Mule
1955 £25 $48
1956-1959 £20 $32
1956
Includes Sooty comic strip
N/D (late 50's/ early 60's)
Comic Strips: Terry Hall's Lenny the Lion, Art: Mevin, Packi's Pantomime, Packi's Christmas Tree By Tony Hart, Mighty Moth and the Cuckoo Clock, Super Nan, The Baker's Dozen, Coco the Clown, Art: Gwynne-Sheer, Luck Homes, Lochy the Funny Wee Monster (2fc), Red Ray Space Ranger, Art: Neville Main-Bom Goes to the Fair, Bom Works Very Hard by Enid Blyton, Art: R Paul Hoye-Robin

the Brave-Muffin, Muffin and the Martian, Art: Neville Main-Art Cody Schoolboy Sheriff-The Flying Fosters
1960-1969 £15 $24
1970-1973 £10 $16
1970 (80pg)
Comic Strips: Basil Brush, Diddymen, Popeye, Mighty Moth, TV Terrors, Bugs Bunny, Arthur, Beetle Bailey, Laurel and Hardy, Mad Movies, Dr Who features Jon Pertwee, Skippy, The Avengers features Tara King
1973-1984 £8 $13
©1974
Comic Strips featuring (fc/tc): Bugs Bunny, Tom & Jerry, The Road Runner, Texas Ted - Artist Frank McDiarmid, Basil Brush Artist - Dick Millington, Pink Panther, TV Terrors, Dad's Army, Mighty Moth, Johnny Morris's Animal Magic, Nelly and her Telly, Popeye, Barney Bear- Artist Bill Titcombe, Dr Who (Jon Pertwee)
©1975-©1979
Comic Strips include: Dr Who (Tom Baker)
1977 (64pg)
Comic Strips featuring: Barney Bear, Basil Brush, TV Terrors, Tom & Jerry, Catain Pugwash, Popeye, Roobarb, Bugs Bunny, Nelly and her Telly, Pink Panther, Dr Who in The Tansbury Experiment, Droopy, Mighty Moth, Dad's Army,
©1978 - 'New Mighty TV Comic Annual'
©1980 (64pg) (fc/tc)
Comic Strips featuring: Tom and Jerry, The Pink Panther, The Incredible Bulk - Artist Steve Maher, Barney Bear - Artist Mevin, Mighty Moth, Basil Brush, Bugs Bunny, Popeye, The Inspector, Droopy, Nelly and her Telly, Texas Ted, TV Terrors
Based on the UK comic
TV CRIMEBUSTERS (TV Publications)
1963
©1962 (Scarce) £25 $40
Includes comic strips, text stories and features on (fc/bw): 77 Sunset Strip, Hawaiian Eye, Danger Man, Interpol Calling, The Avengers (Steed/Keel), Roaring Twenties, The Four Just Men, The Pursuers, Charlie Chan, Dixon of Dock Green
TV DETECTIVES (Brown Watson)
1980
© 1979 (64pg) (fc/bw) £10 $16
Editor: Raymond Wergan
Writers: Lauri Denni, John Kercher, Terence York, Joseph Bell
Features: Baretta, The New Avengers, Starsky & Hutch, Charlies Angels, Target, The Professionals, The Return of The Saint, CHiPs, The Rockford Files, Kojak, McMillan & Wife, Columbo, Lee Majors, Lindsay Wagner and Richard Anderson, Cannon, McCloud, Harry O, Serpico
TV EXPRESS (TV Publications)
1961-1962 £10 $16
Art: Ron Embleton
TV FAVOURITES (World)
1970's £6 $10
1976
Comic Strips: Bugs Bunny, Porky Pig, Tweety & Sylvester, Daffy Duck
1977
Comic Strips: Bugs Bunny, Porky Pig, Tweety & Sylvester, Daffy Duck
1978

TV Tornado 1971

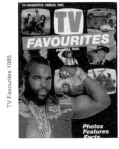

TV Favourites 1985

2000 AD 1979

Comic Strips: Bugs Bunny, Tweety & Sylvester, Yosemite Sam and Daffy Duck, Foghorn Leghorn, Wile E Coyote, Porky Pig
Based on Warner Brothers cartoon characters

TV FAVOURITES (Opal Quill)
1985 £8 $13
Writer: Simon Weir
Features: Airwolf, Magnum, Chips, Hart to Hart, Boy George, A Team, Mr T, Knight Rider, Dukes of Hazzard, Michael Jackson, Dallas, The Fall Guy, Barry Manilow, Blue Thunder, Dynasty, Fame

TV FILM
1960 £10 $16

TV FUN (Amalgamated Press)
1957-1960
1957 £15 $24
1958-1960 £12 $19
Based on the UK comic

TV MIRROR ANNUAL (Amalgamated Press)
1950's £15 $24
1956
Features autographed portraits of (tc/bw): Benny Hill, Peter Cushing, Arthur Askey, Josephine Douglas, Harry Corbett and Sooty, Eve Boswell, Wilfred Pickles and Mabel, Barbara Kelly, Donald Swan, Bob Monkhouse, Yvonne Mitchell, Harry Secombe, Eric Robinson, Peter Dimmock, Winifred Atwell, Beverley Sisters, Dave King, Kenneth Horne, Ruby Murray, Gary E Daniel, Joan Regan, Eamonn Andrews, Richard Dimbleby, Jack Warner, David Attenborough, Petula Clark, Gilbert Harding, Steve Race, Leslie Mitchell, Katie Boyle
Photo cover (fc)

TV TIMES SPACE ANNUAL
1970 £10 $16

TV TORNADO (World)
1968-1971
1968 £15 $24
©1967 (96pg) (fc)
Comic Strips:Tarzan in The Mystery Island, The Man From U.N.C.L.E. in The Toffee Nuts Affair, The Green Hornet in The Phantom Gang, Bonanza in The Cartwright Way, Magnus Robot Fighter in Giant From Planet X, The Phantom in The Web of Spidera, Flash Gordon in Con Man of Space, Dan Dan the TV Man by Denis Gifford (UK)
Dell/Gold Key reprints
Text Stories: Tarzan, The Man From U.N.C.L.E., The Green Hornet, Voyage to the Bottom of the Sea, Magnus Robot Fighter, The Saint
Large format
1969-1971 £10 $16
©1970
Comic Strips: The Lone Ranger in Garland's Grudge (8fc), Voyage to the Bottom of the Sea in Neptunius (9tc) , Henry the Ninth (8tc) Tarzan of the Apes in They attack by Night (9 fc), The Danger Limited (8tc), The Saint in All You Rings You Keeps (8fc)
Text Stories: Voyage to the Bottom of the Sea - Menace From Mindanao, Double First for the Saint, Tarzan and the Screaming Skull, Double Trouble
Based on the UK comic

TV WESTERN FAVOURITES COMIC Annual (World)
N/D 1950's £15 $24
Features: Lone Ranger, Roy Rogers, Gunsmoke, Lassie, Rin Tin Tin

TWEETY & SYLVESTER (World)
1974 £6 $10
Based on the Warner Brothers cartoon characters

TWILIGHT ZONE (World)
1964 (Scarce) £20 $32
Dell/Gold Key reprints
Based on the TV sci fi series

TWINKLE (D.C.Thomson)
1970's-present
1970's £6 $10
1980's £5 $8
1990's £3 $5
Comic Strips include: Nancy the Little Nurse, Tick and Tock, Sam, Molly and her Dollies, Bertie Broomstick, The Blobs, My Baby Brother, Elfie, Patch, Witch Winkle, Belinda, Jenny Wren, Goody Gumdrops, Polly Perkins, Patsy Panda, Elfie, Sam, Bouncy, Vicki, Fairy Fay, Jean Genie, Penny Crayon, Silly Milly, Sally and Scamp.
Based on the UK pre-school comic

TWO RONNIES (Brown Watson)
1979 £8 $13
Based on the BBC TV comedy show starring Ronnie Barker and Ronnie Corbett

2000 A.D. (Fleetway)
1978-1995
1978 £15 $24
1979-1980 £12 $19
1981-1991 £10 $16
1982
Comic Strips: Milli-Way Sixty Six (5), Writer: Gerry Finley-Day, Art: Eric Badbury
1983
Comic Strips: Rogue Trooper (untitled) (9), Writer: Gerry Finley-Day, Art: Boluda
1984 (128pg)
Cover Art: Ian Gibson
Comic Strips: Sam Slade Robo-Hunter (fc)- Writer: Staccato-Art: Ian Gibson, Judge Anderson in The Haunting (bw): Writer: Staccato-Art: Kim Raymond, Bonjo From Beyond the Stars (bw): Art: O'Neill, Invasion (bw): Art: Kennedy, Judge Dredd (bw): Writer: John Wagner-Art: Ian Gibson, Rogue Trooper in First of the Few (bw): Writer: Alan Moore-Art: J. Redondo, Flesh (bwx2): Writer: R.E. Wright-Art: Sola, Judge Dredd in The Beast in 24B (fc(: Writer: Staccato-Art: Ron Smith, A Day in the Death of Torquemada (bw): Writer: Pat Mills-Art: Kevin O'Neill, Tharg's Future-Shocks (bw): Writer: Jack Adrian-Art: Brian Bolland, Ro-busters (bw): Writer: Alan Moore-Art: Joe Eckers, Judge Dredd - selected strips from the Daily Star newspaper- Writer: John Wagner-Art: Ron Smith
Text Story: Strontium Dog in The Iraldi Job (bw)
Features include: Skizz, How He Came To Be- Writer: Alan Moore, How a 2000AD Cover is Created!- Art: Brian Bolland, Cover to Cover Thrill-Power- 2000AD cover gallery (18 issues-bw), Billy Dee Williams Interview
1985 (96pg)
Comic Strips: Slane (fc), Writer: Pat Mills,Art: Massimo Belardinelli, Strontium Dog (bw), Writer: T.B. Grover, Art: C. Ezquerra, Judge Dredd (fc), Writer: T.B. Grover, Art: Ian Gibson, Good Morning, Sheldon, I Love You! (bw), Writer: T.B. Grover, Art: Casanovas, Tharg's Future-Shocks (bw): Writer: C. Lowder, Art: C. Ezquerra, Earn Big Money While You Sleep (bw): Writer: Alan Grant-Art:

Vegas 1980

Valentine 1974

Victor 1964

VI

Casanovas, Rogue Trooper (fc): Writer: Ian Rogan, Art: Robin Smith, The A.B.C. Warriors in Red Planet Blues (fc): Writer: Alan Moore, Art: Dillon/Higgins, Judge Dredd - selected strips from the Daily Star newspaper- Writer: John Wagner, Alan Grant-Art: Ron Smith
Text Story (bw): Zragman: Writer: Alan Grant-Art: Eric Bradbury
Features include (bw): Massimo Belardinelli Interview, Heroes Before 2000AD (Dan Dare, Kelly's Eye, Steel Claw, Robot Archie, House of Dolmann), Tharg's Day at the Printers (bw photo feature), How The Dredd Was Drawn-Ian Gibson Reveals All (from breakdowns to finished art), Top Covers of '83
1986 (96pg)
Cover Art: Massimo Belardinelli
Comic Strips: ACE trucking Co. in Any Space Any Time (fc): Writers: Grant/Grover-Art: Belardinelli, Shako! (three-parts bw), Judge Dredd in On The Waterfront (fc): Writer: Grover, Art: Gibson, Strontium Dog (fc): Writer: Alan Grant-Art: Carlos Ezquerra, Rogue Trooper (fc): Writer: Sim-1, Art:Cam Kennedy, Judge Dredd - selected strips from the Daily Star newspaper- Writer: John Wagner, Alan Grant-Art: Ron Smith
Text Story (bw): Diary of a Mad Citizen: Writer: Alan Grant-Art: Eric Bradbury
Features (bw): Rogue Trooper Quiz Special!
1988
Comic Strips: Torquemada's Second Honeymoon
Ro-busters: Writer: P Mills, Art: K. O'Neill, She Devils: Writer: Wagner E Grant, Art: McCarthy, Riot & Ewins, Ro-busters: Writer: Pat Mills, Art: Dave Gibbons, Ro-busters: Writer: Pat Mills, Art: Kevin O'Neill, Complaint: Writer: Alan Grant, Art: C.Ezquerra
1992-1995-'Yearbook' £10 $16

UFO (City)
1971 £12 $18
Based on Gerry Anderson's live-action TV sci-fi series

UNCLE MAC'S CHILDREN'S HOUR Book (Purnell)
n/d 1950's £15 $24
'Uncle Mac of the BBC'
Editor: Derek McCullough

UNCLE MAC'S STORY Book (Sampson Low)
1950's £15 $24

'V' (World)
1986 (64pg) £8 $13
Comic Strip (fc): Nightmare (6)
Text stories, games and photo feature
Photo cover
Based on the TV sci-fi series
VALIANT Book of TV's SEXTON BLAKE
See: SEXTON BLAKE

VAN DER VALK
1979
©1978 £8 $13
Photo cover
Based on the ITV detective series starring Barry Foster

VANILLA ICE Special (Grandreams)
1991 £3 $5
Writer: Fiona Bruce - Design/Layout: Louise Ivimy
Photo features
Based on the pop star
VALENTINE (Fleetway/IPC)
1960's-1970's

1960's	£10	$16
1970's	£8	$13

1974 (80pg)
Comic Strips (bw): Disco Girl, The Jackson 5 - Back Home in Indiana, The Beauty Business...., This is our Street, Who'd be a Model?, The Saturday Girls
Features: The Osmonds, Michael Jackson, David Cassidy
Pin Ups: The Williams Twins, Rick Springfield, Marty Kristian, Donny, The Osmonds, Ben Murphy, Steve Hodson, Jack Wild, Slade, Michael Jackson, The Jackson Five, Tony Blackburn, David Cassidy
Based on the UK girls teenage magazine
VALENTINE POP SPECIAL
1957-1960's

1950's	£15	$24
1960's	£10	$16

1962 -No.5
VALIANT (Fleetway)
1964-1984

1964	£20	$32
1965	£15	$24
1966	£12	$19
1967-1970	£10	$16
1971-1984	£8	$13

1976 (144pg)
Comic Strips (bw/tc) feature: Kelly's Eye, Captain Hurricane, Micky the Mimic, Kid Pharoah, Janus Stark, Challege Charlie, The Nutts (fc), Adam Eterno (fc), Billy Bunter (fc), Mowser, Lincoln Green Mob, The House of Dolmann
Plus b/w photo feature on the making of an Airfix model-kit
Based on the UK comic
VEGAS (Stafford Pemberton)
1980 (64pg) £8 $13
Comic Strips: Buried Alive (7fc), The Missing Blond (6fc), Motorcycle Nightmare (6fc)
Photo cover and Photo Features
Based on the TV private-eye series starring Robert Urich
VICTOR Book For Boys (D.C. Thomson)
1964-1992

©1963	£20	$32
©1964	£15	$24
©1965	£12	$19
1967-1969	£10	$16
1970-1979	£8	$13
1980-1992	£6	$10

Based on the UK comic
VICTORIA PLUM 'Angela Rippon's' (Purnell)
1983-1985 (64pg)
Text Stories and picture strips
Art: Colin Petty
Based on the books by Angela Rippon
VIDEO ROCK
1985 £6 $10
Features: Spandau Ballet, Belle Stars, Ozzy
VIDEO SUPERSTARS (Opal Quill)
1985 £6 $10
Writer: Jay Dore
Features: Thompson Twins, Spandau Ballet, Billy Joel, Duran Duran, ABC in Mantrap, Kajagoogoo,Elton John, Eurythmics, Paul

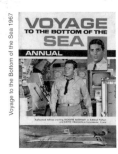

Voyage to the Bottom of the Sea 1967

Wacky Races 1977

Wagon Train 1960

Young, Culture Club, Michael Jackson, Toyah, The Pretenders, Tracey Ullman, Madness, Big Country, Howard Jones, Style Council, Wham, Bananarama

VISIONARIES
1989   £6 $10
Based on the animated TV series
VOLTRON 'Defender of the Universe' (World)
1987 (64pg) (fc)   £6 $10
Text stories
Based on the Japanese animated TV series
VOYAGE TO THE BOTTOM OF THE SEA (World)
1966-1968
1966   £20 $32
1967   £15 $24
1968   £12 $19
©1966 (98pg)
Comic Strip (fc): Robinson Crusoe of the Depths (29)
Gold Key reprint
Text Stories: The Kingdom of Davy Jones, The Statue Makers, The One That Got Away, Vanderbecken Sails Again, Trapped In Lost Atlantis
Photo cover featuring Richard Basehart as Admiral Nelson and David Hedison as Commander Crane (fc)
Based on the Irwin Allen TV series
VULCAN (Fleetway)
1977   £10 $16
Features Don Lawrence reprints
Softback
Based on the UK comic
WAC (Wide Awake Club) 'Look-In' (Purnell)
1987-1990
1987-1988   £4 $7
1987(64pg)
Writer: Phil Parsons-Art: Kevin A Smith, Harry North, Mike Dorey, Harry Hargreaves
Features: Jaki Graham, Amazulu, Jim Diamond, Jon Moss (Culture Club), Mark Reilly, D C Lee, Chris Ryan, Bananarama, Housemartins, Simply Red, Owen Paul, Aha, Five Star
1989 (64pg)   £5 $8
Writer: Phil Parsons-Art: Andy Lanning
Features: Hue & Cry, Sinitta, Wet Wet Wet, Shakin Stevens, Michaela Strachen, Kim Wilde, The Proclaimers, Danny Wilson, Cry Before Dawn, Pepsi and Shirlie, Batman 1960's TV series, Bros
1990 (64pg)   £4 $7
Features: The Royal Family, Carol Vorderman, Michaela Strachen, Kylie Minogue
Based on the Childrens ITV series starring Michaela Strachen
WACKY RACES (Brown Watson)
1974
©1973   £10 $16
'Featuring MotorMouse and Autocat'
Comic Strips: It's Go Go for Kokomo (10tc), Scooby Doo in Tricky Treats (2tc), Dick Dastardly presents - Hold that Hillbilly (25fc), Free Wheeling to Wheeling (8fc),The Cattanooga Cats in The Go-Go-Gone Buggy (6fc), Wacky Races - Dastardly and Muttley in their Flying Machines - It's Flop and Go-Go (7fc), Dick Dastardly presents Greasy Rider (8tc)
Based on the Hanna Barbera animated TV series
WACKY RACES and the HARLEM GLOBETROTTERS

(Brown Watson)
1976   £10 $16
Comic Strips: Motoring Madness with... Beat the Clock through Yellowrock (11tc), Dastardly & Muttley Scarlet Runners (6fc), Wilds and Wizards (25fc), Dastardly & Muttley - The Gunners (6fc), Mish Mash Missouri Dash (8fc), The Scavenger Scramble (13fc)
Based on the Hanna Barbera cartoon characters
WAGON TRAIN (World/Daily Mirror/Peveril)
1959-1964
1959   £15 $24
1960-1964   £12 $19
©1959 (96pg) (World) (fc)
Text Stories: Joe Morrissey-Art: Walter Howarth
Comic Strips (2x16): Broken Treaty, Trouble At Sierra - Dell reprints
Text Stories: The Ben Honeytree Story, The Enoch Owen Story, The Belinda Wilkins Story, The Silas Jeffreys Story, The Elspeth Ballantyne Story, The Danny Ferguson Story
Photo cover featuring Ward Bond and Robert Horton (fc)
©1959 (Daily Mirror) (128pg) (tc)
Writer: Maurice Templar-Art: S Chapman
Text Stories (tc):The Lone Indian, The Prairie Fire, The Lonely Ranch, The Mystery Of Echo Valley, Monarch Of The Pass, The Swamp, The Second Seth, The Story Of Chief Killing Bull, The Peril Of The Tumbling Canyon, The River Crossing, "Some Men With Fevvers!"
Painted frontpiece (fc)
Photo cover featuring Flint McCullough (Robert Horton) and Major Seth Adams
(Ward Bond) (bw tint)
©1960 (Daily Mirror) (128pg) (tc)
Writer: Maurice Templar-Art: R Wilson & J Challen
©1962 (Peveril Books) (96pg) (bw)
'Starring Robert Horton as Flint McCullough and John McIntire as Chris Hale'
Comic Strips: Two Trails To Take (10)
Reprint from Dell's Wagon Train #11
Sioux Ambush (15)-features Ward Bond, Side Trip To Trouble (13), The Varmint Trap (4), No Place To Camp (1)-features Ward Bond
Art: Alex Toth
Picture Strips: (1x2) Artists Of The Old West, Coin of Destiny
Text Stories: The Eddy Freeman Story, The Suzy Starbuck Story, The Frank Gabriel Story, The Sagetown Skeptic
Endpaper art features Horton and McIntire
Photo cover featuring Robert Horton and John McIntire (fc)
Large format
Based on the TV Western series
WALT DISNEY'S PUZZLE TIME
1981   £6 $10
WAR PICTURE LIBRARY ANNUAL
1978   £6 $10
Text Stories: Suicide Ridge, The Curse, Lonely battle. It has features such as The Cannons Roar, Roll of Honour and The Red Devils
WARLORD Book For Boys (D.C. Thomson)
1976-1984
1976-1979   £8 $13
1980-1984   £6 $10
World War II comic strips
Based on the UK comic

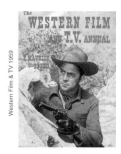

Western Film & TV 1959

Whoopee 1979

William Tell 1960

WCW - WORLD CHAMPIONSHIP WRESTLING (Marvel)
1993 (64pg) (fc)   £5 $8
Comic Strips: Battle Royal (22), Heel (20): Writer: Mike Lackey-Art:
Ron Wilson
Marvel Comics reprints
Text Story: Sting's Metal Mayhem
Photo Pin Ups/Profiles: Ravishing Rick Rude, Sting, Z-Man, El
Gigante, Johnny B. Badd, P.N. News
Photo cover featuring Sting
WESTERN ROUND-UP Annual (World)
1956-1959
1956   £15 $24
1957-1959   £12 $19
©1956 - Includes Gene Autry, Roy Rogers, Dale Evans, Johnny
Mack Brown
Dell reprints
©1957 - Includes Gene Autry, Roy Rogers and Trigger, Range Rider
Dell reprints
©1958 -Includes Wagon Train, Wells Fargo, Range Rider
Dell reprints
WESTERN FILM
1950's (with dj)   £35 $56
(without dj)   £25 $40
WESTERN TV and FILM (Macdonald & Co/Purnell)
1958-1964
1959 (Macdonald & Co)   £12 $19
1964 (Purnell)   £10 $16
WET WET WET Special (Grandreams)
1989   £3 $5
Based on the UK pop group
WF Special (Grandreams)
1992-1994
1992 (64pg)   £3 $5
Features: Hulk Hogan and other wrestlers
WHAM! (Odhams/Hamlyn)
1966-1973
1966   £12 $19
1967-1969   £10 $16
1970-1973   £8 $13
Based on the UK comic
WHAM! & POW! (Odhams)
1974   £8 $13
Based on the UK comic
WHAM! Special (Grandreams)
1985-1987   £6 $10
©1984 (64pg) (fc)
Writer: John Kercher
Features: The Tour, The Beginning, Keeping Fit, A Week with Wham
©1985 (64pg) (fc)
Writer: John Kercher
Features: George's Solo Career, The Wham Story, The Pressures of
Success, What Andy and George Think of Each Other, The Music
©1986 (64pg) (fc)
Writer: John Kercher
Based on the UK pop group
WHAT A MESS
1991   £6 $10
Based on the Childrens animated series by Frank Muir

WHITNEY HOUSTON Special (Grandreams)
1989 (64pg) (fc)   £6 $10
Editor: Jayne Lanigan, Writer: Robin Mackintosh
Based on the singer/actress
WHISKERS (Kemsley Newspapers Ltd)
1948-1952
1950-1952   £20 $32
WHIZZER AND CHIPS (Fleetway)
1970-1999
1970   £8 $13
1971-1979   £6 $10
1980-1989   £5 $8
1990-1999   £3 $5
Based on the UK comic
WHOOPEE (Fleetway)
1975-1987
1975   £8 $13
1976-1981   £5 $8
1982-1987   £3 $5
Based on the UK comic
WILD WEST Comic Annual (World)
1953-1961
1953   £15 $24
1954-1961   £10 $16
©1952 - Includes John Wayne
John Wayne Adventure Comics reprints
©1953 - Wild Bill Pecos, Lobo the Wolf Boy
The Westerner reprints
WILLIAM TELL (Adprint)
1960
©1959 (96pg) (fc/bw)   £15 $24
Comic Strips: New Win in Old Bottles (4bw), Mad Dog (4bw),
Text Stories: The Emperor's Hat, The Hostages, The Secret Death,
Secret Weapon, The Assassins, The Elixir, The Traitor
Adapted by: Terence Walker
Art: Gerry Embleton
Based on the TV series starring Conrad Phillips.
WILLIAM TELL (Marvel)
1990 (64pg)
Editor: Dan Abnett
Comic Strip: The Stallion (20fc)
Writer: Ian Rimmer-Art: Jeff Anderson, Simon Coleby
Text Story: The Dukes of Zahringen
Writer: Andrew Brenner-Art: Gary Frank, Stewart Johnson
The Alchemist: Writer: John Tomlinson-Art: Antony Williams
Photo cover
Based on the TV Series starring Will Lyman
WIND IN THE WILLOWS "Look-In" (ITP)
1984-1987
N/D 1985 (64pg) (fc)   £7 $11
Writer: Frances Kennett
1986 (64pg) (fc)
Writer: Angus P Allan
Art: Michael Noble
1987 (64pg) (fc)
Writer: Angus P Allan
Art: Bill Titcombe
Based on the ITV puppet animation series

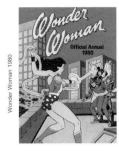

WINNIE THE POOH (EgmontWorld)
1990's-2000　　　　　　　　　　£6　　$10
2000 (64pg)
Editor: Lisa Carless, Designer: Jonathan Gilbert
Picture Stories (fc): Flooded Out!, Trumpet Trouble, In Training,
Tigger's Go-Kart, The Magic Set, The Conker
Based on the Walt Disney cartoon
WIZBIT (Grandreams)
1989 (64pg)　　　　　　　　　　£3　　$5
Writer: Barry Murray-Art: Derek Matthews
Presented by Paul Daniels
Magic tricks
WOLF CUB (PearsonPurnell)
1950's-1960's
1950's　　　　　　　　　　　　£10　　$13
1960's　　　　　　　　　　　　£8　　$13
WOMBLES (World/Egmont World)
1970's-1990's
1970's　　　　　　　　　　　　£8　　$13
1970's (World)
Original text and character material: Elizabeth Beresford
Drawn from Ivor Wood's original film puppets by David Fryer
Art: David Fryer
1980's　　　　　　　　　　　　£7　　$11
1990's　　　　　　　　　　　　£5　　$8
1991 (World)
Art: Edgar Hodges
1999 (Egmont World) (64pg) (fc)
Writer: Elizabeth Beresford-Additional material by Graham Wise and
Geoff Cowans-Art: Alan Willow & Mark Ripley
Picture Strips (2x4): Things that go Whoosh in the Night..., Madame
Cholet's Day Off
Includes text stories and photo features
Based on the Childrens puppet animation series
WONDER WOMAN (Egmont/London Editions)
1980-1982　　　　　　　　　　£10　　$16
1980 (Egmont) (64pg) (fc)
Cover Art: Paul Green-Endpaper: Brian Bolland
Comic Strips : Chessmen of Death (10),
This War Has Been Cancelled (30): Writer: Martin Pasko based on a
Writer: Alan Brennert-Art: Bob Brown and Vince Colletta
Give Her Liberty -- And Give Her Death! (7)-Writer: Martin Pasko-
Art: Kurt Schaffenberger
Justice League of America reprint
The Maniacs Of Mercury (10)
1981 (Egmont) (64pg) (fc)
Cover Art: Brian Bolland-Endpaper: Gary Leach
1982 (London Editions)
Comic Strips : The Mystery of the Atom World! (10), Voyage of the
Sorcerers
Lost (12): Writer: Jack C. Harris-Art: Jack Abel
The Claws of The Cheetah (16)
Writer: Martin Pasko-Art: Jose Delbo & Vince Colletta
Land of the Scaled Gods (23): Writer: Gerry Conway-Pencils: Jose
Delbo-Inks: Joe Giella
Wonder Girl in Mr Jupiter Is Dead! (2 part-10): Writer: E Nelson
Bridwell-Art: Ric Estrada & John Calnan
Based on the DC Comics character
WONDERFUL WORLD OF DISNEY (Fleetway)

1977-1979　　　　　　　　　　£8　　$13
1977(72pg)
Comic Strips: Pinocchio, Brer Rabbit, The Sword in the Stone
Text Stories: Aristocats, Snow White and the Seven Dwarfs, Peter
and the Wolf
1978 (80pg)
Comic Strips: Winnie the Pooh, Dumbo, Pinocchio, Lady & the
Tramp, Donald & Daisy, Mickey Mouse
Text Stories: Brer Rabbit, Robin Hood, Perri, Baloo (Jungle book),
Goofy, Bluebell (Peter Pan), Aristocats
WOODBINDA (World)
1971
©1970 (70pg)　　　　　　　　　　£7　　$11
Photo cover
Based on the Australian TV Series
WOOFITS (Stafford Pemberton)
1981 (64pg)　　　　　　　　　　£6　　$10
WOODY WOODPECKER
1960's-1980's
1960's　　　　　　　　　　　　£8　　$13
1970's-1980's　　　　　　　　　£6　　$10
1983 (Fleetway) (80pg) (fc/bw)
Comic Strips: Gone With The Whirlwind (bw), Cool Music (bw), The
Singing Woodpecker (bw), Finders Keepers (bw), The Lost Wild
West (bw), The Jinxed Journey (fc), Wonder Woody (bw), Gliding
Gladiators (bw), The Tahiti Rectangle (bw)
Gold Key/Whitman reprints
Includes feature on how to draw Woody, Splinter and Knothead
Based on the cartoon character
WOOZIES (Stafford Pemberton)
1977 (64pg)　　　　　　　　　　£6　　$10
Writer: Margaret Berry, Art: Andrea Smith
WORLD OF KNOWLEDGE (Fleetway)
1982 (128pg)　　　　　　　　　　£3　　$5
WORLD OF SHOW JUMPING (Stafford Pemberton)
1978 (72pg)　　　　　　　　　　£4　　$7
Edited: Margaret Dempsey
Pictures by Ed Lacey
WORLD OF SPORT
1979-1981　　　　　　　　　　£6　　$10
©1978 (Brown Watson)
Features: Kevin Keegan, Tony Currie, Mike Haliwood, Brian Moore,
John Conteh, Brendan Foster, Ian BothamRay Wilkins, Barry Sheen,
Peter Barnes, Trevor Francis, Dicky Davies, Kent Walton
©1980 (Grandreams) (64pg)
Editor: John Barraclough-Writer: Peter Bills
Features: Dickie Davies, Severiano Ballesteros, Brian Kidd, Ron
Greenwood, Kenny Carter, Wayne Bridges, Jean Pierre Rives, John
Watson, Vince Hilaire, Brian Moore, Ingemar Stenmark, Emlyn
Hughes, Terry Griffiths, Alex Higgins, Eric Bristow, Alan Minter,
Robin Cousins, Graham Gooch, Johnny Francome, Johnny Saint,
Viv Richards, Terry McDermot, Ian St John, Brough Scott
Based on the ITV sports show
WORZEL GUMMIDGE (Purnell/Brown Watson/Grandreams)
1980-1984　　　　　　　　　　£6　　$10
©1979 (Purnell)-Published 1980
Text Stories: Worzel's Washing Day, A Home Fit for Scarecrows,
Aunt Sally, The Crowman, A Little Learning, Worzel Pays a Visit,

Worzel Gummidge 1982

X Men Collectors Edition

Z Cars 1967

The Scarecrow Hop
©1980 (Brown Watson) (64pg)
Comic Strips: Pigeon Post (6fc), Disaster Fund (6 tc), Four Footed Fear (3fc), Worzel's Party (6fc), The Star Turn (4tc)
Photo cover
©1981 (Grandreams) (64pg)
Comic Strips: Out of his Briny Mind (8bw), A Real Pantomime (8fc), Luck of the Devil (8bw)
Art: John Cooper
Photo cover
©1982 (Grandreams) (64pg) (fc/bw)
Comic Strips (8x2bw): Worzel's Flight of Fancy, Worzel-Superstar
Art: John Cooper
Includes photo stories & features
©1983 (Grandreams) (64pg)
Comic Strips (bw): Aunt Sally's Valentine (4), Lucky for Some (4), Worzel's Prize Performance (2), Resolution Confusion (2), A Fishy Business (4)
Art: John Cooper
Photo cover
Based on the Childrens ITV series starring Jon Pertwee and Geoffrey Bayldon and Una Stubbs

WOW! (Fleetway)
1984	£4	$7

WUZZLES (Grandreams)
1987-1989	£5	$8
Based on the animated TV series and toy range

WWF Official Annual (Grandreams/World)
1992-1996	£3	$5
©1991 (Grandreams)
1st annual
©1995
A Year in Review. The Dawning of a New Generation
1996 (World)

X-MEN 'Collector's Edition' (Marvel/ Grandreams)
N/D 1982-1983 (64pg) (fc)	£8	$13
©1981
Comic Strip: Chapter 1 - What is The Power (28)- Chapter 2 - Mission Murder (34)
Editor: Stan Lee-Writer: Roy Thomas-Pencils: Neal Adams-Inks: Tom Palmer
Uncanny X-Men reprints
Based on the Marvel comics characters

X-MEN (Marvel)
1990's	£5	$8
©1996
Cover: Jim Lee and Bob Wiacek
Editor: Alan Cowsill
Comic Strips: Follow The Leader (48fc), Writer: Scott Lobdell, Pencils: Chris Bachalo, Inks: Dan Panosian
Mandripoor Knights (22fc), Writer: Chris Claremont, Pencils: Jim Lee, Inks: Scott Williams
Zounds of Silence by Larry Hama, and Michael Golden, Art: Robin Text Story: Grave Danger. Art: Tim Sale
Endpaper: McDaniel

YOGI BEAR (World)
1960's	£10	$16
Based on the Hanna-Barbera cartoon character

YOUNG MARVELMAN (Miller)

1954-1961
1954 (Scarce) - softcover	£50	$80
1955 (Scarce) - softcover	£40	$60
1956 - hardcover	£30	$48
1957-1960	£20	$32
1961 - card cover	£15	$24
Based on the UK comic

YOUNG MASTERMIND (World)
1978-1980 (64pg)	£3	$5
Art: Annabel Spenceley & Christine Horrocks
Packed full of questions and answers

YOUNG MAVERICK
1980
©1979	£8	$13
Based on the TV Western series starring Charles Frank and Susan Blanchard

'Z' CARS (World)
1964-1967
1964	£12	$19
1965-1967
©1963-©1966
Writer: Ian Kennedy Martin
Based on the BBC TV police series

ZANE GREY'S WESTERN Annual (World)
1966-1967	£10	$16
©1965
Comic Strips (fc): Zane Grey's The Rainbow Trail (27), Zane Grey's Knights of the Range (27), True Western Adventures Tom Horn--- Range Rider (4), Zane Grey's Wild Horse Mesa (27)
Dell/Gold Key reprints
©1966 (96pg)
Comic Strips (fc): Wilderness Ranch (27), The End of the Daltons (4), Twin Sombreros (27), 30,000 On the Hoof (27)
Dell/Gold Key reprints

ZIG & ZAG (Grandreams)
1994 (48pg)	£3	$5
Based on the TV puppet characters

ZOIDS (Marvel/Grandreams)
1987	£5	$8
©1986 (64pg)
Based on the animated TV series

ZOO FRIENDS
1950's-1960's	£8	$13

ZOO TIME
1960's	£8	$13
Based on the ITV childrens animal series with Desmond Morris

ZORRO (Daily Mirror)
1960-1961
1960	£20	$32
©1959 (128pg) (b/w) (with dj)
Writer: Steve Frazee, Adapted by: Arthur Groom
Art: John Challen
Photo Cover
1961	£15	$24
©1960
Photo Cover featuring Guy Williams (tc)
Based on the Disney TV series featuring characters created by Johnston McCulley

Black Bob 1952

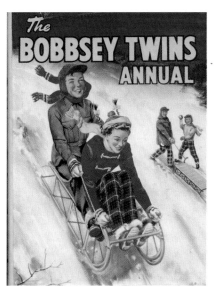

Lone Ranger 1953   **Bobbsey Twins 1958**

Topper 1958

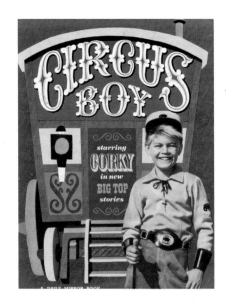

Circus Boy 1960

Cheyenne 1961

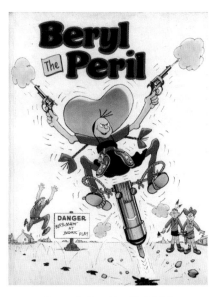

Beryl the Peril 1962

Beano 1962

Roy of the Rovers 1963

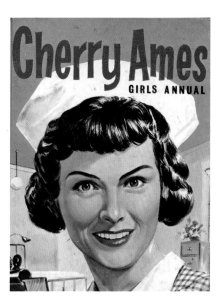

Cherry Ames 1964

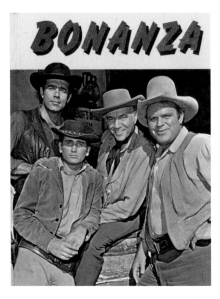

Bonanza 1965

Beverly Hillbillies 1966

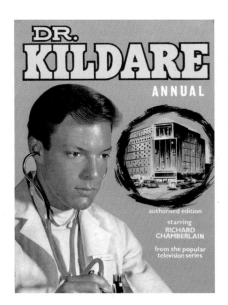

Dr Kildare 1964

The Avengers 1970

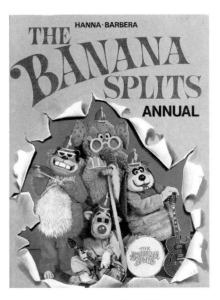

Banana Splits 1971

Hurricane 1971

Catweazle 1972

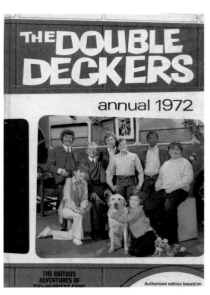

Double Deckers 1972

Battle Picture Weekly 1977

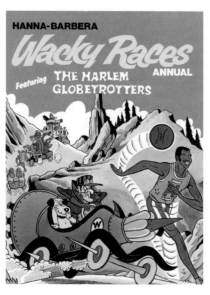

Wacky Races 1977

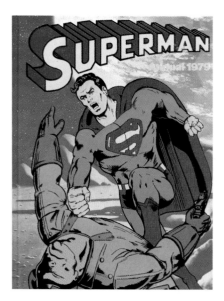

Superman 1979

Fab 208 1979

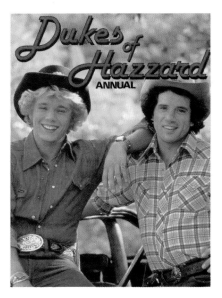

Dukes of Hazzard 1980

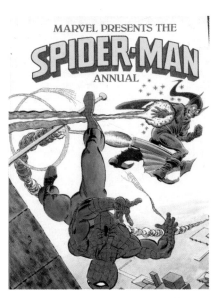

Spiderman 1981

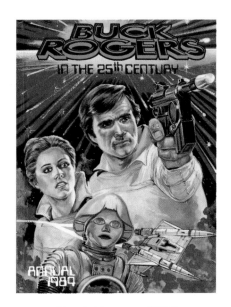

Buck Rogers 1984

Masters of the Universe 1985

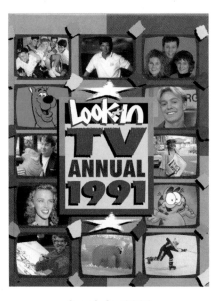

Look In 1991

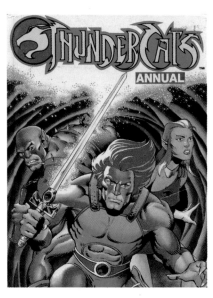

Thundercats 1991

Beverly Hills 90210 1994

Mummies Alive 1999

Beryl the Peril 1962

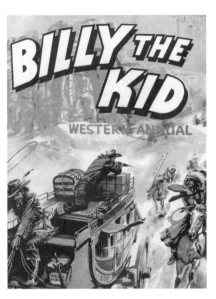

Billy the Kid 1959

Dr Who 1966

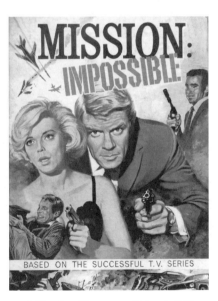

Mission Impossible 1970

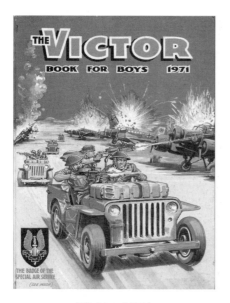

Victor 1971

Basil Brush 1972

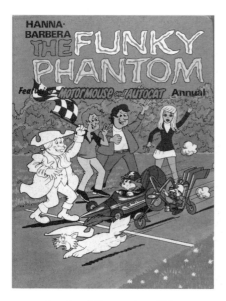

Funky Phantom 1975

Holmes and Yoyo 1978

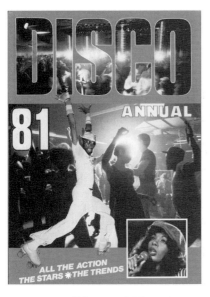

Disco 1981

X-Men 1982

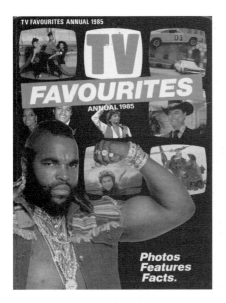

TV Favourites 1985

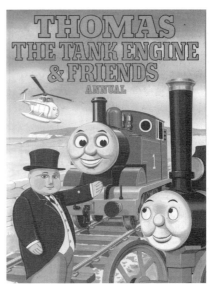

Thomas the Tank Engine 1987

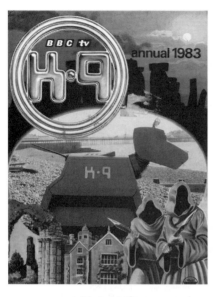

K-9 1983

Rupert 1994

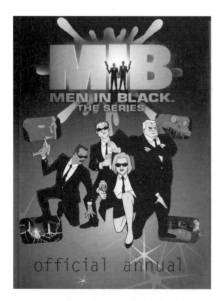

Men in Black 1999

My Little Pony 1999

TV/MOVIE/POP CROSS REFERENCE GUIDE

The following guide is alphabetically listed for use as a cross reference to locate TV Series, Movies, Actors/Actresses and Pop/Rock Stars hidden within the pages of various annuals. Many girl's teenage titles, comics titles, magazine titles and pop titles contain features on stars and series who weren't granted their own annuals. Some stars and series appeared in both their own annuals and the titles listed in this cross reference.

So if you're searching for 77 Sunset Strip, The Beatles, Gerry Anderson or Charlie's Angels you'll find these and many others featured in this reference guide.

10cc feature - Cheggers 1980
10cc feature - Disco 45 1977
10cc feature - FAB 208 1976
10cc feature - Top of the Pops 1977
10cc feature - Top Pop Scene 1975
10cc feature/pin-up - Pop Group 1977
10cc feature/pin-up - Record Mirror & Disc 1977
5 Star feature - Look-In 1988
5 Star feature - Look-In 1989
5 Star pin up - Girl 1988
77 Sunset Strip - TV Crimebusters ©1962
77 Sunset Strip feature - ITV Annual for Boys and Girls 1964
A Bridge Too Far movie - Photoplay 1978
A Team comic strip - Look-In 1988
A Team feature - TV Favourites 1985
Abba comic strip - Look-In ©1980
Abba feature - Blue Jeans 1980
Abba feature - Cheggers 1980
Abba feature - Daily Mirror Pop Club 1978
Abba feature - Disco 45 1978
Abba feature - FAB 208 1979
Abba feature - Look-In ©1977
Abba feature - Look-In ©1978
Abba feature - Pop Group 1978
Abba feature - Superstars 1978
Abba feature (2pg) - Daily Mirror Book for Boys and Girls 1981
Abba feature/pin-up - Pop Group 1977
Abba feature/pin-up - Record Mirror & Disc 1977
Abba pin up - Diana 1979
Abba pin up - Diana 1982
Abba pin up - Disco 45 1977
Abba pin up - Girl 1983
Abba pin up - Look-In ©1977
Abba pin up - Look-In ©1978
Abba pin up - Look-In ©1981
Abba pin up - Mates 1980
Abba small feature - Look-In Pop ©1982
ABC feature - Pop Superstars 1984
ABC feature - Video Superstars 1985
Adam and the Ants - Diana 1983
Adam and the Ants pin up - Look-In ©1980
Adam Ant feature - Jackie 1986
Adam Ant feature - Look-In ©1982
Adam Ant feature - Look-In Pop ©1982
Adam Ant pin up - Girl 1984
Adam Ant pin up - Look-In Pop ©1982
Adam Ant pin up - My Guy 1983
Adam Ant pin up - My Guy 1984
Adam Ant small feature - Jackie 1983
Adam Ant small feature - Jackie 1984
Adam Faith small feature - Boyfriend 1968
Addams Family small feature - Look-In 1990

Adrian Paul cover photo - Oh Boy! 1985
Adrian Paul small photo - Oh Boy! 1983
Adrian Wright pin up - Look-In ©1972
Aha fact file and pin up - Jackie 1988
Aha feature - Look-In 1987
Aha feature and pin up - Girl 1988
Aha pin up - Girl 1987
Air Supply feature - Daily Mirror Pop Club 1982
Airwolf endpaper - Look-In 1987
Airwolf feature - TV Favourites 1985
Al Pacino feature - Photoplay 1978
Al Pacino feature/pin-up - Photoplay 1975
Alan Hudson feature - Boyfriend 1973
Alan Hudson pin up - Look-In ©1975
Alan McClusky of O M D small feature - Jackie 1984
Alan Price pin-up - Boyfriend 1968
Alannah Currie of Thompson Twins feature - Jackie 1986
Alessi Brothers pin up - Mates 1979
Alessi Brothers pin up - Mates 1980
Alex Harvey pin-up - Record Mirror & Disc 1977
Alf feature - Look-In 1988
Alf feature - Look-In 1989
Alf Garnett feature - Star TV & Film 1968
Ali MacGraw feature - Photoplay 1974
Ali MacGraw pin-up - Photoplay 1979
Alias Smith and Jones (Duel/Murphy) photo cover/endpaper - TV Action 1974
Alias Smith and Jones (Duel/Murphy) text story - TV Action 1974
Alice Cooper feature - Music Scene 1974
Alice Cooper feature/pin-up - Top of the Pops 1974
Alice Cooper pin up - Music Scene 1974
Alice Cooper pin-up - Popswop ©1973
Alister Kerr feature - Mates 1979
All Saints small feature - Mandy 2000
All Saints small feature - Mandy 2000
Allan Clarke pin up - Look-In ©1974
Altered Images feature - Look-In Pop ©1982
Altered Images feature - Pop Superstars 1984
Altered Images feature - Radio 1984
Altered Images pin up - Look-In Pop ©1982
Altered Images pin up - Oh Boy! 1985
Alvin Lee pin up - Boyfriend 1973
Alvin Stardust feature - Diana 1979
Alvin Stardust feature - FAB 208 1976
Alvin Stardust feature - Mirabelle Sunshine Pop Book 1975
Alvin Stardust feature - Music Star 1976
Alvin Stardust pin up - Diana 1986
Alvin Stardust pin up - Look-In ©1974
Alvin Stardust pin up - Look-In ©1975
Alvin Stardust pin up - Mirabelle Sunshine Pop Book 1975
Alvin Stardust pin-up - Top of the Pops 1975
Alvin Stardust small feature - Look-In ©1974

Amen Corner feature/pin-up - Fab 208 1969
Amii Stewart small feature - Blue Jeans 1981
An Investigation into Murder movie - Photoplay 1975
Andrew McCarthy small feature - Blue Jeans 1988
Andy & David Williams feature - Pink 1974
Andy & David Williams pin up - Mirabelle Sunshine Pop Book 1975
Andy Brown feature - Boyfriend 1971
Andy Gibb feature - Mates 1979
Andy Gibb feature/pin-up - Pink 1982
Andy Gibb pin up - Mates 1979
Andy Gibb pin up - Mates 1980
Andy Gibb pin up - My Guy 1982
Andy Ruffell feature - Look-In 1986
Andy Summers small feature - Blue Jeans 1982
Andy Williams feature - FAB 208 1972
Animals feature - Radio Luxembourg Record Stars ©1965
Ann Margret pin-up - Photoplay 1974
Ann Margret pin-up - Photoplay 1976
Ann Miller feature - Hollywood Album - Ninth
Anna Kashfi pin up - Hollywood Album - Twelfth ©1958
Anne Kirkbride (Dierdre from Coronation Street) feature - Diana 1983
Annie Lennox small feature - Blue Jeans 1982
Anthea Turner feature - Top of the Pops 1992
Anthony Quinn feature - Hollywood Album - Twelfth ©1958
Arrows pin up - Mates 1977
Art Garfunkel pin-up - Top of the Pops 1977
Arthur Askey pin-up - TV Mirror 1956
Arthur of the Britons endpaper - Look-In ©1973
Ava Gardner feature - Hollywood Album - Ninth
Avengers (Steed/Keel) - TV Crimebusters ©1962
Ayshea pin up - Look-In ©1971
B A Robertson small feature - Jackie 1981
Baccara pin up - Look-In ©1978
Bachelors feature - Radio Luxembourg Record Stars ©1965
Bad Company feature - FAB 208 1976
Bad Company feature - Superstars 1979
Banana Splits comic strip - All Stars Television Annual 1973
Bananarama feature - Pop Superstars 1985
Bananarama feature - Video Superstars 1985
Barbara Bach pin-up - Photoplay 1978
Barbara Kelly pin-up - TV Mirror 1956
Barbra Streisand feature/pin-up - Photoplay 1971
Barbra Streisand feature/pin-up - Photoplay 1974
Barbra Streisand feature/pin-up - Photoplay 1975
Barbra Streisand feature/pin-up - Photoplay 1976
Barbra Streisand pin-up - Photoplay 1978
Barclay James Harvest feature - Daily Mirror Pop Club 1982
Baretta feature - TV Detectives ©1979
Barry Blue feature - Top Pop Scene 1975
Barry Manilow feature - Daily Mirror Pop Club 1982
Barry Manilow feature - Girl 1984
Barry Manilow feature - TV Favourites 1985
Barry Newman feature - Photoplay 1973
Barry Newman pin-up - Photoplay 1974
Barry Sheene feature - Superstars 1978
Barry Sheene feature - Superstars 1979
Barry White feature - Superstars 1978
Batman & Robin feature - Star TV & Film 1968
Batman TV series small feature - Look-In 1990
Bay City Rollers feature - Daily Mirror Pop Club 1978

Bay City Rollers feature - FAB 208 1976
Bay City Rollers feature - FAB 208 1979
Bay City Rollers feature - Mates 1977
Bay City Rollers feature - Mates 1978
Bay City Rollers feature - Music Star 1976
Bay City Rollers feature - Record Mirror & Disc 1977
Bay City Rollers feature - Supersonics 1979
Bay City Rollers feature - Top Pop Scene 1975
Bay City Rollers feature/pin-up - Pink 1978
Bay City Rollers feature/pin-up - Pop Group 1977
Bay City Rollers pin up - Mates 1978
Bay City Rollers pin-up - Pink 1979
Bay City Rollers pin-up - Top of the Pops 1977
Beach Boys pin up - Boyfriend 1974
Beach Boys feature - Pop Group 1978
Beach Boys feature - Teen Beat-Pop Ten ©1969
Beach Boys pin-up - Boyfriend 1968
Bear Island movie - Photoplay 1980
Beat pin-up - Top of the Pops 1982
Beatles feature - Radio Luxembourg Record Stars ©1965
Beatles feature - Teen Beat-Pop Ten ©1969
Beatles feature - Teen Beat-Pop Ten 1967
Beatles feature - Tony Blackburn Pop Special 2
Beatles feature - Tony Blackburn Pop Special 3
Beatles feature and pin up - Boyfriend 1971
Beatles feature/illustration - Diana 1982
Beatles feature/pin-up - Fab 208 1969
Beatles Growing Up - 3 page picture strip - Judy 1975
Beatles pin-up - Pop Group 1977
Beatles small feature - Blue Jeans 1993
Bee Gee Barry Gibb pin up - Boyfriend 1971
Bee Gees Andy Gibb feature - FAB 208 1980
Bee Gees feature - Cheggers 1980
Bee Gees feature - Pop Group 1978
Bee Gees feature - Teen Beat-Pop Ten ©1969
Bee Gees feature - Tony Blackburn Pop Special 3
Bee Gees feature/illustration - Diana 1982
Bee Gees feature/pin-up - Fab 208 1969
Ben Murphy feature - Popswop ©1973
Ben Murphy feature/pin-up - Popswop ©1973
Ben Murphy pin up - FAB 208 1973
Ben Murphy pin up - FAB 208 1975
Ben Murphy pin up - Look-In ©1974
Ben Murphy pin-up - Valentine 1974
Ben Murphy pin-up - Valentine 1974
Ben Murphy small feature - Pink 1978
Benedict Taylor - Diana 1983
Benny Hil feature - Look-In TV Comedy ©1974
Benny Hill comic strip - Look-In ©1975
Benny Hill comic strip - Look-In ©1976
Benny Hill comic strip - Look-In ©1977
Benny Hill comic strip - Look-In ©1978
Benny Hill comic strip - Look-In ©1979
Benny Hill comic strip - Look-In TV Comedy ©1975
Benny Hill endpaper - Look-In ©1980
Benny Hill feature - Look-In ©1979
Benny Hill feature - Look-In TV Comedy ©1975
Benny Hill pin-up - TV Mirror 1956
Bert Weedon feature - ITV Annual for Boys and Girls 1964
Bert Weedon pin up - Crackerjack ©1962
Betty Boo feature/pin-up - Top of the Pops 1992
Betty Boo pin up - Eagle Yearbook 1992
Beverley Sisters pin-up - TV Mirror 1956
Beverly Hillbillies small feature - Look-In 1990
Bewitched pin up - Mandy 2000

Pin Up = 1 page pin up * Feature = ½ page article or more * Small feature = ¼ page article or less

Bewitched small feature - Look-In 1990
Bewitched small feature - Mandy 2000
Bewitched small feature/pin-up - Mandy 2000
Big Country feature - Jackie 1986
Big Country feature - Video Superstars 1985
Bilbo Baggins pin up - Mates 1977
Billy Fury pin up - Crackerjack ©1962
Billy Idol feature - Supersonics 1979
Billy Idol pin up - My Guy 1983
Billy Joel feature - Daily Mirror Pop Club 1982
Billy Joel feature - Pop Superstars 1985
Billy Joel feature - Video Superstars 1985
Bionic Woman feature - Look-In ©1977
BJ and the Bear pin up - Look-In ©1980
Bjorn Borg fact file - Diana 1982
Bjorn Borg endpaper - Look-In ©1981
Bjorn Borg feature - Superstars 1978
Black Beauty comic strip - Look-In ©1974
Black Beauty comic strip - Look-In ©1981
Black Beauty comic strip - Look-In 1989
Black Beauty endpaper - Look-In ©1974
Black Sabbath feature - Daily Mirror Pop Club 1978
Black Sabbath feature - Music Scene 1974
Bless This House comic strip - Look-In ©1974
Bless This House comic strip - Look-In ©1975
Bless This House comic strip - Look-In TV Comedy ©1974
Bless This House comic strip - Look-In TV Comedy ©1975
Bless This House feature - Look-In TV Comedy ©1974
Bless This House photo story - Look-In ©1974
Blockbusters endpaper - Look-In 1990
Blondie 2pg feature - Daily Mirror Book for Boys and Girls 1981
Blondie feature - Cheggers 1980
Blondie feature - Look-In ©1979
Blondie feature - Top of the Pops 1982
Blue Thunder feature - TV Favourites 1985
Bob Dylan feature - Top Pop Stars 1968
Bob Dylan small feature - Boyfriend 1971
Bob Geldof feature - Supersonics 1979
Bob Geldof pin up - Look-In ©1980
Bob Geldof pin up - My Guy 1981
Bob Geldof small feature - Blue Jeans 1980
Bob Geldof small feature - Blue Jeans 1981
Bob Geldof small feature - Blue Jeans 1982
Bob Geldof small feature - Jackie 1981
Bob Marley feature - Pop Group 1978
Bob Marley feature - Supersonics 1979
Bob Monkhouse pin-up - TV Mirror 1956
Bob Wallis pin up - Crackerjack ©1962
Bobbie Gentry pin up - Boyfriend 1971
Bobby Ball comic strip - Look-In 1987
Bobby Davro feature - Look-In 1988
Bobby Vinton feature - Radio Luxembourg Record Stars ©1965
Bon Jovi pin up - Girl 1988
Boney M feature - Cheggers 1980
Boney M feature - Disco 81 1981
Boney M feature - Look-In ©1979
Boney M small feature - Blue Jeans 1980
Boomtown Rates illustration/fact file - Diana 1981
Boomtown Rats feature - Cheggers 1980
Boomtown Rats feature - FAB 208 1980
Boomtown Rats pin up - Mates 1981
Boomtown Rats pin up - Oh Boy! 1980
Boris Becker feature - Look-In 1987

Bow Wow Wow feature - Pop Superstars 1984
Boy Dominic endpaper - Look-In ©1974
Boy George endpaper - Look-In ©1983
Boy George feature - Jackie 1985
Boy George feature - TV Favourites 1985
Brat Pack feature - Blue Jeans 1990
Brenda Lee feature - Radio Luxembourg Record Stars ©1965
Brenda Lee pin up - Crackerjack ©1962
Brian Connolly feature - Mirabelle Sunshine Pop Book 1975
Brigitte Bardot feature - Photoplay 1973
Britt Ekland pin-up - Photoplay 1974
Bros feature - Look-In 1989
Bros feature/pin-up - Top of the Pops 1992
Bros pin up - Blue Jeans 1990
Bros pin up- Jackie 1989
Bros small feature - Blue Jeans 1993
Brother Beyond pin up - Blue Jeans 1990
Brotherhood of Man feature - Cheggers 1980
Bruce Jenner pin up - My Guy 1982
Bruce Johnston small feature - Boyfriend 1968
Bruce Lee feature - Photoplay 1975
Bruno Brookes feature - Top of the Pops 1992
Bryan Ferry feature - Superstars 1978
Bryan Ferry feature - Top of the Pops 1982
Bryan Ferry pin-up - Pink 1980
Bryan Ferry pin-up - Record Mirror & Disc 1977
Bryan Ferry pin-up - Top of the Pops 1977
Buck Rogers in the 25th Century pin up - Look-In ©1981
Bucks Fizz - Diana 1983
Bucks Fizz feature - My Guy 1984
Bucks Fizz feature - Radio 1984
Bucks Fizz pin up - Girl 1988
Bucks Fizz pin up - Look-In Pop ©1982
Bucks Fizz pin up - Oh Boy! 1985
Bucks Fizz pin-up - Diana 1985
Burt Bacharach feature - Look-In ©1972
Burt Reynolds feature/pin-up - Photoplay 1974
Burt Reynolds pin-up - Photoplay 1975
Burt Reynolds pin-up - Photoplay 1976
Buster Bloodvessel feature - Girl 1984
Buster pin up - Mates 1978
Candi Staton feature - Superstars 1979
Cannon & Ball comic strip - Look-In ©1982
Cannon & Ball comic strip - Look-In ©1984
Cannon & Ball comic strip - Look-In 1986
Cannon & Ball comic strip - Look-In 1988
Cannon & Ball endpaper - Look-In ©1983
Cannon & Ball endpaper - Look-In 1989
Cannon & Ball feature - Look-In ©1982
Cannon feature - TV Detectives ©1979
Cannon photo story - TV Action 1974
Captain Sensible star file - Jackie 1986
Car 54 Where Are You? small feature - Look-In 1990
Caravan to Vaccares movie - Photoplay 1975
Carl Wayne pin up - Boyfriend 1971
Carly Simon feature - Superstars 1979
Carol Hawkins pin up - Look-In ©1972
Carol Vorderman feature - Look-In 1990
Caroline Mortimer feature - Star TV & Film 1968
Carpenters feature - Daily Mirror Pop Club 1978
Carpenters feature - Pop Group 1978
Carpenters feature - Supersonics 1979
Carpenters feature - Superstars 1978

Pin Up = 1 page pin up * Feature = ½ page article or more * Small feature = ¼ page article or less

Carpenters feature/pin-up - Top of the Pops 1975
Carpenters pin up - Judy 1979
Carroll Baker pin up - Hollywood Album - Twelfth ©1958
Carry On feature - Look-In TV Comedy ©1975
Casablanca movie - Photoplay 1979
Cat Stevens feature - Music Scene 1974
Cat Stevens feature - Pink 1974
Cat Stevens feature - Superstars 1978
Cat Stevens small feature/pin-up - Boyfriend 1968
Catweazle comic strip - Look-In ©1972
Catweazle feature - All Stars Television Annual 1973
Catweazle feature - Look-In ©1971
Charles Bronson pin-up - Photoplay 1976
Charles Bronson pin-up - Photoplay 1979
Charlie Chan - TV Crimebusters 1977
Charlie's Angels feature - Look-In ©1978
Charlie's Angels feature - Look-In ©1979
Charlie's Angels feature - Look-In ©1980
Charlies Angels feature - TV Detectives ©1979
Charlie's Angels pin up - Look-In ©1978
Charlie's Angels quiz - My Guy 1981
Charlotte Rampling pin-up - Photoplay 1975
Charlton Heston feature - Hollywood Album - Twelfth ©1958
Charlton Heston feature/pin-up - Photoplay 1973
Chas Smash pin up - My Guy 1984
Chas Smash small feature - Blue Jeans 1983
Cheryl Baker small feature - Look-In Pop ©1982
Chesney Hawkes pin-up - Top of the Pops 1992
Chic feature - Disco 81 1981
Chicago feature - Pop Group 1978
Chicago feature - Superstars 1978
Chidren's Ward small feature - Look-In 1991
Child feature - FAB 208 1980
Child pin up - Mates 1978
Child pin up - Mates 1980
Child pin up - Mates 1981
Child small feature - Blue Jeans 1980
China Crisis pin up - Girl 1988
CHiPs feature - TV Detectives ©1979
CHiPs feature - TV Favourites 1985
Chris Atkins pin up - My Guy 1982
Chris Atkins pin up - My Guy 1983
Chris Barber pin up - Crackerjack ©1962
Chris Foreman of Madness small feature - Jackie 1984
Chris Quentin pin up - My Guy 1981
Chrissie Hynde small feature - Blue Jeans 1982
Christian Slater feature - Blue Jeans 1993
Christian Slater feature - Jackie 1991
Christian Slater pin up - Jackie 1993
Christian Slater star file - Jackie 1993
Christopher Lee feature - Photoplay 1971
Christopher Lee feature - Photoplay 1974
Christopher Plummer feature - Photoplay 1971
Christopher Reeve (painted Superman portrait) - Diana 1983
Christopher Reeve feature - Look-In ©1983
Christopher Reeve feature - Photoplay 1980
Chuck Berry feature - Radio Luxembourg Record Stars ©1965
Cilla Black feature - FAB 208 1972
Cilla Black feature - FAB 208 1973
Cilla Black feature - Look-In 1989
Cilla Black feature - Star TV & Film 1968
Cilla Black small photo - Fab 208 1969

Claire Bloom pin up and feature - Hollywood Album - Twelfth ©1958
Clark Gable feature - Hollywood Album - Twelfth ©1958
Clark Gable pin-up - Photoplay 1980
Clark Gable small feature - Jackie 1991
Claudia Cardinale feature - Photoplay 1973
Cleopatra small feature - Mandy 2000
Cleopatra small feature - Mandy 2000
Cliff Richard cover - Top Pop Stars 1962
Cliff Richard cover - Top Pop Stars 1964
Cliff Richard feature - Boyfriend 1973
Cliff Richard feature - Disco 45 1978
Cliff Richard feature - FAB 208 1972
Cliff Richard feature - FAB 208 1973
Cliff Richard feature - Film Show 1963
Cliff Richard feature - Girl 1984
Cliff Richard feature - Look-In ©1981
Cliff Richard feature - Pop Weekly 1969
Cliff Richard feature - Radio Luxembourg Record Stars ©1965
Cliff Richard feature - Star TV & Film 1968
Cliff Richard feature - Superstars 1979
Cliff Richard feature - Tony Blackburn Pop Special 2
Cliff Richard feature - Top of the Pops 1974
Cliff Richard feature/illustration - Diana 1982
Cliff Richard full page autographed colour photo - ITV Annual for Boys and Girls 1964
Cliff Richard pin up - Crackerjack ©1962
Cliff Richard pin up - Daily Mirror Pop Club 1982
Cliff Richard pin up - Diana 1981
Cliff Richard pin up - Girl 1982
Cliff Richard pin up - Judy 1980
Cliff Richard pin up - Look-In ©1981
Cliff Richard pin up - My Guy 1982
Cliff Richard pin up - My Guy 1984
Cliff Richard pin-up - Boyfriend 1968
Cliff Richard pin-up - Popswop ©1973
Cliff Richard pin-up - Top of the Pops 1982
Cliff Richard pin-up - Top of the Pops 1992
Cliff Richard small feature - Blue Jeans 1982
Cliff Richard small feature - Look-In Pop ©1982
Clint Eastwood cover/feature/pin-up - Photoplay 1980
Clint Eastwood fact file - Diana 1982
Clint Eastwood feature - Photoplay 1975
Clint Eastwood feature - Superstars 1979
Clint Eastwood feature/pin-up - Photoplay 1971
Clint Eastwood feature/pin-up - Photoplay 1973
Clint Eastwood feature/pin-up - Photoplay 1978
Clint Eastwood pin-up - Photoplay 1976
Clodagh Rodgers - pin up - Boyfriend 1971
Cockney Rebel feature - Pop Group 1978
Cockney Rebel feature - Record Mirror & Disc 1977
Colin Baker feature - Blue Peter Twenty One ©1984
Colin Blunstone feature - Look-In ©1972
Colin Blunstone feature - Mirabelle Sunshine Pop Book 1975
Colin Blunstone feature/pin-up - Pink 1974
Columbo feature - TV Detectives ©1979
Comedians feature - Look-In TV Comedy ©1974
Corey Feldman feature - Jackie 1991
Corey Haim feature - Jackie 1991
Cornell Borchers pin up - Hollywood Album - Twelfth ©1958
Corrs small feature - Mandy 2000
Corrs small feature - Mandy 2000

Pin Up = 1 page pin up * Feature = ½ page article or more * Small feature = ¼ page article or less

Cosgrove Hall feature - Look-In 1988
Craig Douglas pin up - Crackerjack ©1962
Craig McLachlan pin up - Eagle Yearbook 1992
Creature Comforts feature - Look-In ©1981
Cromwell movie feature - Photoplay 1971
Crosby Stills and Nash feature - Superstars 1979
Culture Club feature - Pop Superstars 1984
Culture Club feature - Pop Superstars 1985
Culture Club feature - Video Superstars 1985
Curiosity Killed the Cat (Ben) fact file - Jackie 1988
Curiosity Killed the Cat feature - Blue Jeans 1988
Curt Smith of Tears for Fears star file - Jackie 1986
Dad's Army comic strip - TV Action 1974
Daleks feature - Look-In ©1978
Dallas feature - TV Favourites 1985
Damian O'Neill small feature - Blue Jeans 1983
Damned feature - Supersonics 1979
Dan Dailey feature - Hollywood Album - Ninth
Dan Dare small feature - Look-In ©1976
Dan Duryea feature - Hollywood Album - Twelfth ©1958
Dan O'Herlihy feature - Hollywood Album - Ninth
Dana Andrews feature and pin up - Hollywood Album - Ninth
Danger Man - TV Crimebusters ©1962
Danger Mouse comic strip - Look-In ©1982
Danni Minogue pin-up - Top of the Pops 1992
Danny Kaye feature - Hollywood Album - Ninth
Danny Williams pin up - Crackerjack ©1962
Daryl Hall pin up - Girl 1988
Dave Clark feature - Radio Luxembourg Record Stars ©1965
Dave Clark Five feature - Tony Blackburn Pop Special 3
Dave Clarke feature - Top of the Pops 1977
Dave Dee small feature - Boyfriend 1968
Dave Hill pin up - Mirabelle Sunshine Pop Book 1975
Dave Hill pin-up - Top of the Pops 1977
Dave King pin-up - TV Mirror 1956
Dave Vanian of the Damned small feature - Jackie 1981
Dave Wakeling pin up - My Guy 1983
David Attenborough pin-up - TV Mirror 1956
David Bowie feature - Daily Mirror Pop Club 1978
David Bowie feature - FAB 208 1976
David Bowie feature - Mirabelle Sunshine Pop Book 1975
David Bowie feature - Music Scene 1974
David Bowie feature - Music Star 1974
David Bowie feature/pin-up - Popswop ©1973
David Bowie feature/pin-up - Record Mirror & Disc 1977
David Bowie feature/pin-up - Top of the Pops 1974
David Bowie feature/pin-up - Top of the Pops 1977
David Bowie pin up - Boyfriend 1974
David Bowie pin up - Daily Mirro Pop Club 1982
David Bowie pin up - Mirabelle Sunshine Pop Book 1975
David Bowie pin up - Music Scene 1974
David Bowie pin up - My Guy 1981
David Bowie pin up - My Guy 1982
David Bowie pin-up - Pink 1974
David Bowie pin-up - Top of the Pops 1975
David Bowie pin-up - Top of the Pops 1982
David Bowie small feature - Jackie 1984
David Bowie small feature - Look-In Pop ©1982
David Carradine - see Kung Fu
David Cassidy comic strip - Look-In ©1973
David Cassidy feature - FAB 208 1972
David Cassidy feature - FAB 208 1973
David Cassidy feature - FAB 208 1976

David Cassidy feature - Jackie 1975
David Cassidy feature - Mirabelle Sunshine Pop Book 1975
David Cassidy feature - Music Star 1974
David Cassidy feature - Music Star 1975
David Cassidy feature - Music Star 1976
David Cassidy feature - Top Pop Scene 1975
David Cassidy feature/pin-up - Pink 1974
David Cassidy feature/pin-up - Popswop ©1973
David Cassidy feature/pin-up - Record Mirror & Disc 1977
David Cassidy feature/pin-up - Valentine 1974
David Cassidy on Hawaii feature - FAB 208 1975
David Cassidy photo cover - Boyfriend 1974
David Cassidy pin up - Look-In ©1973
David Cassidy pin up - Look-In ©1974
David Cassidy pin-up - Top of the Pops 1974
David Cassidy pin-up - Top of the Pops 1975
David Easter pin up - Girl 1987
David Easter pin up - My Guy 1981
David Essex endpaper - Diana 1981
David Essex feature - Cheggers 1980
David Essex feature - FAB 208 1975
David Essex feature - FAB 208 1976
David Essex feature - Mates 1977
David Essex feature - Mates 1977
David Essex feature - Mates 1978
David Essex feature - Mates 1982
David Essex feature - Mirabelle Sunshine Pop Book 1975
David Essex feature - Music Star 1976
David Essex feature - Pink 1978
David Essex feature - Popswop ©1973
David Essex feature - Supersonics 1979
David Essex feature - Top of the Pops 1977
David Essex feature/pin-up - Record Mirror & Disc 1977
David Essex pin up - Diana 1979
David Essex pin up - Judy 1981
David Essex pin up - Look-In ©1974
David Essex pin up - Look-In ©1975
David Essex pin up - Mates 1977
David Essex pin up - Mates 1980
David Essex pin up - Mates 1981
David Essex pin up - Mirabelle Sunshine Pop Book 1975
David Essex pin up - My Guy 1981
David Essex pin up - My Guy 1982
David Essex pin up - My Guy 1983
David Essex pin up - Oh Boy! 1980
David Essex pin up - Oh Boy! 1985
David Essex pin-up - Diana 1985
David Essex pin-up - Photoplay 1975
David Essex pin-up - Top of the Pops 1975
David Essex small feature - Blue Jeans 1981
David Essex small feature - Jackie 1981
David Essex small feature - Look-In ©1974
David Hasselhoff feature - Look-In 1991
David Hodo pin up - My Guy 1982
David Jaymes of Modern Romance small feature - Jackie 1984
David Lambert feature - Pink 1974
David Lean feature - Photoplay 1971
David Nixon feature - Look-In ©1972
David Nixon pin up - Look-In ©1971
David Soul feature - Disco 45 1978
David Soul feature - Oh Boy! 1979
David Soul illustrated pin up - Judy 1979
David Soul illustrated pin up - Judy 1980

Pin Up = 1 page pin up * Feature = ½ page article or more * Small feature = ¼ page article or less

David Sylvian feature - My Guy 1984
David Sylvian pin up - My Guy 1983
David Sylvian small feature - Blue Jeans 1983
David Van Day pin up - My Guy 1984
David Wilkie feature - Superstars 1978
Dead End Kids feature - Jackie 1978
Dean Martin feature - Radio Luxembourg Record Stars ©1965
Dean Martin pin up - Hollywood Album - Ninth
Debbie Gibson feature - Look-In 1989
Debbie Harry feature - FAB 208 1980
Debbie Harry feature - Look-In ©1980
Debbie Harry pin up - Daily Mirror Pop Club 1982
Debbie Harry pin up/fact file - Diana 1981
Debbie Harry small feature - Blue Jeans 1980
Debbie Harry small feature - Blue Jeans 1981
Debbie Harry small feature - Blue Jeans 1982
Debbie Harry small feature - Blue Jeans 1983
Deep Purple feature - Music Scene 1974
Dempsey & Makepeace quiz - Look-In 1986
Dennis Roussos feature - Daily Mirror Pop Club 1978
Dennis Waterman feature - Superstars 1978
Dennis Waterman pin up - My Guy 1983
Dennis Waterman pin-up - Photoplay 1979
Dennis Waterman small feature - Blue Jeans 1980
Depeche Mode feature - Pop Superstars 1984
Depeche Mode small feature - Look-In Pop ©1982
Deryck Guyler pin up - Look-In ©1971
Detroit Spinners feature - Top Pop Scene 1975
Dewey Martin feature - Hollywood Album - Ninth
Dexy's Midnight Runners feature - Pop Superstars 1984
Dexys Midnight Runners pin-up - Top of the Pops 1982
Dianne Foster feature - Hollywood Album - Twelfth ©1958
Dick Emery feature - Look-In TV Comedy ©1974
Dick Powell feature - Hollywood Album - Ninth
Dick Turpin comic strip - Look-In 1986
Dick Turpin endpaper - Look-In ©1979
Dickie Valentine pin up - Crackerjack ©1962
Dillinger movie - Photoplay 1975
Dire Straits feature - Daily Mirror Pop Club 1982
Dixon of Dock Green - TV Crimebusters ©1962
Doctor at Sea comic strip - Look-In ©1974
Doctor Dolittle see Rex Harrison
Doctor Hook small feature - Jackie 1981
Doctor in the House/At Large feature - Look-In ©1972
Doctor on the Go comic strip - Look-In ©1975
Doctor on the Go comic strip - Look-In ©1976
Doctor on the Go comic strip - Look-In ©1977
Doctor on the Go comic strip - Look-In TV Comedy ©1975
Doctor Who feature - Blue Peter Eighteenth ©1981
Dollar 2pg feature - Daily Mirror Book for Boys and Girls 1981
Dollar feature - Diana 1983
Dollar pin up - Girl 1982
Dollar pin-up - Pink 1980
Dollar small feature - Blue Jeans 1983
Dolores Hart pin up - Hollywood Album - Twelfth ©1958
Don Mclean feature - Daily Mirror Pop Club 1982
Donald Swan pin-up - TV Mirror 1956
Donna Percy pin up - Hollywood Album - Ninth
Donna Summer feature - Cheggers 1980
Donna Summer feature - Disco 81 1981
Donna Summer pin up - Look-In ©1978
Donny & Marie Osmond pin up - Mates 1977
Donny Osmond feature - Blue Jeans 1993

Donny Osmond feature - FAB 208 1975
Donny Osmond feature - FAB 208 1976
Donny Osmond feature - Mates 1978
Donny Osmond feature - Mirabelle Sunshine Pop Book 1975
Donny Osmond feature - Music Star 1974
Donny Osmond pin up - Mates 1978
Donny Osmond pin up - Mirabelle Sunshine Pop Book 1975
Donny Osmond pin-up - Pink 1974
Donny Osmond pin-up - Popswop ©1973
Donny Osmond pin-up - Top of the Pops 1975
Donny Osmond pin-up - Top of the Pops 1977
Donny Osmond pin-up - Valentine 1974
Donovan Leitch feature - Boyfriend 1971
Donovan pin-up - Boyfriend 1968
Donovan pin-up - Fab 208 1969
Donovan pin-up - Tony Blackburn Pop Special 3
Doobie Brothers feature - Pop Group 1978
Dorothy Malone pin up - Hollywood Album - Twelfth ©1958
Dr Who (Jon Pertwee) comic strip - TV Action 1974
Dr Who (Jon Pertwee) photo cover - TV Action 1974
Dr. Hook feature - Pop Group 1978
Dracula movie - Photoplay 1980
Droopy comic strip - TV Action 1974
Dukes of Hazzard feature - TV Favourites 1985
Duran Duran - 4 page feature - Blue Jeans 1987
Duran Duran feature - Girl 1984
Duran Duran feature - My Guy 1984
Duran Duran feature - Pop Superstars 1984
Duran Duran feature - Pop Superstars 1985
Duran Duran feature - Radio 1984
Duran Duran feature - Video Superstars 1985
Duran Duran Poster - Barbie 1985
Duran Duran Poster - Barbie 1986
Dustin Hoffman feature - Photoplay 1973
Dustin Hoffman feature - Superstars 1978
Dustin Hoffman feature/pin-up - Photoplay 1971
Dusty Springfield feature - Radio Luxembourg Record Stars ©1965
Dynasty feature - TV Favourites 1985
Eagles feature - Disco 45 1977
Eamonn Andrews pin-up - TV Mirror 1956
Earth Wind & Fire feature - Daily Mirror Pop Club 1982
Eastenders feature - Blue Jeans 1987
Echo & the Bunnymen pin up - Girl 1987
Ed Stewart feature - Look-In ©1974
Ed Stewart pin up - Look-In ©1972
Eddie and the Hot Rods feature - Superstars 1979
Eddie Kidd small feature - Jackie 1981
Edmund Purdom pin up and feature - Hollywood Album - Ninth
Edwyn Collins of Orange Juice small feature - Jackie 1984
Electric Light Orchestra feature - Girl Talk 1978
Elizabeth Taylor feature - Film and Television Parade 1950's
Elizabeth Taylor pin-up - Photoplay 1973
Elliott Gould pin-up - Photoplay 1980
ELO feature - Daily Mirror Pop Club 1978
ELO feature - Pop Group 1977
ELO feature - Pop Group 1978
ELO pin-up - Top of the Pops 1977
Elton John feature - Boyfriend 1973
Elton John feature - Cheggers 1980
Elton John feature - Daily Mirror Pop Club 1982

Pin Up = 1 page pin up * Feature = ½ page article or more * Small feature = ¼ page article or less

Elton John feature - Disco 45 1978
Elton John feature - FAB 208 1976
Elton John feature - Jackie 1975
Elton John feature - Music Scene 1974
Elton John feature - Pink 1978
Elton John feature - Top of the Pops 1976
Elton John feature - Video Superstars 1985
Elton John feature/pin-up - Popswop ©1973
Elton John feature/pin-up - Record Mirror & Disc 1977
Elton John pin up - Judy 1980
Elton John pin up - Music Scene 1974
Elton John pin-up - Pink 1974
Elton John pin-up - Top of the Pops 1974
Elton John pin-up - Top of the Pops 1977
Elton John pin-up - Top of the Pops 1982
Elvis Presley comic strip - Look-In Pop ©1982
Elvis Presley cover - Top Pop Stars 1963
Elvis Presley feature - FAB 208 1976
Elvis Presley feature - FAB 208 1980
Elvis Presley feature - Look-In ©1979
Elvis Presley feature - My Guy 1983
Elvis Presley feature - Radio Luxembourg Record Stars ©1965
Elvis Presley feature - Top of the Pops 1974
Elvis Presley feature/illustration - Diana 1982
Elvis Presley pin up - Crackerjack ©1962
Elvis Presley pin up - Oh Boy! 1980
Emanuels feature - Sindy ©1984
Emerson Lake & Palmer feature - Music Scene 1974
EMF feature - Top of the Pops 1992
Emilio Estevez small feature - Blue Jeans 1988
Emperor Rosko feature - Boyfriend 1971
Eric Clapton feature - Boyfriend 1971
Eric Clapton pin up - Music Scene 1974
Eric Flynn pin up - Look-In ©1971
Eric Robinson pin-up - TV Mirror 1956
Erik Estrada pin up - My Guy 1981
Erik Estrada small feature - Jackie 1981
Errol Flynn small feature - Jackie 1991
Eruption feature - Disco 81 1981
Eurthymics feature - Daily Mirror Pop Club 1982
Eurthymics pin up - Girl 1988
Eurythmics feature - Pop Superstars 1984
Eurythmics feature - Pop Superstars 1985
Eurythmics feature - Video Superstars 1985
Eve Boswell pin-up - TV Mirror 1956
Everly Brothers feature - Boyfriend 1973
Faces pin-up - Popswop ©1973
Fall Guy comic strip - Look-In 1987
Fall Guy feature - Look-In ©1982
Fall Guy feature - TV Favourites 1985
Fame - see Gene Antony Ray
Fame feature - TV Favourites 1985
Family Dogg feature - Boyfriend 1971
Famous Five endpaper - Look-In ©1979
Famous Five feature - Look-In ©1978
Famous Five feature - Look-In ©1979
Farrah Fawcett-Majors feature - Superstars 1979
Father Dear Father feature - Look-In TV Comedy ©1974
Faye Dunaway pin-up - Photoplay 1971
Faye Dunaway pin-up - Photoplay 1974
Feargal Sharkey small feature - Blue Jeans 1982
Fenn Street Gang comic strip - Look-In ©1972
Fenn Street Gang photo story - Look-In ©1973
Fergal Sharkey pin up - Girl 1987

Fireball XL5 4pg bw feature with rare behind the scenes pictures - ITV Annual for Boys and Girls 1964
Five Star feature - Sindy 1988
Five Star small feature - Blue Jeans 1988
Fleetwood Mac feature - Superstars 1979
Flintlock endpaper - Look-In ©1976
Flintlock feature - Jackie 1978
Flintlock feature - Look-In ©1976
Flintlock feature - Look-In ©1977
Flintlock feature/pin-up - Pink 1978
Flintlock pin up - Look-In ©1977
Flintlock pin up - Mates 1978
Follyfoot comic strip - Look-In ©1972
Follyfoot endpaper - Look-In ©1972
Follyfoot feature - All Stars Television Annual 1973
Fonz feature - see Happy Days
Fonz feature - Superstars 1979
Fonzie feature - FAB 208 1979
Fonzie feature - Jackie 1978
Four Just Men - TV Crimebusters ©1962
Four Tops feature - Pop Group 1978
Francis Rossi of Status Quo small feature - Jackie 1981
Frank Ifield pin up - Crackerjack ©1962
Frank Sinatra feature - Tony Blackburn Pop Special 3
Frank Sinatra small feature - Jackie 1991
Frank Zappa pin up - Boyfriend 1973
Frankie Miller feature - Cheggers 1980
Freddie Starr feature - Look-In TV Comedy ©1974
Frenzy movie - Photoplay 1973
Fun Boy 3 feature - Pop Superstars 1984
G Band pin up - Mates 1978
Gallagher & Lyle feature - Pop Group 1978
Garfield feature - Look-In 1991
Gary Davies feature - Top of the Pops 1992
Gary Glitter feature - Jackie 1975
Gary Glitter feature - Mirabelle Sunshine Pop Book 1975
Gary Glitter feature - Pink 1974
Gary Glitter feature - Top of the Pops 1976
Gary Glitter feature/pin-up - Record Mirror & Disc 1977
Gary Glitter feature/pin-up - Top of the Pops 1974
Gary Glitter pin up - Look-In ©1974
Gary Glitter pin up - Mates 1977
Gary Glitter pin up - Mirabelle Sunshine Pop Book 1975
Gary Glitter pin-up - Top of the Pops 1975
Gary Glitter small feature - Look-In ©1974
Gary Numan feature - Mates 1982
Gary Numan feature - Sindy 1984
Gary Numan pin up - My Guy 1982
Gary Numan pin up - My Guy 1983
Gary Numan pin up - My Guy 1984
Gary Numan small feature - Look-In Pop ©1982
Gary Warren small feature - Look-In ©1972
Gene Antony Ray pin up - Oh Boy! 1985
Gene Autry feature - Hollywood Album - Ninth
Gene Hackman pin-up - Photoplay 1974
Gene Pitney feature - Radio Luxembourg Record Stars ©1965
Gene Wilder feature - Superstars 1978
Genesis feature - Music Scene 1974
Genghis Khan feature - Film and Television Parade 1950's
Geoff Downes of the Buggles small feature - Jackie 1981
Geoffrey Davies pin up - Look-In ©1976
George Best feature - Boyfriend 1973
George Best feature - FAB 208 1973
George Best feature/pin-up - Fab 208 1969

147

Pin Up = 1 page pin up * Feature = ½ page article or more * Small feature = ¼ page article or less

George Best pin up - FAB 208 1973
George Harrison feature - Daily Mirror Pop Club 1978
George Harrison feature - Superstars 1979
George Michael feature - Look-In 1986
George Michael pin up - Blue Jeans 1986
George Nader pin up - Hollywood Album - Twelfth ©1958
George Segal pin-up - Photoplay 1975
Georgie Best feature - FAB 208 1972
Georgie Fame feature - Radio Luxembourg Record Stars ©1965
Georgie Fame feature - Tony Blackburn Pop Special 3
Georgie Fame pin-up - Boyfriend 1968
Gerry Anderson feature - Look-In ©1976
Gerry Anderson feature - Look-In ©1977
Gerry Sundquist pin up - My Guy 1981
Gerry Sundquist pin up - My Guy 1983
Gianni pin up - Boyfriend 1973
Gilbert Harding pin-up - TV Mirror 1956
Gilbert O'Sullivan feature - Mirabelle Sunshine Pop Book 1975
Gilbert O'Sullivan feature - Music Scene 1974
Gilbert O'Sullivan pin-up - Top of the Pops 1975
Gilbert O'Sullivan pin-up - Top of the Pops 1977
Gillian Blake pin up - Look-In ©1972
Gillian Blake pin up - Look-In ©1973
Girl from UNCLE see Stefanie Powers
Gladys Knight feature - Disco 45 1978
Glen Campbell pin-up - Photoplay 1971
Glenda Jackson pin-up - Photoplay 1973
Glenda Jackson pin-up - Photoplay 1974
Glitter Band feature - FAB 208 1976
Glitter Band feature - Top Pop Scene 1975
Glitter Band pin-up - Pop Group 1977
Gloria Estefan pin up - Eagle Yearbook 1992
Gloria Talbot pin up and feature - Hollywood Album - Ninth
Glyn E Daniel pin-up - TV Mirror 1956
Glynis Johns feature - Hollywood Album - Ninth
Go West pin up - Girl 1987
Goldie Hawn (painted Private Benjamin portrait) - Diana 1983
Goldie Hawn feature/pin-up - Photoplay 1971
Gone with the Wind feature - Diana 1985
Goodies feature - Look-In TV Comedy ©1975
Gordon Hill pin up - Look-In ©1976
Grace Kelly feature - Hollywood Album - Ninth
Grange Hill feature - Blue Peter Eighteenth ©1981
Grease feature - Cheggers 1980
Grease feature - Diana 1985
Greg Evigan pin-up - Pink 1980
Gunter Netzer pin up - Look-In ©1973
Gus Goad - My Guy 1983
Haircut 100 pin up - Look-In Pop ©1982
Hanna-Barbera feature - Look-In TV Comedy ©1974
Happy Days feature - Look-In ©1979
Happy Days feature - Oh Boy! 1979
Happy Days small feature - Look-In 1990
Hardy Boys feature - Mates 1981
Harrison Ford pin-up - Diana 1985
Harry O feature - TV Detectives ©1979
Harry Secombe feature - All Stars Television Annual 1973
Harry Secombe pin-up - TV Mirror 1956
Hart to Hart feature - TV Favourites 1985
Hart to Hart pin-up - Diana 1985
Hart to Hart small feature - Look-In ©1984
Hart to Hart small feature - Look-In 1986

Hawaii Five-O photo cover - TV Action 1974
Hawaii Five-O photo story - TV Action 1974
Hawaiian Eye - TV Crimebusters ©1962
Hawaiian Eye feature - Danger in the Deep - 8 pg Story by Alan Fennell with photos from the series - ITV Annual for Boys and Girls 1964
Hazel O'Connor feature - Daily Mirror Pop Club 1982
Heaven 17 feature - Pop Superstars 1984
Heaven 17 pin up - Girl 1988
Helen Reddy feature - Photoplay 1978
Helen Shapiro full page autographed colour photo - ITV Annual for Boys and Girls 1964
Helen Shapiro pin up - Crackerjack ©1962
Hello pin-up - Top of the Pops 1977
Henry King feature - Hollywood Album - Ninth
Henry Winkler pin up - Look-In ©1978
Herd feature/pin-up - Fab 208 1969
Hermans Hermits feature and pin up - Boyfriend 1971
Hollies feature - Pop Group 1978
Hollies feature - Teen Beat-Pop Ten ©1969
Hollies feature - Tony Blackburn Pop Special 3
Home & Away feature - Look-In 1991
Hot Chocolate feature - Disco 45 1977
Hot Chocolate feature - Pop Group 1978
Hot Chocolate feature - Top Pop Scene 1975
Hot Chocolate feature/pin-up - Record Mirror & Disc 1977
Hot Chocolate pin-up - Top of the Pops 1977
How! feature - Look-In ©1978
Howard Jones feature - Pop Superstars 1985
Howard Jones feature - Video Superstars 1985
Howard Keel feature - Hollywood Album - Ninth
Human League feature - Pop Superstars 1984
Human League feature - Radio 1984
Human League pin up - Eagle Yearbook 1992
Human League pin up - Look-In Pop ©1982
Humphrey Bogart small feature - Jackie 1981
Hywel Bennett feature - Photoplay 1973
Hywell Bennett pin-up - Fab 208 1969
I Dream of Jeannie small feature - Look-In 1990
Ian Drury pin up/fact file - Diana 1981
Ian Dury pin-up - Top of the Pops 1982
Ian McShane pin-up - Photoplay 1980
Ian Mitchell Band pin up - Mates 1981
Ian Mitchell pin up - My Guy 1981
Ian Ogilvy feature - Look-In ©1978
Ian Ogilvy pin up - Look-In ©1978
Icehouse feature - Pop Superstars 1984
Iggy Pop feature - Superstars 1979
Interpol Calling - TV Crimebusters ©1962
INXS pin up - Girl 1988
Jack Hargreaves feature - Look-In ©1972
Jack Hargreaves feature - Look-In ©1973
Jack Jones feature - Superstars 1979
Jack Lemmon feature - Hollywood Album - Ninth
Jack Lemmon feature/pin-up - Photoplay 1971
Jack Nicholson feature - Superstars 1978
Jack Palance pin up and feature - Hollywood Album - Ninth
Jack Warner pin-up - TV Mirror 1956
Jack Wild feature - All Stars Television Annual 1973
Jack Wild feature - FAB 208 1972
Jack Wild pin up - FAB 208 1973
Jack Wild pin-up - Valentine 1974
Jack Wild small feature - Look-In ©1972
Jackson 5 pin-up - Pop Group 1977

Jackson Five pin-up - Valentine 1974
Jacksons feature - Pink 1974
Jacksons feature - Top of the Pops 1974
Jacksons pin up - Mates 1979
Jacksons pin up - Mates 1980
Jacqueline Bisset pin-up - Photoplay 1974
Jacqueline Bisset pin-up - Photoplay 1980
Jakki Brambles feature - Top of the Pops 1992
Jam feature - Pink 1979
Jam feature - Supersonics 1979
Jam feature - Top of the Pops 1982
Jam pin up - Mates 1982
James Arness pin up and feature - Hollywood Album - Twelfth ©1958
James Bond feature - Look-In ©1977
James Cann feature/pin-up - Photoplay 1976
James Cann pin-up - Photoplay 1974
James Coburn feature - Star TV & Film 1968
James Coburn pin-up - Photoplay 1971
James Coburn pin-up - Photoplay 1975
James Dean small feature - Jackie 1991
James Stacy pin up - FAB 208 1973
Jane Asher small photo - Fab 208 1969
Jane Fonda 'Barbarella' illustration/fact file - Diana 1983
Jane Fonda feature - Photoplay 1974
Jane Fonda feature - Photoplay 1979
Jane Fonda pin-up - Photoplay 1978
Jane Powell feature - Hollywood Album - Ninth
Jane Russell feature - Hollywood Album - Ninth
Jane Seymour cover/feature - Photoplay 1974
Janet Jackson pin up - Girl 1988
Janet Jackson pin-up - Top of the Pops 1992
Jan-Michael Vincent feature - Look-In 1986
Jan-Michael Vincent feature/pin-up - Photoplay 1974
Jason Connery feature - Look-In 1987
Jason Donovan feature - Look-In 1990
Jason Donovan feature - Top of the Pops 1992
Jason Donovan pin up - Jackie 1991
Jason Donovan small feature - Blue Jeans 1993
Jason Priestly pin-up - Jackie 1993
Jaws feature - Diana 1985
Jay Morley Jr feature - Hollywood Album - Ninth
Jean Jacques Burnel pin up - My Guy 1982
Jean Wallace pin up - Hollywood Album - Twelfth ©1958
Jeanne Crain pin up and feature - Hollywood Album - Twelfth ©1958
Jeff Chandler feature - Hollywood Album - Ninth
Jeff Chandler pin up - Hollywood Album - Twelfth ©1958
Jeff Phillips pin up - Mates 1979
Jeff Richards pin up and feature - Hollywood Album - Ninth
Jennie McKeown of the Belle Stars small feature - Jackie 1984
Jennifer Capriati feature - Look-In 1991
Jenny Agutter feature - Photoplay 1978
Jermaine Jackson pin up - My Guy 1983
Jermaine Stewart pin up - Girl 1988
Jerry Lee Lewis feature - Radio Luxembourg Record Stars ©1965
Jerry Lewis pin up - Hollywood Album - Ninth
Jerry Shirley pin-up - Pink 1974
Jessica Lange feature - Photoplay 1978
Jesus of Nazareth endpaper - Look-In ©1977
Jethro Tull feature - Pop Group 1978
Jethro Tull pin up - Boyfriend 1973

Jets feature - Look-In 1988
Jill St. John pin-up - Photoplay 1973
Jim Capaldi pin-up - Top of the Pops 1977
Jim Kerr of Simple Minds small feature - Jackie 1984
Jim McInven pin up - My Guy 1984
Jim Morrison feature - Boyfriend 1971
Jim Reeves feature - Radio Luxembourg Record Stars ©1965
Jim Stafford feature - Top Pop Scene 1975
Jimmy Baio pin up - My Guy 1982
Jimmy Connors feature - Superstars 1978
Jimmy Cricket feature - Look-In 1988
Jimmy Osmond pin up - Mirabelle Sunshine Pop Book 1975
Jimmy Pursey pin up - Look-In ©1980
Jimmy Pursey small feature - Blue Jeans 1981
Jimmy Pursey small feature - Blue Jeans 1982
Jimmy Savile feature - Radio Luxembourg Record Stars ©1965
Jimmy Saville feature - Star TV & Film 1968
Jimmy Tarbuck feature - Look-In TV Comedy ©1974
Jo Ann Pflug pin-up - Photoplay 1973
Joan Armatrading feature - Daily Mirror Pop Club 1982
Joan Armatrading feature - Superstars 1978
Joan Collins pin up and feature - Hollywood Album - Twelfth ©1958
Joan Regan pin-up - TV Mirror 1956
Joanna Lumley feature - Look-In ©1979
Joanne Conway feature - Look-In 1988
Joanne Woodward feature - Hollywood Album - Twelfth ©1958
Joanne Woodward pin up - Hollywood Album - Twelfth ©1958
Joe Brown full page autographed colour photo - ITV Annual for Boys and Girls 1964
Joe Dolan pin up - Boyfriend 1971
Joe Jackson pin up - My Guy 1982
Joe Jackson small feature - Jackie 1984
Joey Tempest fact file - Jackie 1988
Joey Travolta pin up - Pink 1980
John Alderton pin up - Look-In ©1971
John Curry feature - Superstars 1979
John Lennon feature - Record Mirror & Disc 1977
John Lloyd pin up - Mates 1979
John Miles pin up - Disco 45 1977
John Peel feature - Daily Mirror Pop Club 1982
John Saxon pin up - Hollywood Album - Twelfth ©1958
John Thaw pin-up - Photoplay 1979
John Travolta feature - Disco 81 1981
John Travolta feature - FAB 208 1979
John Travolta feature - FAB 208 1979
John Travolta feature - Look-In ©1979
John Travolta feature - Mates 1980
John Travolta feature - Photoplay 1979
John Travolta illustrated pin up - Judy 1981
John Travolta pin up - Mates 1980
John Travolta pin-up - Photoplay 1980
John Travolta small feature - Blue Jeans 1980
John Wayne feature - Photoplay 1971
John Wayne feature - Photoplay 1973
John Wayne feature/pin-up - Photoplay 1974
Johnathan King feature - Disco 45 1977
Johnny Bristol feature - Top Pop Scene 1975
Johnny Cougar pin up - My Guy 1981
Johnny Depp feature - Blue Jeans 1993

Johnny Depp feature - Jackie 1991
Johnny Fingers small feature - Blue Jeans 1980
Johnny Logan pin up - My Guy 1982
Johnny Logan pin-up - Pink 1982
Johnny Morris feature - Star TV & Film 1968
Johnny Nash pin up - Boyfriend 1974
Johnny Rotten feature - Supersonics 1979
Jon Voight feature - Photoplay 1971
Josephine Douglas pin-up - TV Mirror 1956
Judas Priest pin up - Daily Mirror Pop Club 1982
Judy Geeson small photo - Fab 208 1969
Julia Roberts feature - Blue Jeans 1993
Julian Cope pin up - My Guy 1984
Julie Andrews feature - Star TV & Film 1968
Julie Andrews feature/pin-up - Photoplay 1971
Julie Andrews feature/pin-up - Photoplay 1975
Julie Covington feature - Cheggers 1980
Julie Covington small feature - Blue Jeans 1980
Julie Felix feature - Star TV & Film 1968
June Christie pin up - Crackerjack ©1962
June Croft small feature - Look-In ©1983
Junior pin up - My Guy 1984
Junior Showtime endpaper - Look-In ©1972
Just William feature - Look-In ©1977
Kajagoogoo feature - Pop Superstars 1985
Kajagoogoo feature - Video Superstars 1985
Kajagoogoo pin up - Girl 1987
Kate Bush feature - FAB 208 1980
Kate Bush pin up - Daily Mirror Pop Club 1982
Kate Bush small feature - Blue Jeans 1980
Kate Garner of Haysi Fantaysee small feature - Jackie 1984
Katie Boyle pin-up - TV Mirror 1956
Kay Kendall pin up and feature - Hollywood Album - Twelfth ©1958
KC and the Sunshine Band pin-up - Pop Group 1977
Keanu Reeves star file - Jackie 1993
Keith Chegwin pin up - Mates 1979
Keith Chegwin small feature - Jackie 1981
Keith Michell feature - Photoplay 1973
Kelly Marie feature - Daily Mirror Pop Club 1982
Ken Goodwin comic strip - Look-In ©1973
Kenneth Horne pin-up - TV Mirror 1956
Kenny Ball pin up - Crackerjack ©1962
Kenny Dalglish pin up - Look-In ©1978
Kenny Everett feature - FAB 208 1972
Kenny Everett feature - Look-In ©1980
Kenny feature - FAB 208 1976
Kenny pin up - Mates 1977
Kenny pin up - Mates 1978
Kenny pin-up - Pop Group 1977
Kenny pin-up - Record Mirror & Disc 1977
Kermit the Frog pin up - Look-In ©1977
Kermit the Frog small feature - Jackie 1981
Kevin Costner pin up - Blue Jeans 1993
Kevin Keegan pin up - Look-In ©1973
Kevin Keegan pin up - Look-In ©1976
Kevin Keegan pin up - Look-In ©1979
Kevin Rowland of Dexy's Midnight Runners small feature - Jackie 1984
Kevin Rowland pin up - My Guy 1984
Kid Jensen feature - Diana 1981
Kid Jensen feature - FAB 208 1972
Kid Jensen small feature - Jackie 1981
Kim Appleby pin-up - Top of the Pops 1992

Kim Novak pin up - Hollywood Album - Twelfth ©1958
Kim Novak pin up and feature - Hollywood Album - Ninth
Kim Wilde feature - Jackie 1986
Kim Wilde pin up - Diana 1986
Kim Wilde pin up - Look-In Pop ©1982
Kim Wilde small feature - Blue Jeans 1983
Kim Wilde small feature - Blue Jeans 1990
King pin up - Girl 1987
Kirk Douglas pin-up - Photoplay 1976
Kiss feature - Daily Mirror Pop Club 1982
Knight Rider comic strip - Look-In 1989
Knight Rider endpaper - Look-In 1986
Knight Rider feature - TV Favourites 1985
Kojak feature - TV Detectives ©1979
Kraftwerk small feature - Look-In Pop ©1982
Kris Kristofferson feature - Photoplay 1978
Kris Kristofferson pin-up - Photoplay 1979
Kung Fu comic strip - Look-In ©1974
Kung Fu feature - Look-In ©1974
Kurt Russel feature - Supersonics 1979
Kylie Minogue feature - Jackie 1991
Kylie Minogue feature - Look-In 1990
Kylie Minogue feature - Top of the Pops 1992
Kylie Minogue pin up - Bunty 1990
Kylie Minogue small feature - Blue Jeans 1990
Lady Caroline Lamb movie - Photoplay 1973
Last Valley movie feature - Photoplay 1971
Led Zeppelin feature - Music Scene 1974
Led Zeppelin feature - Pop Club 1979
Lee Curreri pin up - Oh Boy! 1985
Lee Jones pin up - My Guy 1984
Lee Majors feature - Look-In ©1976
Lee Majors feature - Look-In ©1978
Lee Majors feature - Look-In ©1982
Lee Majors feature - TV Detectives ©1979
Lee Majors pin up - Look-In ©1976
Lee Majors pin up - Look-In ©1977
Lee Majors pin up - Look-In ©1978
Lee Marvin feature - Photoplay 1971
Lee Marvin pin-up - Photoplay 1976
Lee Marvin pin-up - Photoplay 1978
Lee Remick pin up - Hollywood Album - Twelfth ©1958
Leif Garrett feature - FAB 208 1980
Leif Garrett pin up - Mates 1980
Leif Garrett pin up - Mates 1981
Leif Garrett pin up - My Guy 1982
Leif Garrett pin up - Oh Boy! 1980
Leif Garrett pin-up - Pink 1980
Lemmy of Motorhead small feature - Jackie 1981
Lena Zavaroni small feature - Blue Jeans 1980
Lene Lovich small feature - Blue Jeans 1982
Leo Sayer feature - Cheggers 1980
Leo Sayer feature - Daily Mirror Pop Club 1978
Leo Sayer feature - Disco 45 1978
Leo Sayer feature - FAB 208 1976
Leo Sayer feature - Girl Talk 1978
Leo Sayer feature - Superstars 1979
Leo Sayer feature/pin-up - Pink 1979
Leo Sayer pin up - Daily Mirror Pop Club 1982
Leo Sayer pin up - My Guy 1981
Leo Sayer pin-up - Pink 1980
Leo Sayer pin-up - Record Mirror & Disc 1977
Leo Sayer pin-up - Top of the Pops 1977
Les Dawson comic strip - Look-In ©1973
Les Dawson feature - Look-In TV Comedy ©1974

Pin Up = 1 page pin up * Feature = ½ page article or more * Small feature = ¼ page article or less

Les Dawson feature - Look-In TV Comedy ©1975
Les Nemes pin up - My Guy 1984
Lesley Anne Down feature - Photoplay 1978
Lesley Anne Down pin-up - Photoplay 1974
Lesley Ash cover - Pink 1980
Lesley Ash cover photo - Mates 1980
Leslie Ash cover - Blue Jeans 1980
Leslie Crowther comic strip - Look-In ©1972
Leslie Crowther feature/comic strip - Look-In ©1971
Leslie Mitchell pin-up - TV Mirror 1956
Leslie Neilsen feature - Hollywood Album - Twelfth ©1958
Level 42 pin up - Girl 1987
Lewis Collins feature/pin up - Diana 1982
Lewis Collins pin up - My Guy 1981
Lewis Collins small feature - Blue Jeans 1980
Lewis Collins small feature - Jackie 1981
Limahl factfile - Barbie 1986
Limahl feature - Pop Superstars 1985
Limahl pin up - Barbie 1985
Limahl pin up - Girl 1988
Linda Ronstadt feature - Superstars 1979
Lindsay Wagner feature - Look-In ©1978
Lindsay Wagner feature - TV Detectives ©1979
Lindsay Wagner pin up - Look-In ©1977
Lindsay Wagner pin up - Look-In ©1978
Lisa Marie Presley small feature - Blue Jeans 1990
Little and Large feature - Look-In ©1977
Liv Ullmann feature - Photoplay 1974
Liza Minnelli feature - Photoplay 1973
Liza Minnelli pin-up - Photoplay 1978
Lloyd Cole and the Commotions pin up - Barbie 1987
Lloyd Nolan feature - Hollywood Album - Twelfth ©1958
Logan's Run pin up - Look-In ©1978
Lol Crème pin up - Disco 45 1977
London Palladium feature - Judy 1979
Lone Ranger small feature - Look-In 1990
Long Duel movie - see Yul Brynner
Lonnie Donegan pin up - Crackerjack ©1962
Lotus Eaters feature - Pop Superstars 1985
Louis Alphonso small feature - Blue Jeans 1983
Louis Armstrong feature - Radio Luxembourg Record Stars ©1965
Lucille Ball feature/pin-up - Photoplay 1975
Lulu feature - Boyfriend 1973
Lulu feature - Top Pop Stars 1967
Lulu pin up - Boyfriend 1971
Lulu small photo - Fab 208 1969
Lynda Day George - see Mission Impossible
Lynne Frederick feature - Photoplay 1978
Lynsey de Paul feature - Mirabelle Sunshine Pop Book 1975
Lynsey de Paul pin up - Mirabelle Sunshine Pop Book 1975
Mac and Katie Kissoon pin-up - Top of the Pops 1977
Madness feature - Pop Superstars 1985
Madness feature - Radio 1984
Madness feature - Video Superstars 1985
Madness feature and pin up - Girl 1984
Madness pin up - Daily Mirror Pop Club 1982
Madness pin up - Diana 1983
Madness pin up - Girl 1987
Madonna feature - Look-In 1987
Madonna feature - Top of the Pops 1992
Madonna pin up - Eagle Yearbook 1992
Madonna pin up - Girl 1987

Madonna pin up- Jackie 1989
Maggie Bell feature - Top Pop Scene 1975
Maggie Bell pin up - Music Scene 1974
Magnum feature - TV Favourites 1985
Magpie feature - All Stars Television Annual 1973
Magpie feature - Look-In ©1971
Magpie feature - Look-In ©1976
Malcolm McLaren feature - Pop Superstars 1984
Mama Cass - pin up - Boyfriend 1971
Mame movie - Photoplay 1975
Mamie Van Doren pin up - Hollywood Album - Ninth
Man About The House comic strip - Look-In ©1976
Man About The House feature - Look-In ©1974
Manfred Mann feature - Radio Luxembourg Record Stars ©1965
Manfred Mann feature - Teen Beat-Pop Ten ©1969
Manfred Mann's Earth Band feature - Pop Superstars 1984
Manhattan Transfer pin up - Diana 1981
Marc Bolan feature - Boyfriend 1971
Marc Bolan feature - Boyfriend 1974
Marc Bolan feature - FAB 208 1973
Marc Bolan feature - Mirabelle Sunshine Pop Book 1975
Marc Bolan feature - Music Scene 1974
Marc Bolan feature/pin-up - Popswop ©1973
Marc Bolan feature/pin-up - Record Mirror & Disc 1977
Marc Bolan feature/pin-up - Top of the Pops 1974
Marc Bolan pin up - Mirabelle Sunshine Pop Book 1975
Marc Bolan pin up - Music Scene 1974
Marc Bolan pin up - Oh Boy! 1980
Mari Wilson small feature - Jackie 1984
Marie feature - FAB 208 1980
Marie Osmond feature - Popswop ©1973
Marie Osmond small feature - Jackie 1981
Marillion pin up - Girl 1987
Marilyn Monroe pin-up - Photoplay 1971
Mark Almond of Soft Cell small feature - Jackie 1984
Mark Goodier feature - Top of the Pops 1992
Mark Hamill pin up - Look-In ©1978
Mark Lester feature - Look-In ©1972
Marlon Brando small feature - Jackie 1991
Marmalade feature - Tony Blackburn Pop Special 3
Marmalade pin up - Boyfriend 1971
Marthe Keller feature - Photoplay 1978
Marti Pellow pin up - Jackie 1991
Martin Kemp pin-up - Photo Love 1985
Martin Kemp small feature - Blue Jeans 1983
Martin Kemp small feature - Jackie 1983
Martin Sheen feature - Photoplay 1978
Marty Kristian feature - Mirabelle Sunshine Pop Book 1975
Marty Kristian pin up - Mirabelle Sunshine Pop Book 1975
Marty Kristian pin-up - Popswop ©1973
Marty Kristian pin-up - Valentine 1974
Marvin Gaye feature - Top Pop Scene 1975
Mary Tamm small feature - Blue Jeans 1980
Matt Dillon pin up - Jackie 1991
Matt Dillon pin up - Blue Jeans 1993
Matt Dillon small feature - Blue Jeans 1988
Matthew Kelly small feature - Look-In ©1983
Maureen O'Hara pin up and feature - Hollywood Album - Twelfth ©1958
Maurice Gibb feature - Boyfriend 1971
May Wynn pin up and feature - Hollywood Album - Ninth
MC Hammer feature/pin-up - Top of the Pops 1992
McCloud feature - TV Detectives ©1979

Pin Up = 1 page pin up * Feature = ½ page article or more * Small feature = ¼ page article or less

McMillan & Wife feature - TV Detectives ©1979
Mel & Kim feature - Look-In 1988
Men at Work feature - Pop Superstars 1984
Men at Work pin up - Oh Boy! 1985
Merrill Osmond feature - Mirabelle Sunshine Pop Book 1975
Mervyn Day pin up - Look-In ©1975
Metal Mickey feature - Look-In ©1981
Meteor movie - Photoplay 1980
Michael Bentine feature - Star TV & Film 1968
Michael Bentine's Potty Time comic strip - Look-In ©1974
Michael Caine feature - Photoplay 1978
Michael Caine feature - Photoplay 1980
Michael Caine pin-up - Boyfriend 1968
Michael Caine pin-up - Photoplay 1973
Michael Caine pin-up - Photoplay 1974
Michael Caine pin-up - Photoplay 1978
Michael Crawford feature - FAB 208 1976
Michael Crawford feature - Look-In TV Comedy ©1974
Michael Crawford pin-up - Boyfriend 1968
Michael Holoway pin up - Look-In ©1976
Michael J Fox fact file - Jackie 1988
Michael J Fox feature - Look-In 1987
Michael J Fox feature - Look-In 1991
Michael J Fox feature - Sindy 1988
Michael J Fox pin up- Jackie 1988
Michael J Fox small feature - Blue Jeans 1988
Michael Jackson feature - Look-In 1990
Michael Jackson feature - Mates 1982
Michael Jackson feature - Music Star 1974
Michael Jackson feature - Music Star 1975
Michael Jackson feature - Pop Superstars 1984
Michael Jackson feature - Pop Superstars 1985
Michael Jackson feature - Supersonics 1979
Michael Jackson feature - TV Favourites 1985
Michael Jackson feature - Video Superstars 1985
Michael Jackson feature/pin-up - Valentine 1974
Michael Jackson pin up - Mirabelle Sunshine Pop Book 1975
Michael Jackson pin-up - Pink 1974
Michael Jackson pin-up - Popswop ©1973
Michael Jackson small feature - Jackie 1984
Michael Kidd feature - Hollywood Album - Ninth
Michael Mullins of Modern Romance small feature - Jackie 1984
Michael Praed - see Robin of Sherwood
Michael York pin-up - Fab 208 1969
Michaela Strachan feature - Look-In 1991
Michaela Strachen pin up - Eagle Yearbook 1992
Mick Bass pin up - My Guy 1983
Mick Channon pin up - Look-In ©1974
Mick Jagger feature - Daily Mirror Pop Club 1978
Mick Jagger feature - FAB 208 1972
Mick Jagger small feature/pin-up - Boyfriend 1968
Mick Robertson - illustrated pin up - Look-In ©1975
Mick Robertson - pin up - Look-In ©1974
Mickey Mouse feature - Look-In ©1978
Mickey Rooney feature - Hollywood Album - Twelfth ©1958
Midge Ure pin up - Girl 1987
Midge Ure pin up - My Guy 1983
Mike & Bernie Winters feature - Look-In TV Comedy ©1974
Mike Batt pin-up - Record Mirror & Disc 1977
Mike D'Abo small feature - Boyfriend 1968

Mike Holoway pin up - My Guy 1983
Mike Nolan pin-up - Photo Love 1985
Mike Oldfield feature - Top of the Pops 1982
Mike Read small feature - Blue Jeans 1983
Mike Reid endpaper - Look-In ©1976
Mike Reid feature - Look-In TV Comedy ©1975
Mike Yarwood - illustrated pin up - Judy 1979
Mindbenders pin-up - Boyfriend 1968
Miss Piggy pin up - Look-In ©1977
Miss Piggy small feature - Jackie 1981
Mission Impossible photo story - TV Action 1974
Mitzi Gaynor pin up - Hollywood Album - Twelfth ©1958
Mona Freeman pin up - Hollywood Album - Ninth
Monie Love pin-up - Top of the Pops 1992
Monkees feature - Boyfriend 1968
Monkees feature - Fab 208 1969
Monkees feature - Star TV & Film 1968
Monkees feature - Teen Beat-Pop Ten1 968
Monkees feature - Tony Blackburn Pop Special 3
Monkees small feature - Look-In 1990
Montgomery Clift small feature - Jackie 1991
Moody Blues feature - Boyfriend 1971
Moody Blues feature - Music Scene 1974
Moody Blues feature - Top Pop Stars 1965
Moonraker movie - Photoplay 1980
Morecambe & Wise cover/feature - Star TV & Film 1968
Morecambe & Wise feature - Look-In TV Comedy ©1974
Mork & Mindy feature - Look-In ©1980
Mork & Mindy pin up - Look-In ©1980
Mork & Mindy small feature - Look-In 1990
Morph feature - Blue Peter Nineteenth Book ©1982
Morten Harket pin-up - Blue Jeans 1988
Mott the Hoople pin-up - Pop Group 1977
Mott the Hoople pin-up - Record Mirror & Disc 1977
Mr Ackerbilk pin up - Crackerjack ©1962
Mr Ed small feature - Look-In 1990
Mr Mister pin up - Girl 1988
Mr T feature - Look-In 1986
Mr T feature - TV Favourites 1985
Mud feature - FAB 208 1976
Mud feature - Music Star 1976
Mud feature - Pink 1978
Mud feature - Pop Group 1978
Mud feature and pin up - Disco 45 1977
Mud feature/pin-up - Pink 1979
Mud feature/pin-up - Pop Group 1977
Mud feature/pin-up - Record Mirror & Disc 1977
Mud pin up - Mates 1977
Mud pin up - Mirabelle Sunshine Pop Book 1975
Mud pin-up - Top of the Pops 1975
Mud pin-up - Top of the Pops 1977
Munsters small feature - Look-In 1990
Muppet Show endpaper - Look-In ©1978
Muppet Show feature - Superstars 1979
Muppets feature - Look-In ©1977
Muppets feature - Look-In ©1980
Muriel Young feature - Radio Luxembourg Record Stars ©1965
Musical Youth pin up - Barbie 1985
Musical Youth small feature - Jackie 1984
Nancy Sinatra feature - Star TV & Film 1968
Nancy Sinatra feature - Tony Blackburn Pop Special 3
Nashville Teens small feature - Boyfriend 1968
Nazareth pin-up - Top of the Pops 1975
Neil Diamond bw pin up - Boyfriend 1973

Pin Up = 1 page pin up * Feature = ½ page article or more * Small feature = ¼ page article or less

Neil Diamond feature - Daily Mirror Pop Club 1982
Neil Diamond feature - Superstars 1979
Neil Rooney pin up - My Guy 1983
Neil Sedaka feature - Top Pop Scene 1975
New Avengers feature - TV Detectives ©1979
New Hearts pin up - Mates 1980
New Kids on the Block feature - Look-In 1991
New Kids on the Block feature - Top of the Pops 1992
New Kids on the Block pin up - Jackie 1991
New Kids on the Block pin up - Jackie 1992
New Seekers feature/pin-up - Popswop ©1973
New Seekers pin-up - Pink 1974
New World pin up - FAB 208 1973
News at Ten feature - Look-In ©1973
Nicholas Hammond feature - Look-In ©1982
Nick Beggs of Kajagoogoo small feature - Jackie 1984
Nick Berry feature - Sindy 1988
Nick Berry pin up- Jackie 1988
Nick Berry pin-up - Blue Jeans 1988
Nick Heyward feature - Oh Boy! 1985
Nick Heyward feature - Pop Superstars 1984
Nick Heyward feature - Pop Superstars 1985
Nick Heyward feature and star file - Jackie 1986
Nick Heyward pin up - Girl 1987
Nick Heyward pin up - My Guy 1984
Nick Heyward small feature - Jackie 1984
Nick Kamen pin up - Girl 1988
Nick Nolte feature - Superstars 1979
Nick Nolte feature/pin-up - Photoplay 1978
Nick Rhodes pin up - Oh Boy! 1985
Nick Van Eede pin up - Mates 1981
Nicky Campbell feature - Top of the Pops 1992
Nik Kershaw feature - Look-In 1986
Nik Kershaw feature - Pop Superstars 1985
Nik Kershaw pin up - Girl 1987
Niki Lauda feature - Superstars 1979
Nikki Richards pin up - My Guy 1981
Noddy Holder feature - Mirabelle Sunshine Pop Book 1975
Noddy Holder feature - Music Star 1974
Noddy Holder pin-up - Pink 1974
Noel Edmonds feature - Daily Mirror Pop Club 1978
Noel Edmonds feature - FAB 208 1972
Noel Edmonds illustrated pin up - Judy 1983
Noel Edmonds pin up - Boyfriend 1973
Noel Edmonds small feature - Jackie 1981
Nolan Sisters small feature - Jackie 1981
Norman Wisdom feature - Look-In TV Comedy ©1975
O M D feature - Pop Superstars 1984
O'Jays pin-up - Pop Group 1977
Oliver Reed feature - Photoplay 1976
Oliver Reed pin-up - Photoplay 1974
Oliver Reed pin-up - Photoplay 1979
Oliver Tobias pin up - My Guy 1981
Oliver Tobias pin-up - Photoplay 1980
Olivia Dehavilland feature - Hollywood Album - Ninth
Olivia Newton John feature - Daily Mirror Pop Club 1982
Olivia Newton John feature - FAB 208 1980
Olivia Newton John feature - Girl 1984
Olivia Newton John feature - Mates 1982
Olivia Newton John feature - Top of the Pops 1975
Olivia Newton John pin up - Diana 1982
Olivia Newton John small feature - Blue Jeans 1980
Omar Sharif pin-up - Photoplay 1971
Omar Sharif pin-up - Photoplay 1975
OMD small feature - Look-In Pop ©1982

On the Buses comic strip - Look-In ©1972
On the Buses comic strip - Look-In TV Comedy ©1974
On the Buses photo story - Look-In ©1973
Orange Juice feature - Pop Superstars 1984
Orange Juice pin up - Oh Boy! 1985
Osibisa feature - Pop Group 1978
Osibisa feature - Superstars 1978
Osmonds feature - Boyfriend 1974
Osmonds feature/illustration - Diana 1982
Osmonds feature - FAB 208 1972
Osmonds feature - FAB 208 1979
Osmonds feature - FAB 208 1980
Osmonds feature - Mirabelle Sunshine Pop Book 1975
Osmonds feature - Music Star 1975
Osmonds feature - Music Star 1976
Osmonds feature - Pop Group 1978
Osmonds feature - Top of the Pops 1975
Osmonds feature - Top Pop Scene 1975
Osmonds feature/pin-up - Popswop ©1973
Osmonds feature/pin-up - Valentine 1974
Osmonds pin up - FAB 208 1973
Osmonds pin up - Look-In ©1974
Osmonds pin-up - Pink 1974
Osmonds pin-up - Pop Group 1977
Osmonds pin-up - Top of the Pops 1974
Osmonds Plan for Living feature - FAB 208 1975
Osmonds small feature - Pink 1978
Owen Paul pin up - Girl 1988
P P Arnold pin up - Boyfriend 1971
P.J. Proby feature - Radio Luxembourg Record Stars ©1965
Partridge Family pin up - FAB 208 1973
Pat Boone pin up and feature - Hollywood Album - Twelfth ©1958
Pathfinders comic strip - Look-In ©1973
Patrick Dempsey feature - Jackie 1991
Patrick Duffy small feature - Blue Jeans 1981
Patrick McGoohan pin-up - Boyfriend 1968
Paul & Linda McCartney feature - Top Pop Scene 1975
Paul Daniels feature - Diana 1982
Paul Di'Anno small feature - Blue Jeans 1982
Paul Jones pin-up - Boyfriend 1968
Paul McCartney & Wings feature - Disco 45 1978
Paul McCartney feature - Pop Club 1979
Paul McCartney feature - Radio 1984
Paul McCartney pin up - Daily Mirror Pop Club 1982
Paul McCartney small feature - Boyfriend 1968
Paul Newman & Joanne Woodward pin-up - Photoplay 1971
Paul Newman cover - Photoplay 1971
Paul Newman pin up - FAB 208 1973
Paul Newman pin up - Hollywood Album - Twelfth ©1958
Paul Newman pin-up - Photoplay 1973
Paul Newman pin-up - Photoplay 1974
Paul Newman pin-up - Photoplay 1976
Paul Newman small feature - Jackie 1991
Paul Nicholas pin up - Mates 1979
Paul Simenon (Clash) feature - Supersonics 1979
Paul Simon feature - Superstars 1978
Paul Stewart feature - Hollywood Album - Ninth
Paul Weller feature - Jackie 1985
Paul Weller feature - My Guy 1982
Paul Weller pin up - Mates 1979
Paul Weller small feature - Blue Jeans 1981
Paul Weller small feature - Blue Jeans 1982

Paul Young fact file - Blue Jeans 1987
Paul Young feature - Jackie 1986
Paul Young feature - Pop Superstars 1985
Paul Young feature - Video Superstars 1985
Paul Young feature/pin-up - Photo Love 1985
Paula Abdul pin up - Eagle Yearbook 1992
Pauline Black small feature - Blue Jeans 1981
Pauline Black small feature - Blue Jeans 1982
Penny Edwards pin up - Hollywood Album - Ninth
Pet Shop Boys pin-up - Top of the Pops 1992
Pet Shop Boys feature and pin up - Blue Jeans 1990
Pet Shop Boys pin up - Girl 1987
Pet Shop Boys pin up- Jackie 1989
Pete Burns pin up - Girl 1987
Peter Blake pin up - My Guy 1981
Peter Cleall pin up - Look-In ©1972
Peter Cushing feature - Photoplay 1971
Peter Cushing pin-up - TV Mirror 1956
Peter Davison - illustrated pin up - Judy 1983
Peter Dimmock pin-up - TV Mirror 1956
Peter Duel feature - FAB 208 1973
Peter Finch feature/pin-up - Photoplay 1974
Peter Firth feature - FAB 208 1972
Peter Frampton feature - Pop Group 1978
Peter Frampton feature - Superstars 1978
Peter Noone feature - Radio Luxembourg Record Stars ©1965
Peter Noone pin-up - Tony Blackburn Pop Special 3
Peter O'Toole feature - Photoplay 1973
Peter O'Toole small feature - Jackie 1991
Peter Pan feature - Film and Television Parade 1950's
Peter Powell feature - FAB 208 1980
Peter Powell feature - Top of the Pops 1982
Peter Powell pin up - My Guy 1981
Peter Powell small feature - Jackie 1981
Peter Sarstedt feature and pin up - Boyfriend 1971
Peter Sellers feature - Photoplay 1976
Peter Sellers feature - Superstars 1979
Peter Shelley feature - Top of the Pops 1977
Peter Vaughn Clarke pin up - Mates 1979
Petula Clark pin-up - TV Mirror 1956
Phil Lynott pin up - My Guy 1983
Phil Lynott pin up - Oh Boy! 1980
Phil Oakey of the Human League small feature - Jackie 1984
Phillip Schofield pin up - Blue Jeans 1990
Phillip Schofield pin up - Jackie 1992
Phoenix Hall small feature - Look-In 1991
Phyllis Kirk feature - Hollywood Album - Twelfth ©1958
Pier Angeli pin up - Hollywood Album - Twelfth ©1958
Pilot feature - FAB 208 1976
Pilot pin up - Look-In ©1975
Pilot pin-up - Pop Group 1977
Pilot pin-up - Record Mirror & Disc 1977
Pilot pin-up - Top of the Pops 1977
Pink Floyd pin up - Boyfriend 1973
Piper Laurie pin up and feature - Hollywood Album - Ninth
Planet of the Apes illustrated pin up - Look-In ©1975
Planet of the Apes pin up - Look-In ©1975
Please Sir! comic strip - Look-In ©1971
Please Sir! comic strip - Look-In ©1972
Please Sir! endpaper - Look-In ©1971
Poco feature - Pop Group 1978
Police 5 feature - ITV Annual for Boys and Girls 1964
Police feature - Daily Mirror Pop Club 1982

Police feature - Pink 1982
Police pin up - Look-In ©1980
Police pin up - Mates 1981
Police pin up - Mates 1981
Police pin up - My Guy 1982
Police pin-up - Top of the Pops 1982
Police small feature - Jackie 1981
Press Gang small feature - Look-In 1991
Pretenders feature - Pop Superstars 1985
Pretenders feature - Video Superstars 1985
Princess Diana pin up - Diana 1986
Procul Harum feature - Pop Group 1978
Professionals feature - FAB 208 1979
Professionals feature - FAB 208 1980
Professionals feature - TV Detectives ©1979
Professionals small feature - Jackie 1981
Protectors (Robert Vaughn) photo cover - TV Action 1974
Protectors photo story - TV Action 1974
Pursuers - TV Crimebusters ©1962
Queen feature - Disco 45 1977
Queen feature - Mirabelle Sunshine Pop Book 1975
Queen feature - Music Star 1976
Queen feature/pin-up - Pop Group 1977
Queen feature/pin-up - Record Mirror & Disc 1977
Queen feature/pin-up - Top of the Pops 1977
Queen pin up - Girl 1988
Queen pin up - Mates 1978
Queen pin up - Mirabelle Sunshine Pop Book 1975
Queen pin up - Oh Boy! 1980
Ralph Macchio small feature - Blue Jeans 1988
Ranking Roger pin up - My Guy 1982
Ray Lake pin up - My Guy 1981
Ray Wilkins pin up - Look-In ©1977
Ray Wilkins pin up - Mates 1982
Razzmatazz endpaper - Look-In ©1982
Real Thing pin up - Mates 1979
Red Box pin up - Girl 1988
Reg Varney pin up - Look-In ©1971
Return of the Antelope endpaper - Look-In 1987
Return of The Saint feature - TV Detectives ©1979
Revillos small feature - Blue Jeans 1982
Rex Allen feature - Film and Television Parade 1950's
Rex Harrison feature - Star TV & Film 1968
Rex Smith pin up - My Guy 1981
Rex Smith pin up - My Guy 1982
Richard Anderson feature - TV Detectives ©1979
Richard Basehart feature - Hollywood Album - Twelfth ©1958
Richard Burton feature - Photoplay 1974
Richard Burton feature - Photoplay 1975
Richard Burton pin-up - Photoplay 1973
Richard Burton pin-up - Photoplay 1976
Richard Davies pin up - Look-In ©1971
Richard Dimbleby pin-up - TV Mirror 1956
Richard Hudson feature - Top Pop Scene 1975
Richard O'Sullivan feature - Diana 1982
Richard O'Sullivan feature - FAB 208 1976
Richard O'Sullivan feature - Look-In ©1979
Richard O'Sullivan feature - Look-In TV Comedy ©1974
Richard Todd photo cover - Film and Television Parade 1950's
Richard Widmark feature - Hollywood Album - Ninth
Rick Astley pin up- Blue Jeans 1990
Rick Parfitt - small feature - Jackie 1983
Rick Springfield pin up - Mirabelle Sunshine Pop Book

Pin Up = 1 page pin up * Feature = ½ page article or more * Small feature = ¼ page article or less

1975
Rick Springfield pin-up - Valentine 1974
Rick Wakeman feature - Superstars 1978
Rita Ray small feature - Blue Jeans 1982
River Phoenix pin up (fc) - Blue Jeans 1993
Roaring Twenties - TV Crimebusters ©1962
Rob Lowe small feature/pin-up - Blue Jeans 1988
Robert de Niro (painted "Raging Bull" portrait) - Diana 1983
Robert de Niro pin-up - Photoplay 1980
Robert Downey Jnr star file - Jackie 1993
Robert Francis feature - Hollywood Album - Ninth
Robert Palmer feature - Girl Talk 1978
Robert Palmer feature - Superstars 1978
Robert Plant feature - FAB 208 1972
Robert Plant pin up - Music Scene 1974
Robert Redford cover/feature - Photoplay 1973
Robert Redford feature - FAB 208 1972
Robert Redford feature - Photoplay 1974
Robert Redford feature/pin-up - Photoplay 1975
Robert Redford feature/pin-up - Photoplay 1976
Robert Redford pin up - FAB 208 1973
Robert Shaw feature - Photoplay 1974
Robert ShawRobert Wagner pin-up - Photoplay 1973
Robert Vaughn pin up - Look-In ©1973
Robert Wagner & Natalie Wood pin-up - Photoplay 1976
Robin Campbell small feature - Blue Jeans 1983
Robin Hood movie - Photoplay 1973
Robin Nedwell pin up - Look-In ©1974
Robin Nedwell pin up - Look-In ©1976
Robin of Sherwood comic strip - Look-In 1988
Robin of Sherwood comic strip - Look-In 1991
Robin of Sherwood endpaper - Look-In ©1984
Robin of Sherwood endpaper - Look-In 1988
Robin of Sherwood feature - Look-In ©1984
Rockford Files feature - TV Detectives ©1979
Rod Hull & Emu endpaper - Look-In TV Comedy ©1974
Rod Stewart feature - Cheggers 1980
Rod Stewart feature - Daily Mirror Pop Club 1978
Rod Stewart feature - Disco 45 1978
Rod Stewart feature - FAB 208 1976
Rod Stewart feature - Music Star 1976
Rod Stewart feature - Oh Boy! 1979
Rod Stewart feature - Superstars 1978
Rod Stewart feature/pin-up - Popswop ©1973
Rod Stewart feature/pin-up - Top of the Pops 1977
Rod Stewart pin up - Boyfriend 1974
Rod Stewart pin up - Daily Mirror Pop Club 1982
Rod Stewart pin up - Diana 1979
Rod Stewart pin up - Disco 45 1977
Rod Stewart pin up - FAB 208 1973
Rod Stewart pin up - Mates 1977
Rod Stewart pin up - Mates 1978
Rod Stewart pin up - Music Scene 1974
Rod Stewart pin up - Pink 1974
Rod Stewart pin-up - Record Mirror & Disc 1977
Rod Stewart pin-up - Top of the Pops 1974
Rod Stewart small feature - Jackie 1981
Rod Taylor pin-up - Photoplay 1975
Roger Black feature - Look-In 1988
Roger Daltrey pin-up - Photoplay 1976
Roger Miller feature - Radio Luxembourg Record Stars ©1965
Roger Moore cover - Star TV & Film 1967
Roger Moore cover/feature/pin-up - Photoplay 1974

Roger Moore feature - All Stars Television Annual 1973
Roger Moore feature - Look-In ©1971
Roger Moore feature - Photoplay 1978
Roger Moore feature - Superstars 1979
Roger Moore feature/pin-up - Photoplay 1975
Roger Moore pin up - FAB 208 1973
Roger Moore pin-up - Photoplay 1976
Roger Taylor pin up - My Guy 1983
Roger Whittaker pin-up - Tony Blackburn Pop Special 3
Roland Rat feature - Look-In 1986
Rolf Harris feature - Look-In 1991
Rolf Harris feature - Star TV & Film 1968
Rolf Harris pin up - Look-In ©1972
Rolling Stones feature - Music Star 1975
Rolling Stones feature - Pop Group 1978
Rolling Stones feature - Radio Luxembourg Record Stars ©1965
Rolling Stones feature - Teen Beat-Pop Ten ©1969
Rolling Stones feature - Tony Blackburn Pop Special 3
Rolling Stones feature - Top of the Pops 1975
Rolling Stones pin-up - Pop Group 1977
Ronald Howard feature - Hollywood Album - Twelfth ©1958
Ronald Reagan feature - Hollywood Album - Ninth
Rory Calhoun pin up - Hollywood Album - Twelfth ©1958
Rory Gallagher feature - Pop Group 1978
Rosetta Stone pin up - Mates 1979
Rossano Brazzi pin up - Hollywood Album - Twelfth ©1958
Roxy Music feature - Disco 45 1977
Roxy Music feature - FAB 208 1976
Roxy Music feature - Music Scene 1974
Roxy Music feature - Pop Group 1977
Roxy Music feature - Record Mirror & Disc 1977
Roy Orbison feature - Radio Luxembourg Record Stars ©1965
Roy Wood feature - Top Pop Scene 1975
Roy Wood feature/pin-up - Top of the Pops 1975
Roy Wood pin-up - Pop Group 1977
Roy Wood pin-up - Record Mirror & Disc 1977
Roy Wood pin-up - Top of the Pops 1977
Rubettes feature - Pop Group 1978
Rubettes feature - Top of the Pops 1977
Rubettes feature - Top Pop Scene 1975
Rubettes feature/pin-up - Pop Group 1977
Rubettes pin-up - Record Mirror & Disc 1977
Ruby Murray pin-up - TV Mirror 1956
Rudolph Nureyev feature - Superstars 1979
Rupert Bear feature - Blue Peter Eighteenth ©1981
Rupert Keegan pin up - Mates 1979
Russ Abbot small feature - Look-In ©1983
Russ Conway pin up - Crackerjack ©1962
Ruth Madocs (Hi de Hi) feature - Diana 1986
Ryan O'Neal feature - FAB 208 1972
Sad Café pin up - Daily Mirror Pop Club 1982
Sad Cafe pin-up - Top of the Pops 1982
Sade star file - Jackie 1986
Sailor pin-up - Pop Group 1977
Sandie Shaw feature - Top Pop Stars 1968
Sandie Shaw pin-up - Tony Blackburn Pop Special 3
Sandie Shaw small photo - Fab 208 1969
Sandra Dee pin up - Hollywood Album - Twelfth ©1958
Sandy Nelson pin up - Crackerjack ©1962
Santana feature - Pop Group 1978
Sapphire and Steel (Joanna Lumley interview with full colour photos) - Diana 1981

155

Sapphire and Steel text story - Look-In ©1981
Scott Baio pin up - Oh Boy! 1980
Scott Engel small feature - Boyfriend 1968
Scott Graham pin up - My Guy 1982
Scritti Politti pin up - Girl 1987
Sean & Chris Penn small feature - Blue Jeans 1988
Sean Connery feature - Film Show 1963
Sean Connery feature - Superstars 1979
Sean Connery pin-up - Photoplay 1973
Sean Kerly feature - Look-In 1990
Searchers feature - Radio Luxembourg Record Stars ©1965
Sebastian Coe feature - Look-In ©1982
Secret Affair pin-up - Top of the Pops 1982
Serpico feature - TV Detectives ©1979
Serpico movie - Photoplay 1975
Sex Pistols feature - Superstars 1979
Shadows feature - Pop Group 1977
Shakin Stevens comic strip - Look-In 1987
Shakin Stevens feature - Blue Peter Twenty One ©1984
Shakin Stevens feature - Diana 1983
Shakin Stevens feature - Look-In ©1983
Shakin' Stevens feature - Radio 1984
Shakin' Stevens feature - Sindy 1984
Shakin Stevens pin up - Barbie 1987
Shakin Stevens pin up - My Guy 1982
Shakin Stevens pin up - My Guy 1983
Shakin Stevens pin-up - Photo Love 1985
Shakin Stevens quiz - Look-In 1987
Shakin' Stevens small feature - Blue Jeans 1981
Shakin Stevens small feature - Jackie 1981
Sham 69 small feature - Blue Jeans 1980
Sharron Davies small feature - Diana 1983
Shaun & Parker feature - FAB 208 1980
Shaun Cassidy feature - FAB 208 1976
Shaun Cassidy feature - FAB 208 1979
Shaun Cassidy feature - Mates 1981
Shaun Cassidy feature - Mates 1982
Shaun Cassidy feature - Supersonics 1979
Shaun Cassidy feature/pin-up - Pink 1979
Shaun Cassidy pin up - Look-In ©1978
Shaun Cassidy pin up - Mates 1981
Shaun Cassidy pin up - Oh Boy! 1980
Shaun Cassidy pin-up - Pink 1980
Sheena Easton feature - Daily Mirror Pop Club 1982
Sheena Easton pin-up - Top of the Pops 1982
Sheena Easton small feature - Blue Jeans 1982
Shelley Winters feature - Hollywood Album - Ninth
Shirley Bassey pin up - Crackerjack ©1962
Shirley Jones pin up and feature - Hollywood Album - Twelfth ©1958
Showaddywaddy Dave Bartram small feature - Blue Jeans 1982
Showaddywaddy feature - FAB 208 1979
Showaddywaddy feature - Pop Group 1978
Showaddywaddy feature - Top Pop Scene 1975
Showaddywaddy feature/pin-up - Pop Group 1977
Showaddywaddy feature/pin-up - Record Mirror & Disc 1977
Showaddywaddy pin up - Mates 1978
Showaddywaddy pin-up - Top of the Pops 1977
Sid James pin up - Look-In ©1971
Simon Bates feature - Top of the Pops 1982
Simon Le Bon & John Taylor fact file - Barbie 1986
Simon Le Bon feature - Sindy 1984

Simon Le Bon pin up - Diana 1986
Simon Le Bon pin up - My Guy 1984
Simon Le Bon small feature - Blue Jeans 1983
Simon Le Bon small feature - Jackie 1983
Simon Le Bon small feature - Look-In ©1983
Simon Mayo feature - Top of the Pops 1992
Simon O'Brien fact file - Jackie 1988
Simon Ward feature - Photoplay 1973
Simple Minds pin up - Girl 1987
Simply Red pin up - Girl 1988
Sinitta pin up - Bunty 1990
Sister Sledge feature - Disco 81 1981
Six Million Dollar Man endpaper - Look-In ©1978
Six Million Dollar Man feature - Look-In ©1977
Slade feature - Boyfriend 1974
Slade feature - Jackie 1975
Slade feature - Music Scene 1974
Slade feature - Music Star 1974
Slade feature - Music Star 1976
Slade feature - Pink 1974
Slade feature - Top Pop Scene 1975
Slade feature/pin-up - Pop Group 1977
Slade feature/pin-up - Popswop ©1973
Slade feature/pin-up - Top of the Pops 1974
Slade feature/pin-up - Top of the Pops 1975
Slade pin up - Boyfriend 1973
Slade pin up - FAB 208 1973
Slade pin-up - Look-In ©1974
Slade pin-up - Record Mirror & Disc 1977
Slade pin-up - Top of the Pops 1977
Slade pin-up - Valentine 1974
Slik feature - Disco 45 1977
Slik feature - Superstars 1978
Slik feature/pin-up - Pink 1978
Slik pin up - Look-In ©1976
Slik pin up - Mates 1978
Small Faces feature - Music Scene 1974
Small Faces feature - Teen Beat-Pop Ten ©1969
Smokey Robinson and the Miracles pin-up - Pop Group 1977
Smokie feature - Cheggers 1980
Smokie feature - Pop Group 1978
Smokie pin up - Disco 45 1977
Smokie pin-up - Record Mirror & Disc 1977
Smurfs comic strip - Look-In ©1981
Smurfs comic strip - Look-In ©1982
Smurfs feature - Look-In ©1980
Smurfs feature - Look-In ©1981
Soft Cell feature - Pop Superstars 1984
Soft Cell small feature - Look-In Pop ©1982
Sonia feature - Look-In 1991
Sonia pin up - Eagle Yearbook 1992
Sonny & Cher feature - Top Pop Stars 1967
Sooty & Harry Corbett pin-up - TV Mirror 1956
Sophia Loren feature - Photoplay 1973
Sophia Loren feature - Photoplay 1975
Sophia Loren feature and photo cover - Film Show 1963
Sophia Loren pin up and feature - Hollywood Album - Twelfth ©1958
Sophia Loren pin-up - Photoplay 1980
Space 1999 comic strip - Look-In ©1977
Space 1999 comic strip - Look-In ©1979
Space 1999 text story - Look-In ©1976
Spandau Ballet feature - Barbie 1987
Spandau Ballet feature - Girl 1988

Pin Up = 1 page pin up * Feature = ½ page article or more * Small feature = ¼ page article or less

Spandau Ballet feature - Oh Boy! 1985
Spandau Ballet feature - Pop Superstars 1984
Spandau Ballet feature - Pop Superstars 1985
Spandau Ballet feature - Video Superstars 1985
Spandau Ballet pin up - Barbie 1986
Sparks feature - Record Mirror & Disc 1977
Sparks feature - Top Pop Scene 1975
Spencer Tracy feature - Hollywood Album - Ninth
Spider-Man TV series feature - Look-In ©1982
Spike Milligan feature - 4 page comic strip - Judy 1969
Splinter feature - FAB 208 1976
Stanley Baxter endpaper - Look-In TV Comedy ©1974
Star is Born movie feature - Superstars 1979
Star Wars feature - Diana 1985
Star Wars feature - Look In ©1978
Starsky & Hutch feature - Pink 1979
Starsky & Hutch feature - Superstars 1978
Starsky & Hutch feature - TV Detectives ©1979
Starsky & Hutch pin-up - Photoplay 1978
Starsky & Hutch small feature - Pink 1978
Status Quo feature - Daily Mirror Pop Club 1982
Status Quo feature - Disco 45 1978
Status Quo feature - Pop Group 1978
Status Quo feature - Tony Blackburn Pop Special 2
Status Quo pin up - Boyfriend 1971
Status Quo pin-up - Pop Group 1977
Status Quo pin-up - Top of the Pops 1975
Status Quo pin-up - Top of the Pops 1982
Steeleye Span feature - Pop Group 1978
Steeleye Span feature - Superstars 1978
Steeleye Span feature/pin-up - Pop Group 1977
Stefanie Powers feature - Star TV & Film 1968
Stephen Duffy pin up - Girl 1987
Stephen Hendry feature - Look-In 1989
Stephen Lewis pin up - Look-In TV Comedy ©1975
Steptoe and Son comic strip and feature - All Stars Television Annual 1973
Steve Coppell pin up - Look-In ©1978
Steve Ellis feature - Boyfriend 1971
Steve Forrest pin up and feature - Hollywood Album - Ninth
Steve Harley feature - FAB 208 1976
Steve Harley feature/pin-up - Top of the Pops 1977
Steve Harley pin up - Look-In ©1975
Steve Harley pin-up - Record Mirror & Disc 1977
Steve Hodson pin up - Look-In ©1972
Steve Hodson pin-up - Look-In ©1973
Steve Hodson pin-up - Valentine 1974
Steve McQueen feature - FAB 208 1972
Steve McQueen feature - Photoplay 1973
Steve McQueen feature - Photoplay 1974
Steve McQueen feature/pin-up - Photoplay 1971
Steve McQueen pin up - FAB 208 1973
Steve McQueen small feature - Jackie 1991
Steve Norman of Spandau Ballet star file - Jackie 1986
Steve Norman pin up - My Guy 1983
Steve Race pin-up - TV Mirror 1956
Steve Strange pin up - My Guy 1983
Steve Strange pin up - My Guy 1984
Steve Warner feature - Photoplay 1975
Stevensons Rocket feature/pin-up - Pink 1978
Stevie Winwood small feature/pin-up - Boyfriend 1968
Stevie Wonder feature - Disco 45 1978
Stevie Wonder pin-up - Tony Blackburn Pop Special 3
Stewart Copeland small feature - Jackie 1983

Sting pin up - Girl 1983
Sting pin up - Look-In ©1980
Sting pin up - My Guy 1981
Sting pin-up - Photo Love 1985
Sting small feature - Blue Jeans 1981
Sting small feature - Jackie 1981
Sting small feature - Jackie 1983
Sting small feature - Jackie 1984
Sting/Police feature - Diana 1982
Stranglers feature - Supersonics 1979
Strawbs feature - Music Scene 1974
Stray Cats feature - Diana 1983
Streetwise small feature - Look-In 1991
Style Council feature - Pop Superstars 1984
Style Council feature - Pop Superstars 1985
Style Council feature - Video Superstars 1985
Style Council pin up - Girl 1988
Stylistics feature/pin-up - Pop Group 1977
Stylistics pin-up - Top of the Pops 1977
Sue Barker small feature - Diana 1983
Sue Barker feature - Superstars 1978
Suggs endpaper - Look-In ©1982
Super Gran endpaper - Look-In 1986
Superman feature - FAB 208 1980
Superman small feature - Jackie 1981
Supremes pin-up - Pop Group 1977
Survival feature - ITV Annual for Boys and Girls 1964
Survival Special feature - Look-In ©1974
Susan George feature - Photoplay 1971
Susan George feature - Photoplay 1978
Susannah York feature - Photoplay 1976
Susannah York pin-up - Photoplay 1973
Suzan Ball pin up and feature - Hollywood Album - Ninth
Suzi Quatro feature - Mirabelle Sunshine Pop Book 1975
Suzi Quatro feature - Music Star 1975
Suzi Quatro feature - see Happy Days
Suzi Quatro feature - Top Pop Scene 1975
Suzi Quatro pin up - Look-In ©1974
Suzi Quatro pin-up - Mirabelle Sunshine Pop Book 1975
Suzi Quatro small feature - Blue Jeans 1980
Suzi Quatro small feature - Blue Jeans 1981
Suzi Quatro small feature - Blue Jeans 1983
Sweet feature - FAB 208 1976
Sweet feature - Music Star 1974
Sweet feature - Record Mirror & Disc 1977
Sweet feature/pin-up - Popswop ©1973
Sweet pin up - Look-In ©1974
Sweet pin-up - Top of the Pops 1974
Sweet pin-up - Top of the Pops 1977
Sword and the Rose feature - Film and Television Parade 1950's
Sylvester Stallone feature - Photoplay 1978
Sylvester Stallone feature - Superstars 1979
T Rex feature - Music Star 1974
Tanita Tikaram feature - Blue Jeans 1990
Target feature - TV Detectives ©1979
Tatum O'Neal feature - Photoplay 1979
Tavares feature - Pop Group 1978
Tavares pin up - Mates 1979
Tears for Fears feature - Barbie 1987
Tears for Fears feature - Pop Superstars 1984
Teddy Johnson & Pearl Carr pin up - Crackerjack ©1962
Terry Hall pin up - My Guy 1984
Terry Jacks feature - Top Pop Scene 1975
Terry Lightfoot pin up - Crackerjack ©1962

Terry Moore pin up - Hollywood Album - Ninth
Terry Sharpe pin up - My Guy 1981
Thank Your Lucky Stars feature - ITV Annual for Boys and Girls 1964
The Abdication movie - Photoplay 1975
The Beat feature - Pop Superstars 1984
The Black Windmill movie - Photoplay 1975
The Blues Band pin up - Daily Mirror Pop Club 1982
The Commodores feature - Cheggers 1980
The Deep movie - Photoplay 1978
The Exorcist movie - Photoplay 1975
The Godfather (Part II) movie - Photoplay 1976
The Goodies feature - FAB 208 1976
The Goodies feature - Judy 1979
The Great Gatsby movie - Photoplay 1975
The Great Waldo Pepper movie - Photoplay 1976
The Guru movie - Fab 208 1969
The Hollies pin up - Boyfriend 1971
The Jacksons feature - Boyfriend 1974
The Jacksons feature - Disco 81 1981
The Jacksons feature - FAB 208 1972
The Jacksons feature - FAB 208 1976
The Jacksons pin up - FAB 208 1973
The Jam pin up - Diana 1983
The Move pin up - Boyfriend 1971
The Muppet Show feature - Judy 1979
The New Seekers pin up - FAB 208 1973
The Osmonds feature - Jackie 1975
The Quest feature - Jackie 1978
The Railway Children 6pg feature - Daily Mirror Book for Girls 1972
The Rubettes feature - FAB 208 1976
The Shadows pin up - Crackerjack ©1962
The Sparks feature - FAB 208 1976
The Tamarind Seed movie - Photoplay 1975
The Three Degrees feature - Disco 81 1981
The Three Musketeers movie - Photoplay 1975
Thereze Bazaar feature - Sindy 1984
Thereze Bazaar small feature - Blue Jeans 1982
Thereze Bazaar small feature - Jackie 1981
Thin Lizzy feature - Disco 45 1978
Thin Lizzy feature - Pop Group 1978
Thin Lizzy pin up - Daily Mirror Pop Club 1982
Thin Lizzy pin-up - Top of the Pops 1982
Thomas Howell small feature - Blue Jeans 1988
Thompson Twins endpaper - Look-In ©1984
Thompson Twins feature - Pop Superstars 1984
Thompson Twins feature - Pop Superstars 1985
Thompson Twins feature - Video Superstars 1985
Thompson Twins pin up - Barbie 1987
Thompson Twins pin up - Girl 1987
Three Degrees pin-up - Pop Group 1977
Thunderbirds feature - Blue Peter Twenty Seven ©1992
Tiffany pin up - Bunty 1990
Tightrope feature - All Stars Television Annual 1973
Timeslip comic strip - Look-In ©1971
Timeslip feature - Look-In ©1971
Timmy Mallett feature - Look-In 1989
Tina Charles feature - Disco 45 1978
Tina Charles small feature - Blue Jeans 1980
Todd Carty small feature - Blue Jeans 1983
Tom Baker feature - Look-In ©1980
Tom Cruise fact file - Jackie 1988
Tom Cruise small feature - Blue Jeans 1988
Tom Jones feature - Boyfriend 1971

Tom Jones feature - Radio Luxembourg Record Stars ©1965
Tom Jones feature - Star TV & Film 1968
Tom Jones pin-up - Boyfriend 1968
Tom Selleck pin-up - Photo Love 1985
Tommy Boyd feature - Look-In 1987
Tommy Cooper feature - Look-In TV Comedy ©1974
Tommy Steele feature - Star TV & Film 1968
Tomorrow People comic strip - Look-In ©1974
Tomorrow People comic strip - Look-In ©1975
Tomorrow People comic strip - Look-In ©1976
Tomorrow People comic strip - Look-In ©1978
Tomorrow People endpaper - Look-In ©1975
Tomorrow People endpaper - Look-In ©1977
Tomorrow People feature - Look-In ©1978
Tomorrow People pin up - Look-In ©1975
Tomorrow People text story - Look-In ©1977
Tony Anholt pin up - Look-In ©1973
Tony Blackburn feature - FAB 208 1972
Tony Blackburn pin up - Boyfriend 1973
Tony Blackburn pin-up - Valentine 1974
Tony Curtis pin up - FAB 208 1973
Tony Curtis small feature - Jackie 1991
Tony Randall pin up and feature - Hollywood Album - Twelfth ©1958
Top of the Pops feature - All Stars Television Annual 1973
Top of the Pops feature - Jackie 1975
Torville & Dean feature - Ace Reports ©1981
Toyah feature - Radio 1984
Toyah feature - Video Superstars 1985
Toyah pin up - Diana 1983
Toyah pin up - Girl 1984
Toyah small feature - Blue Jeans 1983
Toyah small feature - Look-In ©1982
Toyah Wilcox small feature - Blue Jeans 1982
Tracey Ullman feature - Barbie 1986
Tracey Ullman feature - Pop Superstars 1985
Tracey Ullman feature - Video Superstars 1985
Treasure Hunt feature - Look-In 1988
Tremeloes feature - Teen Beat-Pop Ten ©1969
Tremeloes feature - Tony Blackburn Pop Special 3
Tremeloes pin-up - Fab 208 1969
Trevor Eve factfile/pin up - Diana 1982
Trevor Eve pin up - My Guy 1981
Trevor Francis pin up - Look-In ©1977
Trini Lopez feature - Radio Luxembourg Record Stars ©1965
Troggs small feature - Boyfriend 1968
Twiggy feature - Superstars 1978
Two Ronnies feature - Look-In TV Comedy ©1974
Tyrone Power small feature - Jackie 1991
U2 feature - Barbie 1987
UB40 pin up - Girl 1988
UFO comic strip - TV Action 1974
Ultravox feature - Pop Superstars 1984
Ultravox feature - Pop Superstars 1985
Ultravox feature - Radio 1984
Ursula Andress feature - Star TV & Film 1968
Ursula Theiss pin up - Hollywood Album - Ninth
Val Doonican feature - Star TV & Film 1968
Valerie French pin up and feature - Hollywood Album - Twelfth ©1958
Valerie Perrine pin-up - Photoplay 1980
Vampira movie - Photoplay 1975
Vanilla Ice feature/pin-up - Top of the Pops 1992

Pin Up = 1 page pin up * Feature = ½ page article or more * Small feature = ¼ page article or less

Veronica Carlson pin-up - Photoplay 1975
Vincent Price feature - Hollywood Album - Ninth
Vincent Price feature - Photoplay 1971
Virginia Mayo pin up and feature - Hollywood Album - Ninth
Wagon Train small feature - Look-In 1990
Walker Brothers pin-up - Boyfriend 1968
Walt Disney feature - Look-In ©1972
Walt Disney feature - Look-In TV Comedy ©1974
Warren Beatty feature - Photoplay 1976
Wayne Fontana small feature - Boyfriend 1968
Wayne Maunder pin up - FAB 208 1973
Wendy James pin up - Eagle Yearbook 1992
Wendy Padbury pin up - Look-In ©1972
Wendy Wu small feature - Blue Jeans 1982
Westlife pin up - Mandy 2000
Westlife pin up - Mandy 2000
Wet Wet Wet pin up- Jackie 1989
Wham feature - Barbie 1987
Wham feature - Blue Jeans 1993
Wham feature - Pop Superstars 1984
Wham feature - Sindy ©1984
Wham feature - Video Superstars 1985
Wham pin up - Barbie 1986
Wham pin up - Diana 1986
Wham small feature - Look-In 1986
White Plains pin-up - Pink 1974
Whitney Houston feature - Blue Jeans 1990
Whitney Houston pin up - Bunty 1990
Who feature - Music Scene 1974
Who feature - Pop Group 1977
Who feature - Pop Group 1978
Who feature - Top of the Pops 1982
Wide Awake Club endpaper - Look-In 1990
Wilfred Pickles & Mabel pin-up - TV Mirror 1956
William Katt pin-up - Photoplay 1979
Williams Twins pin-up - Valentine 1974
Wings feature - Cheggers 1980
Wings feature - FAB 208 1976
Wings feature - Pop Group 1978
Wings feature - Top of the Pops 1975
Wings feature/pin-up - Record Mirror & Disc 1977
Wings pin-up - Top of the Pops 1977
Winifred Atwell pin-up - TV Mirror 1956
Winona Ryder feature - Blue Jeans 1993
Winona Ryder star file - Jackie 1993
Wizzard feature - FAB 208 1976
World of Sport feature - Look-In ©1971
Worzel Gummidge comic strip - Look-In ©1984
Worzel Gummidge endpaper - Look-In ©1980
Worzel Gummidge endpaper - Look-In ©1981
Worzel Gummidge feature - Look-In ©1980
Worzel Gummidge pin up - Look-In ©1981
X Ray Spex small feature - Blue Jeans 1980
XTC feature - Daily Mirror Pop Club 1982
Yazoo feature - Pop Superstars 1984
Yazz feature - Look-In 1990
You Only Live Twice feature - Star TV & Film 1968
Yul Brynner feature - Hollywood Album - Twelfth ©1958
Yul Brynner feature - Star TV & Film 1968
Yvonne Mitchell pin-up - TV Mirror 1956
Zardoz movie - Photoplay 1975
Zsa Zsa Gabor feature - Hollywood Album - Twelfth ©1958

NOTES

NOTES

NOTES

NOTES

NOTES

NOTES

NOTES

NOTES

NOTES

23/5/02 - Elgin.

Kenny Dalglish Soccer Annual.   Cost 50p
Value £8.

Dennis He Menace. 1968 Cost 40p Value £25

THE BEEZER 1972 Cost 40p Value £10

THE AVENGERS 1969 Cost 40p Value £20

DR WHO   1975 Cost 40p Value £15

PIXIE + DIXIE 1974   valu £10